EXPONENTIAL ATTRACTORS
FOR DISSIPATIVE
EVOLUTION EQUATIONS

OTHER TITLES IN THE SAME SERIES

Analysis of the K-Epsilon Turbulence Model, by B. Mohammadi and O. Pironneau. 1994, 212 pages.

Exact Controllability and Stabilization - The Multiplier Method, by V. Komornik. 1994, 168 pages.

Global Classical Solutions for Quasilinear Hyperbolic Systems, by Li Ta-tsien. 1994, 328 pages.

Recent Advances in Partial Differential Equations, by M.-A. Herrero and E. Zuazua. 1994, 160 pages.

RAM Research in Applied Mathematics
Series Editors : P.G. CIARLET and J.-L. LIONS

EXPONENTIAL ATTRACTORS FOR DISSIPATIVE EVOLUTION EQUATIONS

A. EDEN

C. FOIAS

B. NICOLAENKO

R. TEMAM

1994

JOHN WILEY & SONS
Chichester • New York • Brisbane • Toronto • Singapore

MASSON
Paris Milan Barcelona

A. EDEN : Department of Mathematics - Arizona State University - Tempe, Arizona.
Department of Mathematics - Boğaziçi Üniversitesi - PK2 Bebek, Istanbul.
C. FOIAS : Department of Mathematics - Indiana University - Bloomington, Indiana.
B. NICOLAENKO : Department of Mathematics - Arizona State University - Tempe, Arizona.
R. TEMAM : Laboratoire d'Analyse Numérique - Université Paris-Sud - Orsay.
Institute for Scientific Computing and Applied Mathematics - Indiana University - Bloomington, Indiana.

La collection **Recherches en Mathématiques Appliquées** a pour objectif de publier dans un délai très rapide des textes de haut niveau en Mathématiques Appliquées, notamment :
— des cours de troisième cycle,
— des séries de conférences sur un sujet donné,
— des comptes rendus de séminaires, congrès,
— des versions préliminaires d'ouvrages plus élaborés,
— des thèses, en partie ou en totalité.

Les manuscrits, qui doivent comprendre de 120 à 250 pages, seront reproduits directement par un procédé photographique. Ils devront être réalisés avec le plus grand soin, en observant les normes de présentation précisées par l'Éditeur.
Les manuscrits seront rédigés en français ou en anglais. Dans tous les cas, ils seront examinés par au moins un rapporteur.
Ils seront soumis directement soit au

The aim of the **Recherches en Mathématiques Appliquées** series (Research in Applied Mathematics) is to publish high level texts in Applied Mathematics very rapidly :
— Post-graduate courses
— Lectures on particular topics
— Proceedings of congresses
— Preliminary versions of more complete works
— Theses (partially or as a whole)

Manuscripts which should contain between 120 or 250 pages will be printed directly by a photographic process. They have to be prepared carefully according to standards defined by the publisher.
Manuscripts may be written in English or in French and will be examined by at least one referee.
All manuscripts should be submitted to

Professor P.G. Ciarlet, Analyse numérique, T. 55,
Université Pierre et Marie Curie, 4, place Jussieu, 75005 Paris
soit au / or to
Professor J.-L. Lions, Collège de France,
11, place Marcelin-Berthelot, 75005 Paris

Tous droits de traduction, d'adaptation et de reproduction par tous procédés, réservés pour tous pays.
Les articles L. 122-4, L. 122-5 et L. 335-2 du Code de la propriété intellectuelle interdisent notamment la photocopie à usage collectif sans autorisation de l'éditeur.

All rights reserved. No part of this book may be reproduced by any means, or transmitted, or translated into a machine language without the written permission of the publisher.
A catalogue record for this book is available from the British Library.

© Masson, Paris, 1994

ISBN Masson : 2-225-84306-8
ISBN Wiley : 0-471-95223-0
ISSN : 0298-3168

MASSON S.A.   120, bd Saint-Germain, 75280 Paris Cedex 06
JOHN WILEY AND SONS Ltd   Baffins Lane, Chichester, West Sussex PO 19 1UD, England

Preface

This work was initiated during the summer of 1989 while the authors were attending at the University of Colorado at Boulder the AMS Summer Research Conference on *The Connection between Inifinite Dimensional and Finite Dimensional Dynamical Systems*; it was then continued and polished while the authors were at the Arizona State University at Tempe, at Indiana University at Bloomington, at the University of Paris-Sud (Orsay), at the IMA at Minneapolis and at the Center for Nonlinear Studies at Los-Alamos.

Our aim was to develop and present the Theory of Exponential Attractors for Dissipative Evolution Equations, mostly of infinite dimension. This book develops an original work not previous published in the literature; announcements of our results appeared in the Comptes Rendus de l'Académie des Sciences de Paris (see [EFNT] in the list of references and also [EFN]) and an earlier version of the work appeared as a preprint of IMA, the Institute for Mathematics and Applications at Minneapolis. In the earlier forms of the work and in related articles Exponential Attractors are also called *Inertial Sets*.

As it is explained in details in the Introductory Remarks of Chapter I, *Exponential Attractors* are "realistic" objects intermediate between the two "ideal" objects which are the *Attractors* and the *Inertial Manifolds*. All three objects describe the long time behaviour of dynamical systems. The global attractor is the smallest object encompassing all the large time dynamics of such a system. However attractors are known to be very complex objects (possibly fractals), very sensitive to perturbations and attracting the orbits at a slow rate. On the other hand inertial manifolds, when they exist, are smooth finite dimensional manifolds which attract all orbits at an exponential rate and they are stable with respect to perturbations. As we shall see Exponential Attractors also attract all orbits at exponential rate, they are stable with respect to perturbation and they exist, as we shall prove, for a broad class of evolutionary equations.

Although this book presents new results, it is partly written in the style of a text book appropriate for a graduate course. The work is self-contained and the prerequisites are at the level of a graduate student.

We wish to thank A. Babin, A. Ben Artzi, A. Debussche, D. Hilhorst, M. Jolly, A. Milani, E. Titi and Z. S. She for their interest and comments. We are also endebted to Linda Arneson and to Vicki Botos for the careful typing and formating of the book. We also want to express our thanks to Ph. Ciarlet and J.L. Lions the editors of this series, for providing us the opportunity to publish as a monograph our work on exponential attractors.

Acknowledgements

This work was supported by the Office of Naval Research, Contract N00014-91-J-1140 and by the Air Force Office of Scientific Research, Universities Research Initiative at Arizona State University. It was partially supported also by the Department of Mathematical Sciences of the National Sciences Foundation, Grants NSF-DMS-9024769 and NSF-DMS-9017174. Partial support by the Research Found of Indiana University and by the Office of the Vice-President for Research at A.S.U. is also acknowledged.

The research presented in this book was also partially supported by the Université de Paris-Sud and the Centre National de la Recherche Scientifique through the Laboratoire d'Analyse Numérique d'Orsay.

Contents

1. Introductory Remarks 1
2. Construction of Exponential Attractors for Maps 9
3. Exponential Attractors for Dissipative Evolution Equations of First Order 25
4. Approximation of Exponential Attractors 35
   4.1. A Simple Galerkin Approximation 35
5. Applications 39
   5.1. Kuramoto-Sivashinsky Equation 39
   5.2. Kolmogorov-Sivashinsky-Spiegel Equation 44
   5.3. 2D Navier-Stokes Equations 53
   5.4. 3D Navier-Stokes Equations 61
   5.5. The Original Burgers Equations 65
   5.6. Chaffee-Infante Reaction-Diffusion Equations 74
6. Exponential Attractors for Second Order Evolution Equations with Damping and Applications 81
   6.1. Functional Set-Up for Second Order Evolution Equations . . . 82
   6.2. Discrete Squeezing Property for Second Order Evolution Equations with Damping 83
   6.3. Applications to Damped Semilinear Wave Equations 89
      6.3.1. Sine-Gordon Equations 89
      6.3.2. Klein-Gordon Type Equations 90
      6.3.3. Systems of Sine-Gordon Equations 91
7. Alternative Construction of Exponential Attractors for Evolution Equations 93
   7.1. Exponential Attractors of Optimal Hausdorff Dimension . . . 94
   7.2. Exponential Attractors of Optimal Outer Lyapunov Dimension 98

8. Inertial Manifolds: A Brief Review and Comparison 111
9. Finite Dimensional Dynamics on Exponential Attractors 119
10. Mañé's Projections and Inertially Equivalent Dynamical Systems 125
    10.1. Generalized Dynamical Systems and the Induced Dynamics
          under Mañé's Projection 128
    10.2. Lifting the Generalized Dynamical System 133
Appendix A. A Constructive Proof of Mañé's Theorem for Hilbert
Spaces 141
Appendix B. A Simple Estimate of the Topological Entropy 161
Appendix C. Mathematical Background of Fractal Sets 165
References 173

Chapter 1
Introductory Remarks

In order to put the study of exponential attractors into perspective we would like to compare them with other sets that arise from the asymptotic behavior of dissipative PDE's. Unquestionably, among the many dissipative PDE's, one stands out as inspiring the most interesting analysis, that is the Navier-Stokes equations. Although the Navier-Stokes equations did not necessarily initiate all the ideas and trends in this subject, they certainly posed the most challenging questions and still require the most careful analysis. Here, instead of trying to follow a historical perspective, we will try to give an a posteriori view on the conceptual developments and their significance in the asymptotic study of Navier-Stokes equations.

In many fluid mechanical flows, the dissipative effects due to diffusion, friction or damping are reflected in the global, infinite-dimensional, phase picture of the partial differential equations modelling these flows. Such equations (with appropriate boundary conditions) are called *dissipative* if they define a forward regularizing flow in an adequate phase space containing an absorbing set. In general, an *absorbing set* is a bounded set that attracts all bounded solutions in finite time, at an exponential rate. The existence of an absorbing set B can be taken as a definition of dissipative PDE's, but in order to develop the subject further, one needs additional properties on B. For the sake of clarity we make a distinction between the case when B is a compact set and call such equations strongly dissipative. The 2D Navier-Stokes equations, the Kuramoto-Sivashinsky equation, the complex Ginzburg-Landau equation and some Reaction-Diffusion equations all fall under this more restricted category. Yet, when the dissipation is a result of a weak damping rather than friction, as it is the case for the weakly damped Sine-Gordon equation as well as the damped KdV equations, the absorbing sets need not be compact anymore ([T1],[H]). Since the main thrust of this study is on strongly dissipative systems, in the introduction we will not dwell on those which are not (see, however, section 6 on hyperbolic damped systems).

Given a compact absorbing set B, and a flow that leaves it positively invariant, the omega limit set of B under the flow has some interesting properties. It is the unique compact set that is both positively and negatively invariant under the flow, which attracts all solutions, eventually. Such a set is called the *global attractor* and it is the largest set that enjoys these properties. Let us remark, however, that the existence of the global attractor can also be guaranteed under weaker conditions (see [T1], [H]). One of the properties that makes the global attractors important objects to study is the fact that sometimes they have finite dimension. Various notions of dimensions have been considered in conjunction with attractors ([Fa]), among them the Hausdorff and fractal dimensions seem to stand up. A fundamental theorem (due to Mallet-Parret [MP]) states that if the linearized flow is exponentially decaying on the attractor for the lower modes, then the attractor has finite Hausdorff dimension. Later on this result has been generalized to Banach spaces (by Mañé [Ma 1-2]) and applied to the two dimensional Navier-Stokes equations [FT1, CF1, CFT1, CFT2, T1-4] and to other nonlinear PDE's that are dissipative [BV, T1, NST1, NST3]. Although the existence of a compact attractor that has finite Hausdorff dimension for 2D Navier-Stokes equations is quite surprising ([FT1], [BV], [La]), more can be obtained if one introduces a new tool into the picture. For Hilbert spaces, where the notion of volumes can be easily expressed, the Lyapunov exponents of the flow on the attractor gives a precise description on the evolution of volumes under the flow. Within this theory, it becomes easier to track various dimensions of attractors. In particular, a result due to Constantin and Foias ([CF1, CF2]) in the context of the 2D Navier-Stokes equations and extended by Constantin, Foias and Temam [CFT1] to the 3D Navier-Stokes and to general dissipative equations states that if the sum of first m Lyapunov exponents is negative, then not only the Hausdorff dimension of the attractor is less than m, but also the fractal dimension is finite and is estimated, up to a universal constant, by m. This result can be used to obtain sharp estimates for the fractal dimension of the attractor of 2D and 3D Navier-Stokes equations (see [CFMT], [CFT2]) that agrees with some of the results in the theory of fully developed turbulene obtained by more heuristic arguments ([Kr], [Ko]); the latter results in dimension two are based on estimating the average rate of transfer of enstrophy towards small scales. We mentioned this particular aspect of the theory in order to show the importance of explicit dimension estimates.

Once the importance of the attractors for the long time behavior of dissipative PDE's is established, the next stage is to unravel and/or compute global bifurcations of the attractor. This turns out to be a quite difficult task. Since the attractor is finite dimensional, it is natural to expect that it can be recovered by solving a large enough system of ODE's, that is the solutions on the attractor satisfy a system of ODE's. An indirect way of obtaining such a system is to imbed the attractor into a smooth finite dimensional manifold. An *inertial manifold* is an exponentially attracting smooth finite dimensional manifold that is forward invariant under the flow [FST, CFNT2]. Clearly, an inertial manifold when it exists will contain the attractor and when constructed properly will satisfy the desired conditions mentioned above. Within the context of ODE's an inertial manifold resembles a global central unstable manifold and can even be constructed by using similar tools. (Note, however, that the two notions do not coincide.)

For the purpose of studying the dynamics, the PDE can then be reduced to a system of Ordinary Differential Equations (ODE's) of relatively low dimension on the inertial manifold: this is called the *inertial form* system. There are several advantages to studying the ODE's resulting from an inertial form analysis. Most important, one needs to solve a much smaller system in order to study the dynamics. Besides the ability to perform accurate simulations, the reduction in size facilitates a numerical bifurcation analysis, and especially an understanding of the geometry of the stable and unstable manifolds connecting saddle orbits. One can then reconstruct the field for the full PDE.

Among the few ways of constructing an inertial manifold, we will briefly expose one method, that of spectral barriers, in Chapter 8 [CFNT3]; we refer the reader to [FST1,2], [T1], [CFNT1-2] or [FSTi] for the others. No matter which method is chosen, a variation of the same type of condition appears; this condition is called *spectral gap condition*. It requires the spectrum of the linear part of the PDE to have large enough gaps so that either the fixed point approach of Lyapunov-Perron or the method of forward evolution of the integral sets, due to Hadamard, will give an invariant set that is exponentially attracting. The spectral gap condition remains of course a restrictive one. Even for simple linear partial differential operators in two-space dimension, it is not always possible to obtain an explicit control over the gaps of consecutive eigenvalues; the simplest such example is the 2D Laplace operator with space periodic boundary conditions for which the eigenvalues are known explicitly, and the gap condition is satisfied by a suitably chosen subsequence (see [CFNT1-3], [MS], [R]). As for the partial differential operators in higher space dimensions, not much is known, except the interesting method of averaging due to Mallet-Paret and Sell that shows the existence of inertial manifolds for Reaction-Diffusion equations in higher space dimension [MS]. As a consequence, even when inertial manifolds exist for 2D or 3D problems, their dimension has not been estimated; see however the recent results of Temam and Wang [TWs] oncoming flawson a sphere (see also [DT], [TWs]. Returning to our quintessential equation, the 2D Navier-Stokes equations, the existence of an inertial manifold is still an open problem in general. Recently, via the spectral gap property of 2D Laplace operators, M. Kwak [Kw] proved the existence of an *inertial form* system for the 2D Navier-Stokes global attractor, for periodic boundary conditions (see also the above quoted reference [TWs] for geophysical flows). This also shows that an image of the attractor lies on a finite-dimensional, Lipschitz (Euclidean) manifold. However, the imbedding map (from the two components velocity vector to a nine-components extended vector), now known as the Kwak-transform, is not a global homeomorphism (its inverse is multivalued); and trajectories of the inertial form outside the attractor are *not invariant under the Navier-Stokes flow*.

If we start optimistically and try to obtain an inertial manifold for the dissipative PDE under consideration, we can resolve some of the theoretical problems related with dissipative PDE's at one shot. However, this is not the only possible scenario. It is perfectly possible that the existence of a finite dimensional attractor implies the existence of a system of ODE's with noncontinuous coefficients. The object of this monograph is to obtain a set on which we have a system of ODE's; we will call this set an Exponential Attractor. By its definition an *exponential attractor* is an exponentially attracting compact set with finite fractal dimension that is invariant under the forward flow. The easiest way of obtaining exponential attractors (sometimes also called *inertial sets*) is by taking the intersection of the absorbing ball with an inertial manifold. Clearly, such a construction, though perfectly legitimate, would carry with it the problems of the theory of inertial manifolds. An alternate approach is to consider the η-neighborhood of an Approximate Inertial Manifold of order η ([FMT2,3], [Ti], [T5]) but these neighborhoods are infinite dimensional. The alternate avenue which is considered here has its own advantages different from the previous ones. Since an absorbing set is also exponentially attracting, though not necessarily finite-dimensional, one can assume without loss of generality that the exponential attractors are subsets of an absorbing set. Combining this with the simple observation that exponential attractors must contain the global attractor, one obtains an idea where to look for an exponential attractor. Most probably, an ϵ-neighborhood of the attractor in a suitable finite dimensional space is an exponential attractor, but a priori it is not easy to determine what that finite dimensional manifold should be. So one must proceed differently. The construction we propose can be thought of as a fractal expansion of the attractor. Geometrically, during the iterative process of this construction, outlined in Chapter 2, we adjoin a generation of points to the attractor at each step, forming a cloud of points around the attractor. A very simplistic description of this method is given below.

First, we cover the absorbing ball with ϵ-balls and choose from each ϵ-ball a number of points that are not converging to the attractor exponentially. It is important to control the dimension of the newly formed cloud of points around the attractor. At the same time, one needs to make sure that this new set can be made invariant under the forward flow without increasing its dimension. At the next generation, one makes use of a covering in which the previous generation of points are centers of $\epsilon/2$-balls. Again, the bad points, that is, the ones that are not converging exponentially, are chosen from each $\epsilon/2$-ball and added to the previous set, and this process continues by induction. The key idea that allows the control on the number of points added at each stage is a form of squeezing property. The squeezing property was first noted in the context of systems of ODE's where it is called exponential dichotomy [Sa-S], and later for Navier-Stokes equations by Foias and Temam [FT1]. Basically, it is a dichotomy principle which says that either the lower modes are dominated by the higher ones or the flow is contracting exponentially. A stronger version of this property, called the cone property, was later observed for the Kuramoto-Sivashinsky equations as well and was utilized in the study of its inertial manifold [FNST1,2]. Here, relying on a weak version, we will be considering a snapshot of this property by choosing a small time t_* and transforming the flow to a map on the absorbing ball. Squeezing property of a discrete map, then, would allow one to carry the construction outlined above, since whenever the points do not converge exponentially, their behavior is determined by a few high modes. Of course, all of this heuristic description should be formalized carefully, which is the purpose of Chapter 2.

For the dissipative nonlinear evolution equations that have compact absorbing balls, a sufficient condition for the existence of an exponential attractor is furnished by a weak Lipschitz condition on the nonlinearity. In the third chapter, we show how to deduce from this condition on the nonlinearity, the squeezing property for a map obtained by discretizing the flow in time. It is very important to note here that, although the existence of the exponential attractor requires information about the asymptotic behavior of the eigenvalues of the linear part, *it does not need any kind of gap condition*. Hence, as the examples in Chapter 5 suggest, this theory is presently applicable to a much wider class of equations than the theory of inertial manifolds.

The applications in Chapter 5 strongly suggest that if one starts with a compact subset of an absorbing ball closer to the attractor, then one obtains much better estimates for the dimension of an exponential attractor. This idea is utilized first for 2D Navier-Stokes equations with periodic boundary conditions where, instead of the usual absorbing set that depends on the H and V norms, one considers a subset of it that is also bounded in $D(A)$. With this choice of absorbing ball, we are able to show that the fractal dimension, up to a logarithmic correction, is of the order of the square of the Grashoff number G. Another example in which we are able to derive good estimates is the case of Chaffe-Infante Reaction-Diffusion equations *in any space dimension*. A careful analysis reveals that there exists a compact subset of an absorbing ball that only includes functions which are bounded in L^∞-norm by a constant; using this subset and restricting the flow on this set, the existence of an exponential attractor is guaranteed. The surprising result is that the dimension estimate for the exponential attractor obtained in this way is not worse than the dimension estimate of the attractor obtained by using the much more powerful theory of Lyapunov exponents. It is also worth mentioning that the existence of inertial manifolds for these equations in space dimension higher than four is still an open question. The Kuramoto-Sivashinsky equation, for which an inertial manifold exists, has an exponential attractor of considerably lower fractal dimension. The same is true for Kolmogorov-Sivashinsky-Spiegel equations. For the convenience of the reader we have compared these results in Chapter 8, where dimension estimates of attractors, exponential attractors, and inertial manifolds are compared. As in [CFT1] we can also show that if the 3D Navier-Stokes equations have a global attractor with a uniformly bounded Reynolds number (as defined in [CFT1]) then the equations also have an exponential attractor; the upper estimate of the fractal dimension of this attractor is comparable with that given in [CFT1] for the global attractor. (see Section 5.4).

An exponential attractor (inertial set), in contrast to a global attractor, enjoys a uniform exponential rate of convergence of the solutions to it once the solution (i.e., the trajectory) is inside an invariant absorbing set. Because of this, exponential attractors possess a deeper and more practical property: they remain *more robust under perturbations and numerical approximations* than global attractors. We elaborate on this point since the literature sometimes gives the perception that attractors are robust under perturbations. One can only establish upper semi-continuity of attractors for approximations of semigroups and partial differential equations [HR], [HLR], [T1]. Specifically, if X_ϵ is the approximation to the attractor X, there exists a spherical

η-neighborhood of X, $\eta = \eta(\epsilon)$, which contains the approximate attractor X_ϵ. The reverse is not true. Similar problems occur in the construction of approximate inertial manifolds: these are in the vicinity of the exact attractor only in the sense of upper-semicontinuity. Whereas, denoting by X and $\mathcal{M}$ the exact global attractor and exponential attractor, and by X_ϵ and $\mathcal{M}_\epsilon$ the approximate ones, we prove at least for classical Galerkin approximations that the exact attractor X is within an η-spherical neighborhood of the approximate exponential attractor $\mathcal{M}_\epsilon$. Moreover, the approximate attractor X_ϵ is within an η-spherical neighborhood of the exact exponential attractor $\mathcal{M}$. Essentially, we also prove that approximate and exact exponential attractors are continuous with respect to the Hausdorff distance, modulo a time-shift (ϵ-dependent), at least for classical Galerkin approximations. The issue of approximations is discussed in Chapter 4. Because of these robustness properties (stability under approximation) we tend to believe that *whenever an attractor is approximated, it is, actually, some kind of exponential attractor that is produced.*

Inspired by the uniform convergence rate, we prefer to call these objects exponential attractors rather than inertial sets. In Chapter 6 we give examples of damped nonlinear equations of second order that admit an exponential attractor. Among the examples we present are the sine-Gordon, Klein-Gordon and systems of sine-Gordon equations. It has been observed (see Mora and Solà-Morales [Mo, MSM]), that when the damping is small, the sine-Gordon equation in one dimension does not have an attracting finite dimensional C^1-manifold. This result excludes the possibility of a C^1-inertial manifold, hence makes the study of finite dimensional fractal objects all the more desirable.

In Chapter 7 we present an alternative construction of exponential attractors for evolution equations [EFN]. We construct exponential attractors of almost optimal Hausdorff dimension and arbitrarily fast rate of convergence in Section 7.1; and in Section 7.2 exponential attractors of almost optimal Lyapunov dimension, with applications to 2D Navier-Stokes flows (both periodic and Dirichlet boundary conditions), and to the 2D Rayleigh-Bénard convection problem.

In Chapter 9 we show how to construct an exponential attractor inside an inertial manifold, should the latter exist for a given evolution equation; we establish the discrete squeezing property for the corresponding inertial form dynamical system. This often yields an exponential attractor of lower fractal dimension than the inertial manifold. The dynamics on the exponential attractor are realized as lifted dynamics from a finite dimensional system on $\mathbf{R}^N$.

In Chapter 10 we address the broader question: is there a natural way of reconstructing the dynamics on the exponential attractor as a finite dimensional dynamical system without direct recourse to the underlying equation? The essential ingredient in our analysis is the existence of Mañé injective projections [Ma3] for compact sets X of finite Hausdorff dimension $d_H(X)$ into $\mathbf{R}^N$ (actually we use a modified version of Mañé's Theorem for which $d_H(X \times X)$ is finite, see Appendix A). An injective projection P by itself is not sufficient to carry back and forth the dynamics from a compact invariant set X to PX. Therefore we are required to search for injective projections P with nicely behaved inverses, e.g., Hölder continuous inverses. In Appendix

A we prove the Hölder version of Mañé's theorem for X in a space of finite-dimension (albeit arbitrarily large). In Section 10.1 we construct generalized dynamical systems outside PX and the induced dynamics on PX under a Hölder-Mañé projection P. In Section 10.2 we lift such a generalized dynamical system back to the full space H, $X \subset H$. We define two dynamical systems as *inertially equivalent* if they have the same exponential attractor X and if their dynamics coincide on X. Finally, we prove that, given an exponential attractor X for an evolution equation in some arbitrarily large but yet finite dimensional space $H \subset \mathbf{R}^N$, there exists an inertially equivalent dynamical system of dimension $\tilde{N} = [2D+1]$, where D is the fractal (box counting) dimension of X. The extension of the Hölder-Mañé theorem to an infinite dimensional space is an open problem.

Chapter 2
Construction of Exponential Attractors for Maps

Let X be a compact, connected subset of a Hilbert space $\mathcal{H}$, let S be a Lipschitz continuous map from X into itself and let us denote the Lipschitz constant of S on X by

$$\operatorname{Lip}_X(S) = L. \tag{2.1}$$

If S is restricted to X, then it possesses a universal attractor $\mathcal{A}$ which is a compact, connected set given by

$$\mathcal{A} = \bigcap_{n=1}^{\infty} S^n X. \tag{2.2}$$

It is well-known that (see [T]) $\mathcal{A}$ attracts all trajectories eventually, that is, the symmetric Hausdorff distance $\rho(S^n X, \mathcal{A})$ goes to 0 as n goes to ∞. However, the rate of convergence to the attractor is not controlled exponentially as the following simple example shows: let $H = \mathbf{R}$, and define $S : [0,1] \to [0,1]$ by $Sx = 1/1+x$, then $\mathcal{A} = \{0\}$, but the rate of convergence to $\mathcal{A}$ is polynomial. To remedy this deficiency we introduce the concept of exponential attractor.

Definition 2.1. A compact set $\mathcal{M}$ is called an exponential fractal attractor for (S, X) if $\mathcal{A} \subseteq \mathcal{M} \subseteq X$ and

(i) $S\mathcal{M} \subseteq \mathcal{M}$,
(ii) $\mathcal{M}$ has finite fractal dimension, d_F,
(iii) there exist positive constants c_0 and c_1 such that

$$h(S^n X, \mathcal{M}) \leq c_0 \exp(-c_1 n), \quad \forall n \geq 1.$$

The pseudodistance used here is the standard asymmetric Hausdorff pseudodistance of two sets defined by $h(A, B) = \max_a \min_b |a - b|_H$, where A and

B are two compact sets. Note, however, that the standard Hausdorff metric $\rho(A, B)$ is defined by

$$\rho(A, B) = \max\{h(A, B), h(B, A)\}.$$

Exponential attractors carry properties both from attractors and inertial manifolds, yet they do not necessarily enjoy a manifold structure. In the case where the continuous dynamical system is known to have an inertial manifold $\mathcal{M}_0$, it is easy to see that $\mathcal{M}_0 \cap X$ is an exponential fractal attractor. In contrast to the construction of inertial manifolds the construction of exponential attractors resembles the "fractal expansion" of the attractor. In the process of construction the controlling property is a stronger version of the dichotomy principle observed for systems of ODE's by Sacker and Sell [Sa-S] and also for Navier-Stokes equations by Foias and Temam [FT1], it is a version of this squeezing property that plays the crucial role in the construction.

Definition 2.2. S has *squeezing property in X* if for some δ in $(0, 1/4)$ there exists an orthogonal projection $P = P(\delta)$ of rank equal to $N_0(\delta)$ such that: for every u and v in X, either

$$|Su - Sv|_H \leq \delta |u - v|_H, \tag{2.3}$$

or

$$|(I - P)(Su - Sv)|_H \leq |P(Su - Sv)|_H. \tag{2.4}$$

Remark 2.1. Although this definition is inspired from the squeezing property of Navier Stokes equations, it is not equivalent to it. Define S as the map induced by Poincaré sections of a Lipschitz continuous semi-flow $S(t)$, $t \geq 0$, at intervals $t = T^*$; that is, $S \doteq S(T^*)$. In essence, the squeezing property in Definition 2.2 is a dichotomy at the specific time T^*. Either a "cone condition" (2.4) is satisfied at T^*; if not, then the relative distance between the two trajectories at $t = T^*$ is contracted by a factor δ with respect to the distance at $t = 0$, as in (2.3). This *neither requires, nor implies any "squeezing" for intermediate times $0 < t < T^*$, nor does it depend on the full past history of the flow*. Also, in contrast to the construction of inertial manifolds, it *does not imply the invariance of the cone* $|(1 - P)(u(t) - v(t))|_H \leq |P(u - v)|_H$ for $t \geq T^*$, if (2.4) is verified at $t = T^*$ (see the review in Chapter 8 and [FNST], [CFNT2] [FST]). In Chapters 3, 5 and 6, we will give explicit determinations of T^* for semi-flows induced by various dissipative parabolic and damped hyperbolic systems.

A different way of describing the squeezing property is as follows: if for u and v in X,

$$|Su - Sv|_H > \sqrt{2} \, |P_{N_0}(Su - Sv)|_H \tag{2.5}$$

then

$$|Su - Sv|_H < \delta |u - v|_H. \tag{2.6}$$

In order to construct an exponential fractal attractor, we will consider subsets of $S^k(X)$ that are maximal with respect to the "cone property" (2.4). Let $\overline{B}_r(a)$ denote the closed ball in $\mathcal{H}$ centered at a in X, with radius r. Set

$$Z \doteq S(\overline{B}_r(a) \cap X), \tag{2.7}$$

and let E denote a subset of Z that is *maximal* for the relation ("cone property")

$$|u - v|_H \leq \sqrt{2}\, |P_{N_0}(u - v)|_H \quad \text{for all} \quad u \text{ and } v \text{ in } E. \tag{2.8}$$

We note that the set E is closed, hence compact. Moreover, the orthogonal projection P_{N_0} is injective on E. Hence, all the covers of E might be lifted from the covers of $P_{N_0}E$. From now on, we will drop the subscript N_0, but always keep in mind that P is an orthogonal projection to an N_0-dimensional space. Using the injectivity of P on E, we can estimate the number of ρ-balls necessary to cover Z in terms of N_0 and ρ.

Lemma 2.1. *For any $2\delta < \theta < 1$, there exists a covering of Z, defined in (2.7), by K_0 θr-balls, centered at y_j, in E with $j = 1, 2, \ldots, K_0$; moreover, K_0 can be estimated by*

$$K_0 \leq \left(\frac{3L}{\theta - 2\delta} + 1 \right)^{N_0}. \tag{2.9}$$

where δ is as given in (2.3).

Proof. Since $PE \subseteq PZ \subseteq P\mathcal{H}$, and using (2.1) and (2.7), diam $(PE) \leq$ diam $(PZ) \leq$ diam $(Z) \leq 2Lr$, given $\rho > 0$ arbitrary, we can cover PE with K_0 balls $B_\rho^{P\mathcal{H}}(Py_j)$ with $y_j \in E$ and $j = 1, 2, \ldots, K_0$. Note that the injectivity of P ensures that Py_j's are distinct points in $P\mathcal{H}$. In order to estimate K_0, we utilize the fact that diam $(PE) \leq 2Lr$. Observe that, if K is the maximum number of ρ-separated points in PE then the ρ-balls centered at these points cover PE, hence $K_0 \leq K$. On the other hand, $\rho/2$-balls centered at Py_j, $j = 1, \ldots, K$ are disjoint and

$$\bigcup_{j=1}^{K} B_{\rho/2}^{P\mathcal{H}}(Py_j) \subseteq B_{\rho/2}^{P\mathcal{H}}(PE) \doteq \{ y \in P\mathcal{H} : \text{dist}(y, PE) < \rho/2 \} \tag{2.10}$$

Since diam $(B_{\rho/2}^{P\mathcal{H}}(PE)) \leq 2Lr + \rho$, from N_0-volume comparisons we obtain that

$$K\omega_{N_0} \cdot \left(\frac{\rho}{2}\right)^{N_0} \leq \omega_{N_0} \left(Lr + \frac{\rho}{2}\right)^{N_0}, \tag{2.11}$$

where ω_{N_0} is the N_0-volume of the unit ball in $\mathbf{R}^{N_0}$. Consequently, we obtain

$$K_0 \leq K \leq \left(\frac{2Lr}{\rho} + 1\right)^{N_0}. \tag{2.12}$$

By expanding the radii in this covering of PE, we claim that we can obtain a covering of E. Once the covering of PE is obtained, by (2.8) we see that

$$|Py - Py_j|_H < \rho \Rightarrow |y - y_j|_H < \sqrt{2}\rho, \quad \forall y \in E, \tag{2.13}$$

hence $\mathcal{U} = \left\{ B_{\sqrt{2}\rho}^H(y_j) \right\}_{j=1}^{K_0}$ will give a covering for E. Now we show that we really get a cover of Z. If $Py \in PE$ then $|Py - Py_i|_H < \rho$ for some

$i \in \{1, 2, \ldots, K_0\}$. If, on the other hand, z is in $Z\setminus E$, then by definition of Z in (2.7) and E in (2.8), there exists $u \in \overline{B}_r(a) \cap X$ such that

$$z = Su$$

and there exists $y = Sv$ in E, with v in $\overline{B}_r(a) \cap X$, such that $|z - y| > \sqrt{2}|P(z - y)|$. From (2.5) and (2.6) it follows that

$$|z - y|_H = |Su - Sv|_H < \delta |u - v|_H \leq 2r\delta. \tag{2.14}$$

Since $y \in E$, there exists $y_j \in E$ such that $|Py - Py_j|_H < \rho$ hence $|y - y_j|_H < \sqrt{2}\rho$,

$$|z - y_j|_H \leq |z - y|_H + |y - y_j|_H \leq 2r\delta + \sqrt{2}\rho < \theta r \tag{2.15}$$

if

$$\rho = \frac{2(\theta - 2\delta)r}{3}. \tag{2.16}$$

Hence by (2.12) and (2.16),

$$K_0 \leq \left(\frac{3L}{\theta - 2\delta} + 1\right)^{N_0} \tag{2.17}$$

Note also that by (2.16), $\sqrt{2}\rho < \theta r$, hence $\mathcal{U}$ is a covering of the desired type. □

Remark 2.2. (i) The argument of the proof is still valid if X is replaced by any of its compact subsets that is invariant.

(ii) If $4\delta < \theta < 1$, then we can choose θ as close to 4δ as we like and $\rho = \delta r$, then the estimate on K_0 takes the following simpler form

$$K_0 \leq \left(\frac{2L}{\delta} + 1\right)^{N_0}.$$

(iii) The squeezing property introduced in Definition 2.2 can be slightly generalized by requiring

$$|(I - P)(Su - Sv)|_H \leq \alpha |P(Su - Sv)|_H$$

instead of (2.4), for some $\alpha > 0$. With this new flexibility, $\sqrt{2}$ becomes $\sqrt{1 + \alpha^2}$ everywhere, namely (2.5), (2.8), (2.13), (2.15) and after (2.17). Consequently, δ must be chosen so that

$$\delta(2 + \sqrt{1 + \alpha^2}) < 1.$$

Then the estimate on K_0 takes the form

$$K_0 \leq \left(\frac{2L\sqrt{1 + \alpha^2}}{\delta} + 1\right)^{N_0}.$$

□

From now on we set

$$\alpha(X) = \log K_0 / \log(1/\theta). \qquad (2.17a)$$

We now proceed, iteratively, to refine the covering given above to coverings of $S^k(X)$, with $k \geq 1$. To start this process, let $R > 0$ and a in X be such that

$$X \subseteq \overline{B}_R(a). \qquad (2.18)$$

Let E_1 denote a subset of $S(\overline{B}_R(a) \cap X) = S(X)$, which is maximal for the relation $|u - v|_H \leq \sqrt{2}|P(u-v)|_H$, for every u and v in E_1. Then by Lemma 2.1, there exists a_{j_1} in E_1 with $1 \leq j_1 \leq K_0$ such that

$$S(X) = S(\overline{B}_R(a) \cap X) \subseteq \bigcup_{j_1=1}^{K_0} \overline{B}_{\theta R}(a_{j_1}) \cap SX \qquad (2.19)$$

with K_0 estimated as in (2.9). We now proceed to refine this cover to obtain a cover for $S^2(X)$. Let $E_{2;j_1}$ be the maximal set with respect to cone property (2.8) in $S(\overline{B}_{\theta R}(a_{j_1}) \cap SX)$, where $1 \leq j_1 \leq K_0$. As in Lemma 2.1, we cover this compact set with M_2 balls $\overline{B}_{\theta^2 R}(a_{j_1;j_2}) \cap SX$, centered at the points a_{j_1,j_2} in $E_{2;j_1}$, with $1 \leq j_2 \leq M_2$. Now by (2.12) and (2.15) with $r = \theta R$, and $\rho = \frac{2}{3}\theta R(\theta - 2\delta)$

$$M_2 \leq \left(\frac{3L}{\theta - 2\delta} + 1\right)^{N_0}. \qquad (2.20)$$

Hence, using the same estimate on M_2 and K_0 allows us to set $M_2 \equiv K_0$. Furthermore, note that

$$\bigcup_{j_1=1}^{K_0} E_{2;j_1} \subset \bigcup_{j_1=1}^{K_0} S(\overline{B}_{\theta R}(a_{j_1}) \cap SX) \subset S^2 X, \qquad (2.21)$$

and

$$S^2(X) \subset \bigcup_{j_1=1}^{K_0} S(\overline{B}_{\theta R}(a_{j_1}) \cap SX) \subset \bigcup_{\substack{j_1=1 \\ 1}}^{K_0} \overline{B}_{\theta^2 R}(a_{j_1,j_2}) \cap S^2 X \qquad (2.22)$$

Proceeding by iteration, we can similarly cover $S^{k+1}(X)$. This is the content of Corollary 2.1. We start with a definition.

Definition 2.3. Let $E_{k+1;j_1,j_2,\ldots,j_k}$ denote a maximal set with respect to the "cone property" (2.8) in the compact set $S(\overline{B}_{\theta^k R}(a_{j_1,j_2,\ldots,j_k}) \cap S^k X)$, for some $a_{j_1,j_2,\ldots,j_k}$ in $E_{k;j_1,j_2,\ldots,j_{k-1}}$ with $j_1, j_2, \ldots, j_k$ in $\{1, 2, \ldots, K_0\}$. Here the balls $\overline{B}_{\theta^k R}(a_{j_1,j_2,\ldots,j_k}) \cap S^k X$ are coming from the cover of $S^k(X)$ at the level of the induction hypothesis, and where the centers $a_{j_1,j_2,\ldots,j_k}$ are chosen from the set $E_{k;j_1,j_2,\ldots,j_{k-1}}$.

Corollary 2.1. *There exists a covering of $S^{k+1}(X)$ such that*

$$S(\overline{B}_{\theta^k R}(a_{j_1,j_2,\ldots,j_k})) \cap S^k X) \subset \bigcup_{j_{k+1}=1}^{K_0} \overline{B}_{\theta^{k+1} R}(a_{j_1,j_2,\ldots,j_{k+1}}) \cap S^{k+1} X \quad (2.23)$$

with $a_{j_1,j_2,\ldots,j_{k+1}}$ in $E_{k+1;j_1,j_2,\ldots,j_k}$; moreover,

$$\bigcup_{\substack{j_1=1 \\ \vdots \\ j_k=1}}^{K_0} E_{k+1;j_1,j_2,\ldots,j_k} \subset \bigcup_{\substack{j_1=1 \\ \vdots \\ j_k=1}}^{K_0} S(\overline{B}_{\theta^k R}(a_{j_1,j_2,\ldots,j_k})) \cap S^k X) \subset S^{k+1} X \quad (2.24)$$

and

$$\begin{aligned} S^{k+1}(X) &\subset \bigcup_{\substack{j_1=1 \\ \vdots \\ j_k=1}}^{K_0} S(\overline{B}_{\theta^k R}(a_{j_1,j_2,\ldots,j_k})) \cap S^k X) \\ &\subset \bigcup_{\substack{j_1=1 \\ \vdots \\ j_k=1 \\ j_{k+1}=1}}^{K_0} \overline{B}_{\theta^{k+1} R}(a_{j_1,j_2,\ldots,j_k,j_{k+1}}) \cap S^{k+1} X. \end{aligned} \quad (2.25)$$

Definition 2.4. We set

$$E^{(k+1)} \doteq \bigcup_{\substack{j_1=1 \\ \vdots \\ j_k=1}}^{K_0} E_{k+1;j_1,j_2,\ldots,j_k} \subset S^{k+1} X \quad (2.26)$$

where $E_{k+1;j_1,j_2,\ldots,j_k}$ is as given in Definition 2.3.

Remark 2.3. All the sets that appear in Definition 2.4 are closed and compact.

We are now ready to construct an exponential fractal attractor for the flow induced by S on X.

Theorem 2.1. *The set $\mathcal{M}$ defined by*

$$\mathcal{M} = \mathcal{A} \cup \left(\bigcup_{j=0}^{\infty} \bigcup_{k=1}^{\infty} S^j(E^{(k)}) \right) \quad (2.27)$$

is an exponential fractal attractor for S. Moreover,
$$d_F(\mathcal{M}) \leq \max\{\alpha(X), N_0\}$$
where $\alpha(X)$ is as defined in (2.17a).

Proof. We first prove that $\mathcal{M}$ has finite fractal dimension. To this end, let us note that Lemma 2.1 already gives an estimate for the fractal dimension of the global attractor:

Lemma 2.2. *The global attractor $\mathcal{A}$ has finite fractal dimension $d_F(\mathcal{A})$, which can be estimated by $\alpha(\mathcal{A})$ where*

$$\alpha(\mathcal{A}) = \frac{\log K_0}{\log(1/\theta)}. \tag{2.28}$$

Proof (of Lemma 2.2). We use the covering idea introduced in Lemma 2.1 and the fact that $S^j(\mathcal{A}) = \mathcal{A}$ for $j = 1, 2, \ldots$. Let $N_\rho(\mathcal{A})$ denote the minimum number of balls, of radius ρ, that is necessary to cover $\mathcal{A}$. Then, if $\theta < 1$ using the covering idea of Lemma 2.1, for $X = \mathcal{A}$ and the fact that $S(\mathcal{A}) = \mathcal{A}$ we obtain a refined covering of $\mathcal{A}$ with $\theta\rho$-balls, where

$$N_{\theta\rho}(\mathcal{A}) = N_{\theta\rho}(S(\mathcal{A})) \leq K_0 N_\rho(\mathcal{A}). \tag{2.29}$$

Now by iteration,
$$N_{\theta^j \rho}(\mathcal{A}) \leq K_0^j N_\rho(\mathcal{A}). \tag{2.30}$$

If we choose $\epsilon > 0$ such that,
$$\theta^{j+1} \rho < \epsilon \leq \theta^j \rho, \tag{2.31}$$

then using the fact that $N_\epsilon(\mathcal{A})$ is a decreasing function of ϵ we obtain that

$$N_\epsilon(\mathcal{A}) \leq N_{\theta^{j+1} \rho}(\mathcal{A}) \leq K_0^{j+1} N_\rho(\mathcal{A}). \tag{2.32}$$

Since, $\log(1/\epsilon) \geq -\log(\theta^j \rho)$, we see that

$$\frac{\log N_\epsilon(\mathcal{A})}{\log(1/\epsilon)} \leq \frac{\log(K_0^{j+1} N_\rho(\mathcal{A}))}{-\log(\theta^j \rho)}. \tag{2.33}$$

Hence,

$$d_F(\mathcal{A}) = \overline{\lim_{\epsilon \to 0}} \frac{\log N_\epsilon(\mathcal{A})}{\log(1/\epsilon)} \leq \lim_{j \to \infty} \frac{\log(K_0^{j+1} N_\rho(\mathcal{A}))}{-\log(\theta^j \rho)}, \tag{2.34}$$

consequently,

$$d_F(\mathcal{A}) \leq \frac{\log K_0}{\log(1/\theta)} = \alpha(\mathcal{A}). \tag{2.35}$$

$\square$

Remark 2.4. Note that, if we use the estimate on K_0 given in (2.9) where all the constants L, δ are on $\mathcal{A}$ instead of X, we obtain, by Remark 2.1(ii), that
$$\alpha(\mathcal{A}) \leq \frac{N_0 \log\left(\frac{2L}{\delta} + 1\right)}{\log(1/\theta)}. \tag{2.36}$$

Next, we proceed to prove that $\mathcal{M}$ has finite fractal dimension in three steps:

Lemma 2.3. *Let* $C_\infty \doteq \overline{\bigcup_{k=1}^{\infty} E^{(k)}}$, *then*
$$d_F(C_\infty) \leq \max\{\alpha(X), N_0\} \tag{2.37}$$
where $\alpha(X)$ is as given in (2.28).

Lemma 2.4. *Let* $\Gamma_\infty \doteq \overline{\bigcup_{j=0}^{\infty} S^j(C_\infty)}$. *Then*
$$d_F(\Gamma_\infty) \leq \max\{\alpha(X), N_0\}. \tag{2.38}$$

Lemma 2.5. *$\mathcal{M}$ as defined in (2.27) is closed and it coincides with*
$$\mathcal{M} = \mathcal{A} \cup \Gamma_\infty. \tag{2.39}$$

As a direct consequence of the above Lemmas, we obtain:

Corollary 2.2.
$$d_F(\mathcal{M}) \leq \max\{\alpha(X), N_0\}. \tag{2.40}$$

We now proceed to prove the Lemmas in their stated order.

Proof (of Lemma 2.3). Let $\{B_1(x_j)\}_{j=1}^{\overline{N}}$ be a cover of X with $\overline{N}$ balls of radius 1, then for any $\bar{\rho} \geq 1$ we have
$$X \subseteq \bigcup_{j=1}^{\overline{N}} B_{\bar{\rho}}(x_j). \tag{2.41}$$

Given $\epsilon > 0$, define N^* such that
$$2\theta^{N^*+1} < \epsilon \leq 2\theta^{N^*}, \tag{2.42}$$
and $\bar{\rho} \in [1, 1/\theta]$ such that
$$\theta^{N^*+1}\bar{\rho} = \epsilon/2. \tag{2.43}$$

The idea of the proof rests upon the observation that
$$C_\infty = \overline{\bigcup_{k=1}^{\infty} E^{(k)}} \subset \overline{\bigcup_{k=1}^{N^*} E^{(k)}} \bigcup S^{N^*+1}(X). \tag{2.44}$$

Indeed,
$$C_\infty = \overline{\bigcup_{k=1}^{\infty} E^{(k)}} \subseteq \overline{\bigcup_{k=1}^{N^*} E^{(k)}} \bigcup \overline{\bigcup_{k=N^*+1}^{\infty} E^{(k)}} \qquad (2.45)$$

which together with $E^{(k+1)} \subset S^{k+1}X \subset S^{N_*+1}X$, $\forall k \geq N_*$ (see (2.26)) implies that,

$$C_\infty \subseteq \overline{\bigcup_{k=1}^{N^*} E^{(k)}} \bigcup S^{N^*+1}(X), \qquad (2.46)$$

which is the relation promised in (2.44).

As before, if $N_\epsilon(Y)$ denote the minimum number of ϵ-balls that is necessary to cover Y, then (2.44) implies that

$$N_\epsilon(C_\infty) \leq \sum_{k=1}^{N^*} N_\epsilon(E^{(k)}) + N_\epsilon(S^{N^*+1}(X)). \qquad (2.47)$$

Since $\epsilon = 2\bar{\rho}\theta^{N^*+1}$, using Lemma 2.1 iteratively, we obtain that
$$N_\epsilon(S^{N^*+1}(X)) = N_{2\bar{\rho}\theta^{N^*+1}}(S^{N^*+1}(X))$$
$$\leq K_0^{N^*+1} \cdot \overline{N}, \qquad (2.48)$$

where $\overline{N}$ is the number of $\bar{\rho}$-balls that cover X. Combining (2.44), (2.47) and (2.48), we obtain

$$N_\epsilon(C_\infty) \leq \sum_{k=1}^{N^*} N_\epsilon(E^{(k)}) + K_0^{N^*+1} \cdot \overline{N}. \qquad (2.49)$$

We now proceed to estimate $N_\epsilon(E^{(k+1)})$ for $k = 0, \ldots, N^* - 1$. By (2.23), (2.24) and (2.26), we have

$$(2.50) \quad \bigcup_{\substack{j_1=1 \\ \vdots \\ j_k=1}}^{K_0} E_{k+1; j_1, \ldots, j_k} = E^{(k+1)} \subseteq \bigcup_{\substack{j_1=1 \\ \vdots \\ j_{k+1}=1}}^{K_0} (\overline{B}_{2\bar{\rho}\theta^{k+1}}(a_{j_1, \ldots, j_{k+1}}) \cap S^{k+1}X).$$

Next we project the above covering to $P\mathcal{H}$ and obtain

$$\bigcup_{\substack{j_1=1 \\ \vdots \\ j_k=1}}^{K_0} PE_{k+1; j_1, \ldots, j_k} = PE^{(k+1)}$$

$$\subseteq \bigcup_{\substack{j_1=1 \\ \vdots \\ j_{k+1}=1}}^{K_0} (\overline{B}_{2\bar{\rho}\theta^{k+1}}^{P\mathcal{H}}(Pa_{j_1, j_2, \ldots, j_{k+1}}) \cap P(S^{k+1}X)). \qquad (2.51)$$

Then we cover each of the $2\bar\rho\theta^{k+1}$-radius balls on the right-hand side of (2.56) with $N^\#$ balls of radius $\epsilon/\sqrt{2}$, where $\epsilon = 2\bar\rho\theta^{N^*+1}$. A simple estimate of $N^\#$ can be obtained by covering the balls $B^{P\mathcal{H}}_{2\bar\rho\theta^{k+1}}$ first with squares and then imbedding these squares into $\epsilon/\sqrt{2}$-balls, namely,

$$N^\# \leq \left(\frac{(2\bar\rho\theta^{k+1})\sqrt{2N_0}}{\epsilon}\right)^{N_0} \leq (2N_0)^{N_0/2}(\theta^{k-N^*})^{N_0}, \tag{2.52}$$

where we have used $\epsilon = 2\bar\rho\theta^{N^*+1}$. Going back to (2.56), we see that, $PE^{(k+1)}$ is covered by $M = (K_0)^{k+1} N^\# \overline{N}$ balls $\{B_i^{P\mathcal{H}}\}_{i=1}^M$ of radius $\epsilon/\sqrt{2}$. Now, we note that by (2.56) again, for any set of indices $j_1, \ldots, j_k$ there are finitely many $\epsilon/\sqrt{2}$-balls that cover $PE_{k+1;j_1,\ldots,j_k}$ where the balls are coming from the cover $\{B_i^{P\mathcal{H}}\}_{i=1}^M$. But, then since $|u-v|_H \leq \sqrt{2}|P(u-v)|_H$ holds for every $u, v \in E_{k+1;j_1,\ldots,j_k}$, the balls with the same centers and with radius ϵ in $\mathcal{H}$ cover $E_{k+1;j_1,\ldots,j_k}$. Hence $M = (K_0)^{k+1} N^\# \overline{N}$ balls, of ϵ-radius, cover $E^{(k+1)}$.

Consequently, combining this last observation with the inequalities (2.54) and (2.57) we can deduce that

$$N_\epsilon(C_\infty) \leq \sum_{k=0}^{N^*-1}(K_0)^{k+1}\overline{N}(2N_0)^{N_0/2}(\theta^{k-N^*})^{N_0} + K_0^{N^*+1}\overline{N}$$

$$\leq \overline{N}(2N_0)^{N_0/2}\theta^{-(N^*+1)N_0}\sum_{k=1}^{N^*}(K_0\theta^{N_0})^k + K_0^{N^*+1}\overline{N}. \tag{2.53}$$

We consider two cases, if $K_0\theta^{N_0} \leq 1$ then by definition, $\alpha = \log K_0/\log(1/\theta) \leq N_0$. So (2.58) simplifies to

$$N_\epsilon(C_\infty) \leq \overline{N}(2N_0)^{N_0/2}\theta^{-(N^*+1)N_0} N^* + K_0^{N^*+1}\overline{N}. \tag{2.54}$$

Substituting into $\theta^{N^*+1} = \epsilon/2\bar\rho$ and $N^*+1 = \log(\epsilon/4\bar\rho)/\log\theta$,

$$N_\epsilon(C_\infty) \leq \overline{N}(2N_0)^{N_0/2}\left(\frac{4\bar\rho}{\epsilon}\right)^{N_0}\frac{\log(4\bar\rho/\epsilon)}{\log(1/\theta)} + K_0^{\frac{\log(4\bar\rho/\epsilon)}{\log(1/\theta)}}\overline{N}$$

$$\leq \overline{N}(2N_0)^{N_0/2}\left(\frac{4\bar\rho}{\epsilon}\right)^{N_0}\frac{\log(4\bar\rho/\epsilon)}{\log(1/\theta)} + \left(\frac{4\bar\rho}{\epsilon}\right)^{\frac{\log K_0}{\log(1/\theta)}}\overline{N}. \tag{2.55}$$

Hence,

$$\varlimsup_{\epsilon\to 0}\frac{\log N_\epsilon(C_\infty)}{\log(1/\epsilon)} \leq N_0. \tag{2.56}$$

In the case where $\theta^{N_0} K_0 \geq 1$, (2.58) simplifies to

$$N_\epsilon(C_\infty) \leq \overline{N}(2N_0)^{N_0/2}\theta^{-(N^*+1)N_0} N^*(K_0\theta^{N_0})^{N^*+1} + K_0^{N^*+1}\overline{N}$$

$$\leq \overline{N}(2N_0)^{N_0/2}N^* K_0^{N^*+1} + K_0^{N^*+1}\overline{N}$$

$$= \overline{N}K_0^{N^*+1}\left[(2N_0)^{N_0/2}N^* + 1\right].$$

Hence
$$N_\epsilon(C_\infty) \leq \overline{N} K_0^{\frac{\log(4\bar{\rho}/\epsilon)}{\log(1/\theta)}} \left[(2N_0)^{N_0/2} \frac{\log(4\bar{\rho}/\epsilon)}{\log(1/\theta)} + 1 \right] \qquad (2.57)$$

Consequently,
$$\varlimsup_{\epsilon \to 0} \frac{\log N_\epsilon(C_\infty)}{\log(1/\epsilon)} \leq \frac{\log K_0}{\log(1/\theta)} = \alpha. \qquad (2.58)$$

□

Proof (of Lemma 2.4). We start by observing that C_∞, being a closed subset of X, is itself compact. Hence, it is sufficient to prove a slightly general version of the Lemma. Namely, if C is compact and $d_F(C) \leq \bar{d} = \max\{\alpha, N_0\}$ then $\Gamma_\infty = \bigcup_{j=0}^{\infty} S^j(C)$ has also finite fractal dimension which is estimated by $\max\{\alpha, N_0\}$. Note that

$$\Gamma_\infty \subset C \cup S(C) \cup \ldots \cup S^n(C) \cup S^{n+1}(X). \qquad (2.59)$$

Let us fix n, such that
$$\theta^{n+1} < \epsilon \leq \theta^n, \qquad (2.60)$$

and then choose $\bar{\rho} \in [1, 1/\theta]$ such that
$$\epsilon = \theta^{n+1}\bar{\rho}. \qquad (2.61)$$

As in the proof of Lemma 2.3, we note that
$$N_\epsilon(\Gamma_\infty) \leq \sum_{j=0}^{n} N_\epsilon(S^j(C)) + N_\epsilon(S^{n+1}(X)). \qquad (2.62)$$

Using the result of the Lemma 2.1 with $r = \bar{\rho}$, $Z = S(B_{\bar{\rho}}(a) \cap C)$, we obtain by iteration
$$N_{\theta^j \bar{\rho}}(S^j(C)) \leq K_0^j N_{\bar{\rho}}(C), \qquad (2.63)$$

where X is replaced by C.

Combining (2.62), (2.63) and using $\epsilon = \theta^{n+1}\bar{\rho}$, we obtain
$$N_\epsilon(\Gamma_\infty) \leq \sum_{j=0}^{n} K_0^j N_{\epsilon\theta^{-j}}(C) + \overline{N} K_0^{n+1}, \qquad (2.64)$$

where $\overline{N}$ is the minimum number of balls of radius 1 necessary to cover the compact set X. As $d_F(C) \leq \bar{d}$, for any $d > \bar{d}$, there exists $\delta_0 = \delta_0(d) > 0$ such that for any $\delta \leq \delta_0$, $\log N_\delta(C) < d \log(1/\delta)$, hence

$$N_\delta(C) < (1/\delta)^d \quad \text{for} \quad \delta \leq \delta_0. \qquad (2.65)$$

On the other hand, for $\delta \geq \delta_0$, using $N_\delta(C) \leq N_{\delta_0}(C)$ we obtain that for $\delta_0 \leq \delta \leq 1$, (if $\delta_0 < 1$)

$$N_\delta(C) \leq N_{\delta_0}(C) \leq (1/\delta_0)^d \leq (\delta/\delta_0)^d (1/\delta)^d \leq c_d (1/\delta)^d, \tag{2.66}$$

where
$$c_d = (1/\delta_0)^d \quad \text{is greater than 1.} \tag{2.67}$$

Consequently, for $\delta \in (0, 1/4)$

$$N_\delta(C) \leq c_d (1/\delta)^d. \tag{2.68}$$

Now returning back to (2.64) and using $\delta = \theta^j \epsilon$, which is less than one, by (2.68) and $\bar{\rho} \leq 1/\theta$, we deduce that

$$\begin{aligned} N_\epsilon(\Gamma_\infty) &\leq \sum_{j=0}^{n} K_0^j c_d \left(\frac{1}{\epsilon \theta^{-j}} \right)^d + \overline{N} K_0^{n+1} \\ &\leq c_d \left(\frac{1}{\epsilon} \right)^d \sum_{j=0}^{n} (K_0 \theta^d)^j + \overline{N} K_0^{n+1}. \end{aligned} \tag{2.69}$$

Again, we consider two cases, if $K_0 \theta^d \leq 1$ then (2.64) can be simplified to

$$N_\epsilon(\Gamma_\infty) \leq c_d \left(\frac{1}{\epsilon} \right)^d n + \overline{N} K_0^{n+1}. \tag{2.70}$$

On the other hand, it follows from (2.66) that

$$n + 1 = \frac{\log(\bar{\rho}/\epsilon)}{\log(1/\theta)}. \tag{2.71}$$

Hence, from (2.70)

$$\begin{aligned} N_\epsilon(\Gamma_\infty) &\leq \frac{c_d}{(\bar{\rho})^d} \left(\frac{\bar{\rho}}{\epsilon} \right)^d \frac{\log(\bar{\rho}/\epsilon)}{\log(1/\theta)} + \overline{N} K_0^{\frac{\log(\bar{\rho}/\epsilon)}{\log(1/\theta)}} \\ &\leq \frac{c_d}{(\bar{\rho})^d} \left(\frac{\bar{\rho}}{\epsilon} \right)^d \frac{\log(\bar{\rho}/\epsilon)}{\log(1/\theta)} + \overline{N} \left(\frac{\bar{\rho}}{\epsilon} \right)^{\frac{\log K_0}{\log(1/\theta)}}, \end{aligned} \tag{2.72}$$

by definition of α, $\alpha = \log K_0 / \log(1/\theta)$ and $d > \bar{d} \geq \alpha$ implies that

$$N_\epsilon(\Gamma_\infty) \leq \left(\frac{\bar{\rho}}{\epsilon} \right)^d \left[\frac{c_d}{(\bar{\rho})^d} \frac{\log(\bar{\rho}/\epsilon)}{\log(1/\theta)} + \overline{N} \right]. \tag{2.73}$$

Finally,

$$\varlimsup_{\epsilon \to 0} \frac{\log N_\epsilon(\Gamma_\infty)}{\log(1/\epsilon)} \leq d + \varlimsup_{\epsilon \to 0} \frac{\log[K_1 + K_2 \log(1/\epsilon)]}{\log(1/\epsilon)} = d, \tag{2.74}$$

where $K_1 = \overline{N} + (c_d/(\bar{\rho})^d)(\log\bar{\rho}/\log(1/\theta)) \leq \overline{N} + c_d$ and $K_2 = (c_d/(\bar{\rho})^d) \times (1/\log(1/\theta))$. This finishes the case where $K_0\theta^d \leq 1$.

In the second case, where $K_0\theta^d \geq 1$, (2.74) simplifies, via (2.76), to

$$N_\epsilon(\Gamma_\infty) \leq \frac{c_d}{(\bar{\rho})^d}\left(\frac{\bar{\rho}}{\epsilon}\right)^d (K_0\theta^d)^n \cdot n + \overline{N}K_0^{n+1}$$

$$\leq \frac{c_d}{(\bar{\rho})^d}\left(\frac{\bar{\rho}}{\epsilon}\right)^d (K_0\theta^d)^{\frac{\log(\bar{\rho}/\epsilon)}{\log(1/\theta)}} \cdot \frac{\log(\bar{\rho}/\epsilon)}{\log(1/\theta)} + \overline{N}\left(\frac{\bar{\rho}}{\epsilon}\right)^{\frac{\log K_0}{\log(1/\theta)}}$$

$$\leq \frac{c_d}{(\bar{\rho})^d}\left(\frac{\bar{\rho}}{\epsilon}\right)^d \left(\frac{\bar{\rho}}{\epsilon}\right)^{\left[\frac{\log K_0}{\log(1/\theta)}-d\right]} \cdot \frac{\log(\bar{\rho}/\epsilon)}{\log(1/\theta)} + \overline{N}\left(\frac{\bar{\rho}}{\epsilon}\right)^{\frac{\log K_0}{\log(1/\theta)}}$$

$$\leq \left(\frac{\bar{\rho}}{\epsilon}\right)^{\frac{\log K_0}{\log(1/\theta)}} \left[\frac{c_d}{(\bar{\rho})^d} \cdot \frac{\log(\bar{\rho}/\epsilon)}{\log(1/\theta)} + \overline{N}\right]. \tag{2.75}$$

As before, using the fact that $\frac{\log K_0}{\log(1/\theta)} = \alpha \leq \bar{d} < d$, we obtain

$$\varlimsup_{\epsilon \to \infty} \frac{\log N_\epsilon(\Gamma_\infty)}{\log(1/\epsilon)} \leq d. \tag{2.76}$$

Consequently, since $d > \bar{d}$ was arbitrary

$$d_F(\Gamma_\infty) \leq \bar{d} = \max\{\alpha(X), N_0\}. \tag{2.77}$$

$\square$

Although the proof of Lemma 2.3 depended on all of the assumptions of Lemma 2.1, the previous proof does not. The crucial relation is the one given by (2.63) and an explicit dimension estimate of C in terms of K_0 and θ.

Corollary (to Lemma 2.4). *Let C be a compact subset of X that contains the attractor $\mathcal{A}$ of (S, X). Assume that C has finite fractal dimension d such that*

$$d_F(G) \leq \alpha \triangleq \frac{\log\beta}{|\log\theta|} \quad \text{with} \quad \beta > 1, \ \theta < 1,$$

and for every $\bar{\rho} \in [1, 1/\theta]$

$$N_{\bar{\rho}\theta^j}(S^j(C)) \leq \beta^j N_{\bar{\rho}}(C).$$

Then the set

$$\Gamma_\infty \triangleq \bigcup_{j=0}^{\infty} S^j(C) \quad \text{is compact}$$

and has finite fractal dimension that can be estimated by

$$d_F(\Gamma_\infty) \leq \alpha.$$

Proof (of Corollary). The set Γ_∞ is a closed subset of X, since $\mathcal{A} \subseteq C \subseteq \Gamma_\infty$. The estimate of its fractal dimension follows from the argument starting from (2.63). $\square$

Remark 2.5 This more general version of Lemma 2.4 will be used in Chapter 7 where an alternative construction of exponential attractors will be presented.

Proof (of Lemma 2.5). In order to prove that

$$\mathcal{M} = \mathcal{A} \cup \left[\bigcup_{j=0}^{\infty} \bigcup_{k=1}^{\infty} S^j(E^{(k)}) \right] \tag{2.78}$$

is a closed set, we proceed by contradiction. Suppose that $\mathcal{M}$ is not closed, then there exists a sequence (x_i, y_i, k_i, N_i) in $X \times X \times \mathbf{N} \times \mathbf{N}$ such that

$$y_i = S^{N_i}(x_i), \quad x_i \in E^{(k_i)}, \quad (y_i, x_i) \to (y_*, x_*) \tag{2.79}$$

but

$$y_* \notin \mathcal{M}.$$

Since $\mathcal{A} \subseteq \mathcal{M}$, it follows that $y_* \notin \mathcal{A}$. If $\{N_i\}$ was an unbounded sequence of natural numbers then $y_i = S^{N_i}(x_i)$ would have implied that $y_* \in \bigcap_{n=0}^{\infty} S^n(X) = \mathcal{A}$ which is not the case. So, there exists N^* such that $N_i = N^*$ for infinitely many i's, by choosing a subsequence, if necessary, we can ensure that

$$y_* = \lim_{i \to \infty} S^{N^*}(x_i) \quad \text{with} \quad x_i \in E^{(k_i)}. \tag{2.80}$$

On the other hand, $k_i \to \infty$ as well. For otherwise, i.e., $k_i \to k_*$, $x_i \in E^{(k_*)}$ as $i \to \infty$ and by compactness of $E^{(k_*)}$, $x_i \to x_*$, hence $x_* \in \mathcal{M}$, a contradiction.

Now $y_* \notin \mathcal{M}$ implies that $x_* \notin E^{(k)}$, for all $k \geq 1$ and $x_* \notin \mathcal{A}$. But $x_i \in E^{(k_i)}$ implies that $x_i \in S^{k_i} X$ (see (2.26)). Hence, as $k_i \to \infty$, at least for a subsequence, dist $(x_i, \mathcal{A}) \to 0$.

Therefore, $x_* = a_*$ is in $\mathcal{A}$, from (2.85) it follows that

$$y_* = S^{N^*}(x_*) \tag{2.81}$$

is also in $\mathcal{A}$, which contradicts the assumption that $y_* \notin \mathcal{M}$.

Next, we proceed to prove $\overline{\mathcal{M}} = \mathcal{M} = \mathcal{A} \cup \Gamma_\infty$. Clearly, it is sufficient to show that $\Gamma_\infty \subseteq \mathcal{M}$, that is for $j \in \mathbf{N}$

$$\operatorname{cl}_H \left[S^j \left(\bigcup_{k=1}^{\infty} E^{(k)} \right) \right] \subseteq \mathcal{A} \cup \bigcup_{j=0}^{\infty} \bigcup_{k=1}^{\infty} S^j(E^{(k)}) = \mathcal{M}. \tag{2.82}$$

As before, let $x_i \in E^{(k)}$ and $x_i \to x_*$; again since $E^{(k)} \subset S^k X$, following the previous argument, we deduce that x_* is in $\mathcal{A}$, hence in $\mathcal{M}$. Since $\mathcal{M}$ is invariant under S, $S^j(x_*)$ is also in $\mathcal{M}$. This proves that

$$\mathcal{M} = \mathcal{A} \cup \Gamma_\infty. \tag{2.83}$$

□

Proof of Corollary 2.2. Since $d_F(\mathcal{A})$ and $d_F(\Gamma_\infty)$ are both dominated by $\bar{d} = \max\{\alpha(X), N_0\}$, for any $d > \bar{d}$, there exists $\epsilon_0 > 0$ such that $\epsilon \leq \epsilon_0$ implies

$$N_\epsilon(\mathcal{A}) \leq (1/\epsilon)^d \quad \text{and} \quad N_\epsilon(\Gamma_\infty) \leq (1/\epsilon)^d. \tag{2.84}$$

Therefore, by (2.92)

$$N_\epsilon(\mathcal{M}) \leq N_\epsilon(\mathcal{A}) + N_\epsilon(\Gamma_\infty) \leq 2(1/\epsilon)^d. \tag{2.85}$$

By definition of d_F,

$$\varlimsup_{\epsilon \to 0} \frac{\log N_\epsilon(\mathcal{M})}{\log(1/\epsilon)} \leq \lim_{\epsilon \to 0} \frac{\log 2 + d\log(1/\epsilon)}{\log(1/\epsilon)} = d. \tag{2.86}$$

Hence, $d_F(\mathcal{M}) \leq \bar{d} = \max\{\alpha(X), N_0\}$. □

We return back to the proof of Theorem 2.1. Until now we have seen that $S(\mathcal{M}) \subseteq \mathcal{M}$ and that $d_F(\mathcal{M}) \leq \max\{\alpha, N_0\}$. It remains to prove that $\mathcal{M}$ is exponentially attracting.

Lemma 2.6. *For every x in X,*

$$\operatorname{dist}_H(S^k(x), \mathcal{M}) < R\theta^k \tag{2.87}$$

where R is chosen so that $X \subseteq \overline{B}_R(a)$ for some a in X, and θ is the fixed number given in Lemma 2.1, e.g. $\theta = (1 + 2\delta)/2$.

Proof. Note that $S^k(x)$ is in $S^k(X)$ hence by (2.25) there exists $a_{j_1, j_2, \ldots, j_k}$ in $E^{(k)}$ such that

$$|S^k(x) - a_{j_1, j_2, \ldots, j_k}|_H \leq \theta^k R. \tag{2.88}$$

Since by construction $E^{(k)} \subseteq \mathcal{M}$, it follows that

$$\operatorname{dist}_H(S^k(x), \mathcal{M}) \leq \theta^k R.$$

A fortiori,

$$\max_{x \in X} \min_{m \in \mathcal{M}} |S^k x - m|_H \leq \theta^k R \tag{2.89}$$

which, in turn, implies that

$$h(S^k X, \mathcal{M}) = O(e^{-ck}) \tag{2.90}$$

where h is the asymmetric pseudo-distance defined in (2.4). In contrast to the case of global attractor where $\rho(S^k X, \mathcal{A}) \to 0$ as $k \to \infty$, for the exponential attractors we can only claim that as $k \to \infty$

$$h(S^k X, \mathcal{M}) \to 0 \tag{2.91}$$

and

$$\rho(S^k X, E^{(k)}) \to 0 \tag{2.92}$$

where the last limit followed from the fact that $E^{(k)} \subset S^k X$, hence $h(E^{(k)}, S^k X) = 0$. □

Remarks 2.5. 1) Another way of looking at the discrete squeezing property (DSP) is through the dichotomy principle described in terms of the kth generation of sets $E^{(k)}$, instead of the cones,

(i) either at some level k, $S^k(x_0) \in E^{(k)}$

(ii) or $\text{dist}_H(S^j(x_0), E^{(j)}) \to 0$ exponentially.

In other words, $\forall x_0 \in X$, if there exists no k for which $S^k(x_0)$ belongs to $E^{(k)}$, then still the distance should converge to zero exponentially. Therefore, $E^{(k)}$ can be considered consisting of elements of X that do not necessarily converge exponentially to $\mathcal{A}$.

2) We also note that the limit points of the set $\cup_k E^{(k)}$ belongs to $\mathcal{A}$, hence

$$\mathcal{E} = \bigcup_k E^{(k)} \bigcup \mathcal{A}$$

is a compact subset of X that attracts all trajectories exponentially, by Lemma 2.6. However, it may not be invariant under the flow, which necessitates the construction of the set $\mathcal{A} \cup C_\infty$, see Lemma 2.37.

Chapter 3
Exponential Attractors for Dissipative Evolution Equations of First Order

The aim of this chapter is to apply the theory of exponential attractors, developed for maps in the previous chapter, to flows that are generated by dissipative evolution equations of the form

$$\frac{du}{dt} + Au + R(u) = 0, \tag{3.1}$$

$$u(0) = u_0. \tag{3.2}$$

Under the appropriate assumptions on the linear term A, the nonlinear term R and the data u_0, not only the existence and uniqueness of solutions are guaranteed, but also, due to the dissipative nature of the specific problem, the existence of a compact absorbing set B will also be assured. First let us summarize the general strategy which will allow us to obtain an exponential attractor for the evolution equation (3.1) and (3.2). Given the solution operator $S(t)$ that maps u_0 to $u(t)$ and the compact absorbing set B, we obtain a map from B into itself, by fixing $t = t_*$ in $S(t)$. Let us call this map S_*, i.e.,

$$S_* = S(t_*). \tag{3.3}$$

It is vital that t_* is chosen, small enough, so that the squeezing property, Definition 2.2, is satisfied for S_* for some $\delta < \frac{1}{8}$ and $N_0 = N_0(\delta)$. Then, using Theorem 2.2., the existence of an exponential attractor $\mathcal{M}_*$ is guaranteed for the map S_* on B. Next, we define

$$\mathcal{M} = \bigcup_{0 \le t \le t_*} S(t)\mathcal{M}_*. \tag{3.4}$$

If the map $F : [0,T] \times \mathcal{M}_* \to \mathcal{M}$ defined by

$$F(t,x) = S(t)x \tag{3.5}$$

is Lipschitz, then it can be shown that $\mathcal{M}$ is still a compact set with finite fractal dimension. Moreover, $\mathcal{M}$ will be exponentially attracting for $(\{S(t)\}_{t\geq 0}, B)$. Now, let us try to be more precise and start with the definition of an exponential attractor.

Definition 3.1. A compact set $\mathcal{M}$ is called an *inertial fractal set* for $((S(t))_{t\geq 0}, X)$ if $\mathcal{A} \subseteq \mathcal{M} \subseteq X$ and

(i) $S(t)\mathcal{M} \subseteq \mathcal{M}$, for $t \geq 0$,

(ii) $\mathcal{M}$ has finite fractal dimension $d_\mathcal{M}$, and

(iii) there exist positive constants a_0 and a_1 such that for all $t \geq 0$,

$$\text{dist}\,(S(t)X, \mathcal{M}) \leq a_0 \exp\{-a_1 t\}.$$

To pose the initial value problem for (3.1), we consider a separable Hilbert space H, and assume that A is a positive, self-adjoint linear operator with $D(A) \subset H$ and has a compact inverse A^{-1}. We further assume that the initial value problem (3.1) and (3.2) is solved by a semi-group of non-linear operators, $\{S(t)\}_{t\geq 0}$, that is continuous from H into $D(A)$, for $t > 0$. For each specific PDE that we will consider in section 5, the existence of an absorbing set, that is a set that absorbs all bounded sets in finite time, has already been shown (see [T], [NST], [FNT], [BV], ...). So, from now on, we assume that the non-linear operator $S(t)$ exists and for $t > 0$:

$$S(t) : H \to D(A) \text{ is continuous}, \tag{3.6}$$

and also, we assume the existence of a compact, invariant absorbing set, of the form

$$B = \{u \in H : |u|_H \leq \rho_0 \text{ and } \|u\|_{D(A^{1/2})} \leq \rho_1\}. \tag{3.7}$$

Since the inverse of A is compact, setting

$$V \doteq D(A^{1/2}), \tag{3.8}$$

makes it clear that V is compactly imbedded in H. For notational simplicity, we denote

$$\|u\| = \|u\|_V = |A^{1/2}u|_H \quad \text{and} \quad |u| = |u|_H. \tag{3.9}$$

To complete the set of assumptions on the equation (3.1), we further assume that the non-linear term

$$R : D(A) \to H \text{ is continuous}, \tag{3.10}$$

and that there exists a compact, invariant subset X of B, and a real number $\beta \in (0, 1/2]$ such that, for every u and v in X,

$$|R(u) - R(v)| \leq c_0 |A^\beta(u-v)|, \tag{3.11}$$

Exponential Attractors for Dissipative Evolution Equations

where c_0 depends on X. Let us remark that although the condition on the non-linearity (3.11) might seem a bit strong, at first sight, by choosing X properly, it can even be guaranteed for 2D Navier-Stokes equations with periodic boundary conditions (see Section 5.3).

Proposition 3.1. *Under the above conditions on the equation* (3.1), *and on the linear and the nonlinear terms, there exists a time* t_*, *such that the discrete operator* $S_* = S(t_*)$ *satisfies the squeezing property given in the Definition* 2.2, *for* $\delta < 1/8$.

Remark 3.1. Let us emphasize that this squeezing property is in some sense stronger than the usual squeezing property for Navier-Stokes equations, where in order to get a contraction at time t_* the difference of solutions are assumed to stay outside of the cone, for all times before t_* (see [FT],...).

Remark 3.2. In contrast to the existing results on the construction of inertial manifolds, here we do not assume any kind of spectral gap condition or the existence of a large spectral barrier for the equation (3.1) (see [CFNT1], [CFNT2], [FST]). Hence, it is natural that we obtain better estimates for the fractal dimension of the exponential attractors (see the examples in Chapter 5).

Proof. First, we introduce the projections that will be utilized. Since A is self-adjoint, positive operator and has a compact inverse, there exists a complete set of eigenvectors $\{w_n\}_{n=1}^{\infty}$ in H, corresponding to the positive eigenvalues $\{\lambda_n\}_{n=1}^{\infty}$, that is

$$Aw_n = \lambda_n w_n, \quad \text{for all } n. \tag{3.12}$$

Moreover, the eigenvalues increase indefinitely,

$$0 \leq \lambda_1 \leq \lambda_2 \leq \ldots \leq \lambda_n \nearrow \infty. \tag{3.13}$$

We set

$$H_n = \text{Span}\{w_1, w_2, \ldots, w_n\}, \tag{3.14}$$

and

$$P_n \text{ is the orthogonal projection onto } H_n. \tag{3.15}$$

Hence,

$$Q_n = I - P_n \text{ is the orthogonal projection onto the orthogonal complement of } H_n. \tag{3.16}$$

Let us assume that t_* has already been given and we are trying to prove the squeezing property, i.e., for every $\delta > 0$ there exists $N_0 = N_0(\delta)$ such that, by (2.3) and (2.4), for u and v in X, with S_* as defined in Proposition 3.1,

$$|Q_{N_0}(S_*u - S_*v)| > |P_{N_0}(S_*u - S_*v)| \tag{3.17}$$

implies that

$$|S_*u - S_*v| < \delta |u - v|. \tag{3.18}$$

A more workable condition, as we will show in the sequel, is obtained from (3.17) by setting
$$w_* = S_* u - S_* v, \tag{3.19}$$
and considering
$$\lambda_* \doteq \frac{\|w_*\|^2}{|w_*|^2}. \tag{3.20}$$

Let us note that, by the choice of the orthogonal projections P_{N_0} and Q_{N_0}, we obtain that $P_{N_0} w_*$ is orthogonal to $Q_{N_0} w_*$ with respect to inner products both in H and V. Hence

$$\lambda_* = \frac{\|P_{N_0} w_* + Q_{N_0} w_*\|^2}{|P_{N_0} w_* + Q_{N_0} w_*|^2} = \frac{\|P_{N_0} w_*\|^2 + \|Q_{N_0} w_*\|^2}{|P_{N_0} w_*|^2 + |Q_{N_0} w_*|^2} \tag{3.21}$$
$$> \frac{1}{2} \frac{\|Q_{N_0} w_*\|^2}{|Q_{N_0} w_*|^2}$$

by (3.17) and neglecting the positive term $\|P_{N_0} w_*\|^2$. But now we can go back to the operator A, to obtain

$$\|Q_{N_0} w_*\|^2 = |A^{1/2}(Q_{N_0} w_*)|^2 = (AQ_{N_0} w_*, Q_{N_0} w_*) \tag{3.22}$$
$$\geq \lambda_{N_0+1} |Q_{N_0} w_*|^2,$$

where the last inequality follows from the fact that the smallest eigenvalue of A over $Q_{N_0+1} H$ is λ_{N_0+1}. Consequently,

$$\lambda_* > \frac{1}{2} \lambda_{N_0+1}. \tag{3.23}$$

So our aim is to show that $\lambda_* > \frac{1}{2} \lambda_{N_0+1}$ implies $|w_*| < \delta |u-v|$. To this end, we start with two solutions u and v of the evolution equation (3.1) with initial values u_0 and v_0, respectively. Setting

$$w(t) \doteq u(t) - v(t), \tag{3.24}$$

we see that $w(t)$ satisfies

$$\frac{dw}{dt} + Aw + R(u) - R(v) = 0, \tag{3.25}$$
$$w(0) = u_0 - v_0 = w_0. \tag{3.26}$$

First, we estimate the Lipschitz constant L for $S(t)$. Taking the inner product of (3.25) with w, in H, we get

$$\frac{1}{2} \frac{d}{dt} |w|^2 + \|w\|^2 + (R(v) - R(u), w) = 0. \tag{3.27}$$

To estimate the non-linear term, we use the assumption (3.8) to deduce

$$|(R(v) - R(u), w)| \leq c_0 |A^\beta w| |w| \leq c_0 |w|^{1-2\beta} |A^{1/2} w|^{2\beta} |w|$$
$$\leq c_0 |w|^{2(1-\beta)} \|w\|^{2\beta}, \tag{3.28}$$

where we have used a standard interpolation combined with the fact that $\beta \in (0, 1/2]$. Finally, by Young's inequality with $p = \frac{1}{\beta}$ and $q = \frac{1}{1-\beta}$, from (3.27) and (3.28) we obtain

$$\frac{1}{2} \frac{d}{dt} |w|^2 + \|w\|^2 \leq c_0 |w|^{2(1-\beta)} \|w\|^{2\beta} \leq \frac{1}{2} c_1 |w|^2 + \frac{\|w\|^2}{2}. \tag{3.29}$$

Finally, neglecting $\|w\|^2$, on the left-hand side of (3.29), we get

$$\frac{d}{dt} |w|^2 \leq c_1 |w|^2, \tag{3.30}$$

here c_1 is a constant that depends only on c_0 and β. By Gronwall's inequality, it follows from (3.30) that

$$L = \text{Lip}_X(S(t)) \leq e^{c_1 t}. \tag{3.31}$$

We return back to the problem of finding the right projection P_{N_0} that will guarantee the squeezing property. From (3.29) we deduce that

$$\frac{d}{dt} |w|^2 + \|w\|^2 \leq c_1 |w|^2. \tag{3.32}$$

Setting

$$\lambda(t) \doteq \frac{\|w(t)\|^2}{|w(t)|^2} \quad \text{and} \quad \xi(t) \doteq \frac{w(t)}{|w(t)|}, \tag{3.33}$$

we obtain,

$$\frac{d}{dt} |w|^2 + (\lambda(t) - c_1) |w|^2 \leq 0. \tag{3.34}$$

By Gronwall's inequality, (3.34) implies that

$$|w(t)|^2 \leq \exp \left\{ -\int_0^t \lambda(\tau) d\tau + c_1 t \right\} |w(0)|^2. \tag{3.35}$$

Taking $t = t_*$ and noting that $w(t_*) = w_*$, as given in (3.19), we obtain

$$|S_* u - S_* v| = |w_*| \leq \delta(t_*) |u_0 - v_0|, \tag{3.36}$$

where

$$\delta_* = \delta(t_*) = \exp \left\{ -1/2 \int_0^{t_*} \lambda(\tau) d\tau + c_1 t_* \right\}. \tag{3.37}$$

At this point, we only know $\lambda_* = \lambda(t_*) > \frac{1}{2}\lambda_{N_0+1}$ by (3.23) and also that λ_{N_0+1} goes to infinity as N_0 goes to infinity. But, the past behavior of the quotient norm $\lambda(\tau)$ for $\tau < t_*$ is not known. The following lemma allows us to control the past of the quotient norm as well.

Lemma 3.1. *Let $\lambda(t)$ and $\xi(t)$ be as defined in (3.33) then $\lambda(t)$ satisfies the differential inequality*

$$\frac{d}{dt}\lambda(t) \leq c_0^2 \lambda^{2\beta}(t). \tag{3.38}$$

Moreover, if $\lambda(t_*) > \lambda_0$ then

$$\int_0^{t_*} \lambda(t)dt \geq \frac{1}{c_3}(1 - e^{-c_3 t_*})\lambda_0 - (c_2/c_3)t_*, \tag{3.39}$$

where c_3 and c_2 depend only on c_0 and β.

Proof. We start by deriving the differential equation that $\lambda(t)$ satisfies. Clearly,

$$\begin{aligned}
\frac{1}{2}\frac{d}{dt}\lambda(t) &= \frac{1}{|w|^2}[(w_t, Aw) - (w_t, w)\lambda(t)] \\
&= \frac{1}{|w|}(w_t, (A - \lambda)\xi) \tag{3.40} \\
&= \frac{1}{|w|}(-Aw - (R(u) - R(v)), (A - \lambda)\xi)
\end{aligned}$$

where the last equality followed from (3.25). However, we also have

$$\begin{aligned}
(\lambda\xi, (A - \lambda)\xi) &= \lambda(\xi, A\xi) - \lambda^2|\xi|^2 = \lambda\|\xi\|^2 - \lambda^2 \\
&= \lambda\frac{\|w\|^2}{|w|^2} - \lambda^2 = 0.
\end{aligned} \tag{3.41}$$

Hence,

$$|(A - \lambda)\xi|^2 = ((A - \lambda)\xi, (A - \lambda)\xi) = (A\xi, (A - \lambda)\xi) = \frac{1}{|w|}(Aw, (A - \lambda)\xi), \tag{3.42}$$

Combining (3.42) with (3.40), we deduce that

$$\begin{aligned}
\frac{1}{2}\frac{d}{dt}\lambda(t) + |(A - \lambda(t))\xi|^2 &= \frac{1}{|w|}(R(u) - R(v), (A - \lambda)\xi) \\
&\leq \frac{1}{|w|}|R(u) - R(v)||(A - \lambda)\xi| \\
&\leq \frac{c_0}{|w|}|A^\beta w||(A - \lambda)\xi| \tag{3.43} \\
&\leq \frac{1}{|w|}c_0|w|^{1-2\beta}\|w\|^{2\beta}|(A - \lambda)\xi| \\
&\leq c_0\lambda^\beta|(A - \lambda)\xi| \\
&\leq \frac{c_0^2}{2}\lambda^{2\beta} + \frac{1}{2}|(A - \lambda)\xi|^2,
\end{aligned}$$

where we have used (3.8), (3.28) and a simple Young's inequality with $p = q = 2$. After simplification,

$$\frac{d}{dt}\lambda(t) \leq c_0^2 \lambda^{2\beta}(t). \tag{3.44}$$

This proves the first part of the Lemma 3.1, as for as the second part, we use Young's inequality with $p = \frac{1}{2\beta}$ and $q = \frac{1}{1-2\beta}$, in the case $\beta < 1/2$ to obtain

$$\frac{d}{dt}\lambda(t) \leq c_3 \lambda(t) + c_2, \tag{3.45}$$

where c_2 and c_3 depends on c_0 and β. In the case $\beta = 1/2$, $c_3 = c_0^2$ and $c_2 = 0$. By Gronwall's inequality (3.45) implies that

$$\lambda(t) \leq e^{c_3(t-t_0)}\lambda(t_0) - (1 - e^{c_3(t-t_0)})\frac{c_2}{c_3}. \tag{3.46}$$

So that, by reversing the inequality for $0 \leq t_0 < t_*$

$$\lambda(t_0) \geq e^{c_3(t_0-t_*)}\lambda(t_*) - c_2/c_3 > e^{c_3(t_0-t_*)}\lambda_0 - c_2/c_3, \tag{3.47}$$

and after integration between 0 and t_*,

$$\int_0^{t_*} \lambda(t_0) dt_0 \geq \frac{1}{c_3}(1 - e^{-c_3 t_*})\lambda_0 - (c_2/c_3)t_*. \tag{3.48}$$

$\square$

As a simple consequence of the above Lemma, (3.37) can be estimated by

$$\delta_* \leq \exp\left\{-\frac{1}{c_3}(1 - e^{-c_3 t_*})\frac{\lambda_{N_0+1}}{2} + ((c_2/c_3) + c_1)t_*\right\}, \tag{3.49}$$

where we have used $\lambda_* = \lambda(t_*) \geq \lambda_{N_0+1}/2$.
Since c_3 depends only on β and c_0, t_* can be chosen initially so that $c_3 t_* = 1$, hence

$$\delta_* \leq \exp\left\{-\frac{1}{2c_3}\lambda_{N_0+1} + \frac{(c_2/c_3) + c_1}{c_3}\right\}. \tag{3.50}$$

Finally, if N_0 is large enough so that

$$\lambda_{N_0+1} > -4c_3 \ln(1/8) + 4((c_2/c_3) + c_1) \tag{3.51}$$

then, by (3.50)

$$\delta_* < 1/8. \tag{3.52}$$

$\square$

This finishes the proof of Proposition 3.1. We summarize the results in a Corollary.

Corollary 3.1. *Under the assumptions of Proposition 3.1, there exist constants c_1, c_2, c_3 that depend only on the constants β, c_0 of (3.11) such that if*

$$t_* = 1/c_3, \tag{3.53}$$

then

$$L_* = \mathrm{Lip}_X(S_*) \le e^{c_1/c_3}. \tag{3.54}$$

Moreover, if N_0 is chosen large enough so that

$$\lambda_{N_0+1} > 12c_3 \ln 2 + 4((c_2/c_3) + c_1) \tag{3.55}$$

then, for every u and v in X,

$$|Q_{N_0}(S_*u - S_*v)| > |P_{N_0}(S_*u - S_*v)| \tag{3.56}$$

implies, for $\delta_* < 1/8$,

$$|S_*u - S_*v| < \delta_*|u - v|. \tag{3.57}$$

In other words, $S_* : X \to X$ is a Lipschitz function with its Lipschitz constant L_* estimated by (3.54) and it satisfies the squeezing property given in the Definition 2.2, with $\delta < 1/8$.

The existence of an exponential attractor for (S_*, X) now follows from Theorem 2.1, but we have more.

Theorem 3.1. *Under the hypothesis of Proposition 3.1, and under the further assumption that the map $F(t, x) = S(t)x$ defined in (3.8) is Lipschitz from $[0, T] \times X$ into X, for any $T > 0$, the flow $\{S(t)\}_{t \ge 0}$ that is determined by (3.1) admits an exponential attractor $\mathcal{M}$ whose fractal dimension can be estimated by*

$$d_F(\mathcal{M}) \le d_F(\mathcal{M}^*) + 1. \tag{3.58}$$

Proof. As a simple consequence of Corollary 3.1 and Theorem 2.1, we obtain that the map $S_* = S(t_*)$ has an exponential attractor $\mathcal{M}_*$, on X, such that

$$h(S_*^n X, \mathcal{M}_*) \le \theta^n R = c_4 \delta_*^n. \tag{3.59}$$

Moreover,

$$d_F(\mathcal{M}^*) \le \max\{N_0, \alpha(X\} \le N_0 \max\{1, c_5\} \tag{3.60}$$

where $c_5 = \ln\left(\frac{2L_*}{\delta_*} + 1\right) / \ln(1/4\delta_*)$ is constant that can be estimated using c_1, c_2 and c_3. Now, we set

$$\mathcal{M} \doteq \bigcup_{0 \le t \le t_*} S(t)\mathcal{M}_*. \tag{3.61}$$

Clearly, $\mathcal{M} \subseteq X$ and by the continuity of the map $F(t, x)$ on $[0, T] \times X$, it is also compact. Also, $\mathcal{A} \subseteq \mathcal{M}_*$ implies, by definition of $\mathcal{M}$, $\mathcal{A} \subseteq \mathcal{M}$. Note, however, that $\mathcal{M}$ is the image of $[0, t_*] \times \mathcal{M}_*$ under F, which is assumed to be Lipschitz. Since Lipschitz functions preserve fractal dimension,

$$d_F(\mathcal{M}) \leq d_F([0, t_*] \times \mathcal{M}_*) \leq d_F(\mathcal{M}_*) + 1. \tag{3.62}$$

To see that $\mathcal{M}$ is invariant under the flow, we consider two cases. If $t \in [0, t_*]$, using $S_*\mathcal{M}_* = S(t_*)\mathcal{M}_* \subseteq \mathcal{M}_*$ we get

$$S(t)\mathcal{M} = \bigcup_{t \leq s \leq t_* + t} S(s)\mathcal{M}_*$$

$$= \left(\bigcup_{t \leq s \leq t_*} S(s)\mathcal{M}_* \right) \cup \left(\bigcup_{t_* \leq s \leq t_* + t} S(s)\mathcal{M}_* \right)$$

$$\subseteq \mathcal{M} \cup \left(\bigcup_{0 \leq s \leq t} S(s)\mathcal{M}_* \right) \subseteq \mathcal{M}. \tag{3.63}$$

As for the case $t > t_*$, we write $t = kt_* + s$ with $k > 0$ and $s \in [0, t_*]$ then

$$S(t)\mathcal{M} = S(kt_*)S(s)\mathcal{M} \subseteq S^k(t_*)\mathcal{M} = S_*^k \mathcal{M}$$

$$\subseteq \bigcup_{0 \leq s \leq t_*} S(s)S_*^k \mathcal{M}_* \subseteq \bigcup_{0 \leq s \leq t_*} S(s)\mathcal{M}_* = \mathcal{M}. \tag{3.64}$$

Finally, for the exponential convergence, for $t = kt_* + s$,

$$h(S(t)X, \mathcal{M}) = h(S(s)S_*^k X, \mathcal{M}) \leq L_* h(S_*^k X, \mathcal{M}_*)$$

$$\leq L_* c_4 \delta_*^k = (L_* c_4) \delta_*^{\frac{t-s}{t_*}} \tag{3.65}$$

$$\leq c_6 (\delta_*^{1/t_*})^t = c_6 \delta_0^t,$$

where c_6 is a constant that depends only on c_1, c_2, c_3 and $\delta_0 = \delta_*^{c_3} < (1/8)^{c_3}$. This finishes the proof that $\mathcal{M}$ is an exponential attractor for $(\{S(t)\}_{t \geq 0}, X)$. □

Remark 3.3. It is clear that the proper choice of the compact, invariant subset X of the absorbing set B is crucial in the estimation of c_0 and β that appears in (3.11), which in turn will determine all the remaining estimates. Of course, the method applied here will be modified slightly to give better estimates for fractal dimension of the exponential attractors in Chapter 5, where we will make the estimates more explicit by determining them in terms of relevant physical parameters.

Remark 3.4. In the limiting case where $\beta = 1/2$, it is possible to give a more explicit estimate for the dimension of the exponential attractor. For simplicity, we will assume that there exists $c_\lambda > 0$, and $\alpha > 0$, such that $\lambda_N \geq c_\lambda N^\alpha$, for all N. Then, as noticed before, $t_* = \frac{1}{c_0^2}$ and $c_2 = 0$, $c_1 = c_3 = c_0^2$; hence, it is sufficient to assume

$$c_\lambda N_0^\alpha 42 c_0^2 \ln 8 + 4c_0^2 = 4c_0^2 (\ln 8 + 1), \tag{3.66}$$

i.e.,
$$N_0 > \left(4(\ln 8 + 1)\left(\frac{c_0^2}{c_\lambda}\right)\right)^{1/\alpha}. \tag{3.67}$$

In such a case $d_F(\mathcal{M}) \leq N_0$, where N_0 is as given in (3.67).

Remark 3.5. Let us note that in the beginning of the argument, i.e., in (3.28), we only needed to assume

$$|(R(u) - R(v), w)| \leq c_0 |w|^{2(1-\beta)} \|w\|^{2\beta}, \tag{3.68}$$

in place of the more restrictive assumption on the nonlinearity given in (3.11). As for Lemma 3.1, it suffices to guarantee (3.39) which can be taken as an assumption, in particular we can assume that there exists $t = t_*$ such that

$$\int_0^{t_*} \lambda(t)\, dt \geq c_4 \lambda(t_*) - c_5 t_*, \tag{3.69}$$

where $c_4 \in (0, 1)$ and $c_5 > 0$. Then we can check the discrete squeezing property for $t = t_*$ and obtain through (3.23) and (3.69) that

$$\int_0^{t_*} \lambda(t)\, dt \geq \frac{1}{2} c_4 \lambda_{N_0+1} - c_5 t_*. \tag{3.70}$$

Returning back to (3.36), which is still valid by (3.68), and utilizing (3.70), we obtain that

$$|w_*| \leq \exp\left\{-\frac{c_4}{4}\lambda_{N_0+1} + \frac{1}{2}(c_5 + c_1)t_*\right\}|w_0|. \tag{3.71}$$

Consequently, the discrete squeezing property will be satisfied by choosing N_0 large enough. Hence, we can replace the condition (3.11) on the nonlinearity R by (3.68) and a condition, i.e., (3.69), on the integrability of the quotient norm $\lambda(t)$. We will see in Chapter 6 that for damped wave equations there is no need to control $\lambda(t)$ at all, since there is no natural candidate for it.

Chapter 4
Approximation of Exponential Attractors

4.1. A Simple Galerkin Approximation

We consider, once again, the abstract evolution equation of the form

$$u_t + Au + R(u) = 0, \tag{4.1}$$
$$u(0) = u_0, \tag{4.2}$$

where A is a positive self-adjoint operator with compact inverse and the nonlinear term R satisfy (3.10), (3.11) and, moreover,

$$R(0) \text{ is in } H. \tag{4.3}$$

The natural problem we would like to address is the approximation of an exponential attractor for (4.1) and (4.2) by exponential attractors of equations that are obtained through (4.1) and (4.2). One of the simplest possible examples is the standard Galerkin approximation of (4.1) and (4.2). Let P be an orthogonal projection on H that commutes with A, typically we will take $P = P_m$ to be the orthogonal projection onto the space spanned by the eigenvectors of A corresponding to the first m eigenvalues of A. Then the projected equations read as

$$y_{mt} + Ay_m + P_m R(y_m) = 0, \tag{4.4}$$

$$y_m(0) = P_m u_0. \tag{4.5}$$

Note that y_m is not necessarily equal to $P_m u$. Clearly, the theory of exponential attractors developed in the previous section for evolution equations of the type (4.1) and (4.2) equally applies to (4.4) and (4.5). Hence, the existence of an inertial $\mathcal{M}_m$ of (4.4) and (4.5) is guaranteed in the absorbing set $B_m = \{y \in P_m H : |y|_H \leq \rho_0 \text{ and } \|y\|_V \leq \rho_1\}$.

In order to study the convergence of the exponential attractor $\mathcal{M}_m$ of the Galerkin approximation of that of the full equation, $\mathcal{M}$, we need to consider the difference of two solutions. Let

$$v_m = u - y_m, \qquad (4.6)$$

then v_m satisfies:

$$v_{mt} + Av_m + R(u) - P_m R(y_m) = 0, \qquad (4.7)$$

$$v_m(0) = (I - P_m)u_0. \qquad (4.8)$$

Hence, by taking H-inner product with v_m, we obtain that

$$\frac{1}{2}\frac{d}{dt}|v_m|_H^2 + \|v_m\|_V^2 = (R(y_m) - R(u), v_m)_H - ((I - P_m)R(y_m), v_m)_H \qquad (4.9)$$

where we have replaced $P_m R(y_m)$ with $R(y_m) - (I - P_m)R(y_m)$. We start estimating the right-hand side of (4.9) in the usual way.

$$\frac{1}{2}\frac{d}{dt}|v_m|_H^2 + \|v_m\|_V^2 \leq |R(y_m) - R(u)|_H |v_m|_H + |R(y_m)|_H |(I - P_m)v_m|_H$$

$$\leq c_0 |v_m|_H^{2(1-\beta)} \|v_m\|_V^{2\beta} + |R(y_m) - R(0)|_H |(I - P_m)v_m|_H$$
$$+ |R(0)|_H |(I - P_m)v_m|_H$$

$$\leq c_1 |v_m|_H^2 + \frac{1}{4}\|v_m\|_V^2 + \left(c_0 \|y_m\|_V^{2\beta} |y_m|_H^{2(1-\beta)} \frac{1}{\sqrt{\lambda_{m+1}}} + \frac{c_2}{\sqrt{\lambda_{m+1}}}\right) \|v_m\|_V$$

$$\leq \frac{3}{4}\|v_m\|_V^2 + c_1 |v_m|_H^2 + \frac{c_0^2}{\lambda_{m+1}}\|y_m\|_V^{4\beta} |y_m|_H^{4(1-\beta)} + \frac{c_2^2}{\lambda_{m+1}}$$

where $c_1 = c_1(c_0, \beta)$ and $c_2 = |f|_H$. Now using the fact that y_m is in the absorbing set B_m, we have $|y_m|_H \leq \rho_0$ and $\|y_m\|_V \leq \rho_1$; therefore,

$$\frac{d}{dt}|v_m|_H^2 + \frac{1}{2}\|v_m\|_V^2 \leq 2c_1 |v_m|_H^2 + (2c_0^2 \rho_0^{4(1-\beta)} \rho_1^{4\beta} + 2c_2^2)/\lambda_{m+1}. \qquad (4.10)$$

Setting

$$\mu_m = \frac{2}{\lambda_{m+1}}\left[c_0^2 \rho_0^{4(1-\beta)} \rho_1^{4\beta} + c_2^2\right], \qquad (4.11)$$

we observe that as $m \to \infty$ $\lambda_m \to \infty$, hence $\mu_m \to 0$. On the other hand, applying the Gronwall's inequality to (4.10) gives

$$|v_m(t)|_H^2 \leq e^{2c_1 t}\left[|(I - P_m)u_0|_H^2 + \frac{1}{2c_1}\mu_m\right], \qquad (4.12)$$

but

$$|(I - P_m)u_0|_H^2 \leq \lambda_{m+1}^{-1}\|u_0\|_V^2 \leq \lambda_{m+1}^{-1}\rho_1^2. \qquad (4.13)$$

This time setting

$$\gamma = 2c_0^2 \rho_0^{4(1-\beta)} \rho_1^{4\beta} + 2c_2^2 + \rho_1^2, \tag{4.14}$$

we obtain that

$$|v_m(t)|_H^2 \leq \frac{e^{2c_1 t}}{\lambda_{m+1}} \gamma. \tag{4.15}$$

In other words, if $\{S_m(t)\}_{t \geq 0}$ denotes the solution semigroup of (4.4) and (4.5) and $\{S(t)\}_{t \geq 0}$ denotes the solution semigroup of the original evolution equations given in (4.1), then for u_0 in X, we have from (4.15)

$$|S(t)u_0 - S_m(t)P_m u_0|_H \leq \lambda_{m+1}^{-1/2} e^{c_1 t} \gamma^{1/2}. \tag{4.16}$$

Now let $\mathcal{M}$ denote an exponential attractor for $(S(t), B)$ and $\mathcal{M}_m$ denote an exponential attractor for $(S_m(t), B_m)$, then for every u in $\mathcal{M} \cap S(t)B$ there exists u_0 in B such that $S(t)u_0 = u$. By definition of an exponential attractor for every bounded subset Y of H and for every bounded set Y_m of $H_m = P_m H$, we have, see Definition 2.1,

$$h(\mathcal{M}, S(t)Y) \leq ce^{-\alpha t} h(\mathcal{M}, Y) \tag{4.17}$$

and

$$h(\mathcal{M}_m, S_m(t)Y_m) \leq ce^{-\alpha_m t} h(\mathcal{M}_m, Y_m). \tag{4.18}$$

In particular, we can utilize this property of exponential attractors for the absorbing sets mentioned above. So starting with u in $\mathcal{M} \cap S(t)B$, there exists u_0 in B such that $S(t)u_0 = u$. On the other hand, by (4.18) there exists u_m in $\mathcal{M}_m$ that depends on t also, such that

$$|u_m - S_m(t)P_m u_0|_H \leq ce^{-\alpha_m t}. \tag{4.19}$$

Consequently,

$$|u_m - u(t)|_H \leq |u_m - S_m(t)P_m u_0|_H + |S_m(t)P_m u_0 - S(t)u_0|_H$$
$$\leq ce^{-\alpha_m t} + \lambda_{m+1}^{-1/2} \gamma^{1/2} e^{c_1 t} \tag{4.20}$$

Let $t = \bar{t}$ be chosen so that

$$\bar{t} = \frac{1}{2(c_1 + \alpha_m)} \ln \left[\frac{\lambda_{m+1}}{\gamma} c^2 \right] \tag{4.21}$$

then by (4.20)

$$|u_m - u(\bar{t})|_H \leq 2ce^{-\alpha_m \bar{t}} = 2c_1 \left[\frac{\gamma}{\lambda_{m+1} c^2} \right]^{\frac{\alpha_m}{2(\alpha_m + c_1)}} \doteq \epsilon_m. \tag{4.22}$$

But as $m \to \infty$, $\epsilon \to 0$, therefore for every u in $\mathcal{M} \cap S(\bar{t})B$ there exists u_m in $\mathcal{M}_m$ such that
$$|u - u_m| < \epsilon_m, \qquad (4.23)$$
that is
$$\max_{u \in \mathcal{M} \cap S(\bar{t})B} \{ \max_{u_m \in \mathcal{M}_m} |u - u_m|_H \} < \epsilon_m. \qquad (4.24)$$
Since $\mathcal{M} \subseteq B$ and $S(\bar{t})\mathcal{M} \subseteq \mathcal{M} \cap S(\bar{t})B$ we deduce that
$$\max_{u \in S(\bar{t})\mathcal{M}} \{ \min_{u_m \in \mathcal{M}_m} |u - u_m|_H \} < \epsilon_m. \qquad (4.25)$$

Also a similar argument will show that
$$\max_{u_m \in S(\bar{t}_1)\mathcal{M}_m} \{ \min_{u \in \mathcal{M}} |u_m - u|_H \} < \epsilon'_m \qquad (4.26)$$
where $\bar{t}_1$ and ϵ'_m are chosen accordingly. We summarize the results outlined above in a theorem.

Theorem 4.1. *Let $\mathcal{M}$ be an exponential attractor for the evolution equation (4.1) and $\mathcal{M}_m$ be an exponential attractor for the Galerkin approximation (4.4). Then for every $\epsilon > 0$, there exists $\bar{t} = \bar{t}(\epsilon)$ and $m = m(\epsilon)$ such that*
$$h(S_m(\bar{t})\mathcal{M}_m, \mathcal{M}) < \epsilon \qquad (4.27)$$
and
$$h(S(\bar{t})\mathcal{M}, \mathcal{M}_m) < \epsilon. \qquad (4.28)$$

Remark 4.2. Since the exponential attractor is not constructed by considering full trajectories, it is natural not to expect a full shadowing effect, see Foias, Sell and Titi for such an effect. However, since the global attractors of each equation are included in the respective exponential attractors, by the invariance of the global attractor we deduce that
$$\mathcal{A}_m = S(\bar{t})\mathcal{A}_m \subseteq S(\bar{t})\mathcal{M}_m \text{ and } \mathcal{A} = S(\bar{t})\mathcal{A} \subseteq S(\bar{t})\mathcal{M}. \qquad (4.29)$$
Consequently, we obtain the following corollary:

Corollary 4.2. *For every $\epsilon > 0$, there exists $m = m(\epsilon)$ such that*
$$h(\mathcal{A}, \mathcal{M}_m) < \epsilon \qquad (4.30)$$
and
$$h(\mathcal{A}_m, \mathcal{M}) < \epsilon. \qquad (4.31)$$

Remark 4.3. It is easily checked that $S_m(\bar{t})\mathcal{M}_m$ in (4.27) and $S(\bar{t})\mathcal{M}$ in (4.28) are themselves exponential attractors for the Galerkin semi-flow and the full semi-flow; in that sense we have *continuity of exponential attractors with respect to the Hausdorff metric*, within the context of Galerkin approximations. This is in sharp contrast to mere upper-semicontinuity of the global attractor with respect to perturbations, see [HR, T1].

Chapter 5
Applications

The methods developed in Chapters 2 and 3 allow one to construct exponential fractal attractors for a large class of dissipative partial differential equations. For equations like Kuramoto-Sivashinsky ([NFST1,2]), Kolmogorov-Sivashinsky-Spiegel ([CNT], [CFNT2]), Ginzburg-Laudau ([DGHN], [C]), etc., although the existence of inertial manifolds have been established, the known dimension estimates for their attractors and their inertial manifolds differ substantially. Hence, starting with an inertial manifold $\mathcal{M}$ for these equations and considering the intersection of this inertial manifold with an absorbing ball may result in exponential fractal attractors of unreasonably high dimension. For comparison of these two approaches the reader is referred to Chapter 6, where a brief review of the theory of inertial manifolds is presented, and various estimates are quoted. On the other hand, for equations like Burgers' with Dirichlet boundary conditions, 2D Navier-Stokes, with periodic boundary conditions, and Reaction Diffusion-Equation, in higher space dimensions, where the existence of an inertial manifold is yet to be shown, it is possible to obtain exponential fractal attractors with reasonable dimension estimates.

In each of the following applications, the existence of an absorbing ball is already known. Following the general method outlined in Chapter 3 and the apriori estimates for the solutions of these equations in terms of the physical parameters, we proceed to derive upper bounds for the fractal dimension of the exponential attractors as constructed in Chapter 3 and Chapter 4.

5.1 Kuramoto-Sivashinsky Equation

Consider
$$u_t + u_{xxxx} + u_{xx} - uu_x = 0 \tag{5.1.1}$$

The Kuramoto-Sivashinsky equations ([Ku], [Si]) have been extensively investigated for chaotic dynamics in [HN], [HNZ], [KNS]. For functions defined on $[-L/2, L/2]$, odd and L-periodic, with $L \geq 1$. Let $H = \{u \in L^2(-L/2, L/2):$

5. Applications

u odd on $[-L/2, L/2]\}$, then one proves [NST1-3] that the set

$$B = \{u \in H : u_x \in L^2(-L/2, L/2), |u|_{L^2} \leq \rho_0 \text{ and } |u_x|_{L^2} \leq \rho_1\}, \quad (5.1.2)$$

with

$$\rho_0 = c_0 L^{5/2} \quad \text{and} \quad \rho_1 = c_1 L^{7/2}, \quad (5.1.3)$$

is absorbing for all bounded subsets of H, where c_0 and c_1 are absolute constants. A direct consequence of these apriori estimates can be obtained using Agmon type inequality, for $u \in B$

$$|u|_{L^\infty} \leq |u|_{L^2}^{1/2} |u_x|_{L^2}^{1/2} \leq (\rho_0 \rho_1)^{1/2} = (c_0 c_1)^{1/2} L^3. \quad (5.1.4)$$

For simplification we will use u' to denote the derivative of u with respect to x, then the initial value problem can be posed as

$$\begin{aligned} u_t + u'''' + u'' - uu' &= 0, \\ u(0) = u_0 \quad \text{in} \quad H. \end{aligned} \quad (5.1.5)$$

Next, we estimate the Lipschitz constant L for the solution operator $S(t)$ over the absorbing set. If $u(t, x)$ and $v(t, x)$ are two solutions of (5.1.1) with initial values u_0 and v_0 respectively in B then the difference

$$w(t, x) \doteq u(t, x) - v(t, x) \quad (5.1.6)$$

satisfy

$$w_t + w'''' + w'' - (2w\bar{u})' = 0, \quad (5.1.7)$$

$$w(0) = u_0 - v_0, \quad (5.1.8)$$

where $\bar{u} \doteq (u + v)/2$ is still in the absorbing ball B. Taking the L^2-inner product with $w(t)$ in (5.1.7) results in:

$$\frac{1}{2}\frac{d}{dt}|w(t)|_{L^2}^2 + |w''(t)|_{L^2}^2 = |w'(t)|_{L^2}^2 - (\bar{u}'(t), w^2(t))_{L^2}. \quad (5.1.9)$$

Since $|w'(t)|_{L^2}^2 \leq |w(t)|_{L^2}|w''(t)|_{L^2} \leq \frac{1}{2}|w(t)|_{L^2}^2 + \frac{1}{2}|w''(t)|_{L^2}^2$ and

$$\begin{aligned} |(\bar{u}'(t), w^2(t))_{L^2}| &= |(\bar{u}(t), 2w(t)w'(t))_{L^2}| \\ &\leq 2|\bar{u}(t)|_{L^\infty}|w(t)|_{L^2}|w'(t)|_{L^2} \\ &\leq 2|\bar{u}(t)|_{L^\infty}|w(t)|_{L^2}^{3/2}|w''(t)|_{L^2}^{1/2} \\ &\leq \frac{3}{4}(2)^{4/3}|\bar{u}(t)|_{L^\infty}^{4/3}|w(t)|_{L^2}^2 + \frac{1}{4}|w''(t)|_{L^2}^2, \end{aligned} \quad (5.1.10)$$

where we have used Young's inequality $ab \leq \frac{a^p}{p} + \frac{b^q}{q}$ with $p = 4$, $q = 4/3$, (5.1.9) simplifies to

$$\frac{1}{2}\frac{d}{dt}|w(t)|_{L^2}^2 + \frac{1}{4}|w''(t)|_{L^2}^2 \leq \frac{1}{2}|w(t)|_{L^2}^2 + 2|\bar{u}(t)|_{L^\infty}^{4/3}|w(t)|_{L^2}^2. \quad (5.1.11)$$

Using $|\bar{u}(t)|_{L^\infty}^2 \le |\bar{u}(t)|_{L^2}|\bar{u}'(t)|_{L^2} \le \rho_0\rho_1 = (c_0 L^{5/2})(c_1 L^{7/2}) = c_0 c_1 L^6$, we obtain from (5.1.11)

$$\frac{d}{dt}|w(t)|_{L^2}^2 + \frac{1}{2}|w''(t)|_{L^2}^2 \le (1 + 4(c_0c_1)^{2/3}L^4)|w(t)|_{L^2}^2 \\ \le (1 + c_2 L^4)|w(t)|_{L^2}^2, \quad (5.1.12)$$

where we set $c_2 = 4(c_0 c_1)^{2/3}$. Neglecting $\frac{1}{2}|w''(t)|_{L^2}^2$ on the left-hand side of (5.1.12) and using Gronwall's inequality, we get

$$|w(t)|_{L^2}^2 \le e^{(1+c_2 L^4)t}|w(0)|_{L^2}^2 \quad (5.1.13)$$

hence,

$$L = \mathrm{Lip}_B(S(t)) \le e^{\frac{1}{2}(1+c_2 L^4)t}. \quad (5.1.14)$$

Following the notation introduced in (3.33), $\lambda(t) = |w''(t)|_{L^2}^2/|w(t)|_{L^2}^2$ and $\xi(t) = w(t)/|w(t)|_{L^2}$ (5.1.12) can be rewritten as

$$\frac{d}{dt}|w(t)|_{L^2}^2 + \left[\frac{1}{2}\lambda(t) - (1 + c_3 L^4)\right]|w(t)|_{L^2}^2 \le 0. \quad (5.1.15)$$

Hence (3.35) takes the form

$$|w(t)|_{L^2} \le \delta(t)|w(0)|_{L^2}, \quad (5.1.16)$$

with

$$\delta(t) = \frac{1}{2}\exp\left\{-\frac{1}{2}\int_0^t \lambda(\tau)d\tau + (1+c_2 L^4)t\right\}. \quad (5.1.17)$$

In order to prove the squeezing property for $S_* = S(t_*)$ we set

$$t_* \doteq L^{-4}, \quad (5.1.18)$$

and assume, by (3.23)

$$\lambda_* \doteq \lambda(t_*) \ge \frac{1}{2}\lambda_{N_0+1}, \quad (5.1.19)$$

where λ_{N_0+1} is the (N_0+1)-th eigenvalue of the operator $Au = u''''$ on H. So that,

$$\lambda_{N_0+1} = \left(2\pi\frac{N_0+1}{L}\right)^4. \quad (5.1.20)$$

Following the argument given in Chapter 3, we look at the differential equation that $\lambda(t)$ satisfies, from (3.43) it follows that

$$\frac{1}{2}\frac{d}{dt}\lambda(t) + |(A - \lambda(t))\xi(t)|_{L^2}^2 = (\xi'(t) - (2\bar{u}\xi)', (A - \lambda(t))\xi(t))_{L^2}, \quad (5.1.21)$$

where the nonlinear term $R(u)$ was taken as $u'' - uu'$.

Using Schwarz's inequality and Young's inequality and neglecting a positive term on the left-hand side, (5.1.21) implies that

$$\frac{d}{dt}\lambda(t) \leq \frac{1}{2}|\xi'(t) - (2\bar{u}(t)\xi(t))'|^2_{L^2}$$
$$\leq |\xi'(t)|^2_{L^2} + 2|2\bar{u}'(t)\xi(t)|^2_{L^2} + 2|2\bar{u}(t)\xi'(t)|^2_{L^2}$$
$$\leq |\xi(t)|_{L^2}|\xi''(t)|_{L^2} + 4|\bar{u}'(t)|^2_{L^2}|\xi(t)|^2_{L^\infty} + 4|\bar{u}(t)|^2_{L^\infty}|\xi'(t)|^2_{L^2}$$
$$\leq |\xi''(t)|_{L^2} + 4\rho_1^2|\xi(t)|_{L^2}|\xi'(t)|_{L^2} + 4|\bar{u}(t)|_{L^2}|\bar{r}(t)|_{L^2}|\xi(t)|_{L^2}|\xi''(t)|_{L^2}$$
$$\leq \lambda(t) + 4\rho_1^2|\xi(t)|^{1/2}_{L^2}|\xi''(t)|^{1/2}_{L^2} + 4\rho_0\rho_1\lambda(t)^{1/2}$$
$$\leq \lambda(t) + 4\rho_1^2\lambda(t)^{1/4} + 4\rho_0\rho_1\lambda(t)^{1/2}, \quad (5.1.22)$$

where we have used the fact that $\lambda(t) = |\xi''(t)|^2_{L^2}$. In order to make the inequality (5.1.22) homogeneous, we introduce a new positive parameter β by

$$\beta \doteq L^4 - 1, \quad (5.1.23)$$

and using Young's inequality with $p = 4/3$, $q = 4$, $a = 4\rho_1^2\left(\frac{2}{\beta}\right)^{1/4}$ and $b = \left(\frac{\beta\lambda(t)}{2}\right)^{1/4}$,

$$4\rho_1^2\lambda(t)^{1/4} \leq \frac{\beta}{2}\lambda(t) + 8(\rho_1^8/\beta)^{1/3}, \quad (5.1.24)$$

and also with $p = q = 2$, $a = 4\rho_0\rho_1(2/\beta)^{1/2}$, $b = (\beta\lambda(t)/2)^{1/2}$, to obtain

$$4\rho_0\rho_1\lambda(t)^{1/2} \leq \frac{\beta}{2}\lambda(t) + \frac{32}{\beta}\rho_0^2\rho_1^2. \quad (5.1.25)$$

So that, combining (5.1.22) with (5.1.23) and (5.1.24)

$$\frac{d}{dt}\lambda(t) \leq (\beta + 1)\lambda(t) + 8\left(\frac{\rho_1^8}{\beta}\right)^{1/3} + \frac{32}{\beta}\rho_0^2\rho_1^2. \quad (5.1.26)$$

By Gronwall's inequality, for $0 \leq t \leq t_*$,

$$\lambda_* = \lambda(t_*) \leq e^{(\beta+1)(t_*-t)}\left(\lambda(t) + \left(8\left(\frac{\rho_1^8}{\beta}\right)^{1/3} + \frac{32}{\beta}\rho_0^2\rho_1^2\right)t_*\right), \quad (5.1.27)$$

so that by (5.1.19), reversing the inequality

$$\lambda(t) \geq \frac{1}{2}\lambda_{N_0+1}e^{(\beta+1)(t-t_*)} - \left[8\left(\frac{\rho_1^8}{\beta}\right)^{1/3} + \frac{32}{\beta}\rho_0^2\rho_1^2\right]t_*. \quad (5.1.28)$$

Integrating (5.1.27) from 0 to t_*, we obtain

$$\int_0^{t_*} \lambda(t)dt \geq \frac{1}{2(\beta+1)}(1 - e^{-(\beta+1)t_*})\lambda_{N_0+1} - \left[4\left(\frac{\rho_1^8}{\beta}\right)^{1/3} + \frac{16}{\beta}\rho_0^2\rho_1^2\right]t_*^2, \quad (5.1.29)$$

hence by (5.1.17)

$$\begin{aligned}\delta_* = \delta(t_*) \\ \leq \frac{1}{2}\exp\Big\{&-\frac{1-e^{-(\beta+1)t_*}}{4(\beta+1)}\lambda_{N_0+1} \\ &+\Big[4\Big(\frac{\rho_1^8}{\beta}\Big)^{1/3}+\frac{16}{\beta}\rho_0^2\rho_1^2\Big]t_*+(1+c_3L^4)t_*\Big\}.\end{aligned} \quad (5.1.30)$$

Substituting the values of ρ_0, ρ_1, β and t_* from (5.1.3), (5.1.18), (5.1.23) into (5.1.29) and utilizing $1 - \exp(-(\beta+1)t_*) = 1 - e^{-1} > 1/2$, we obtain

$$\delta_* \leq \frac{1}{2}\exp\Big\{-\frac{1}{8L^4}\lambda_{N_0+1}+c_3\Big\}, \quad (5.1.31)$$

where c_3 depends only on c_0 and c_1, coming from (5.1.3). Also using the value for λ_{N_0+1} from (5.1.20)

$$\delta_* \leq \frac{1}{2}\exp\Big\{-\frac{2\pi^4}{L^8}(N_0+1)^4+c_3\Big\}. \quad (5.1.32)$$

Hence, if

$$N_0 \doteq c_4 L^2 \quad \text{where} \quad c_4 = \Big(\frac{2\ln 2+c_3}{2\pi^4}\Big)^{1/4}, \quad (5.1.33)$$

then $\delta_* < 1/8$. Summarizing the results as a Corollary to Theorem 3.1, we have shown:

Proposition 5.1. *The Kuramoto-Sivashinsky equation as given in (5.1.1) admits an exponential fractal attractor $\mathcal{M}_0$ in B, as in (5.1.2), whose fractal dimension is estimated by*

$$d_F(\mathcal{M}_0) \leq c_7 L^2, \quad (5.1.34)$$

where c_7 is a constant that depends only on the absolute constants c_0 and c_1 as given in (5.1.3).

Moreover, there exist positive constants c_6 and c_9 such that for all $t \geq 0$

$$\text{dist}_{L^2}(S(t)B, \mathcal{M}_0) \leq c_9 e^{-c_6 L^4 t}. \quad (5.1.35)$$

Proof. First we set $t_* = L^{-4}$, then since by (5.1.14) $S_* = S(t_*)$ is a Lipschitz function on B with

$$L_* = \text{Lip}_B(S(t_*)) \leq \exp\frac{1}{2}(1+c_2L^4)t_* \leq e^{c_5},$$

and satisfies the squeezing property, by Theorem 2.1, S_* admits an exponential fractal attractor $\mathcal{M}_* \subseteq B$ such that

$$d_F(\mathcal{M}_*) \leq \max\{\alpha(B), N_0\} \leq N_0 \max\left\{1, \frac{\log\left(\frac{2L_*}{\delta_*}+1\right)}{\log(1/\theta_*)}\right\}. \quad (5.1.36)$$

Using $L_* \leq e^{c_5}$, $N_0 = c_4 L^2$, $\delta_* = e^{-c_6}$, by (5.1.31), and $\theta_* = 4\delta_*$, the fractal dimension can be estimated by

$$d_F(\mathcal{M}_*) \leq c_7 L^2, \quad (5.1.37)$$

where c_7 depends only on c_0 and c_1. By defining

$$\mathcal{M}_0 = \bigcup_{0 \leq t \leq t_*} S(t)\mathcal{M}_*, \quad (5.1.38)$$

we see as in the proof of Theorem 3.1 that $\mathcal{M}_0$ is an exponential fractal attractor and

$$d_F(\mathcal{M}_0) \leq 2c_7 L^2. \quad (5.1.39)$$

Moreover, by (3.65)

$$\text{dist}_{L^2}(S(t)B, \mathcal{M}_0) \leq c_8 L_* \left[(\delta_*)^{1/t_*}\right]^t \leq c_9 (\delta_*^{L^4})^t \leq c_9 e^{-c_6 L^4 t}. \quad (5.1.40)$$

$\square$

Remark 5.1. We have implicitly assumed that the map $(t, x) \to S(t)x$ is Lipschitz from $[0, T] \times B$ into B, this can be easily verified.

5.2 Kolmogorov-Sivashinsky-Spiegel Equation

A variant of the Kuramoto-Sivashinsky equation, with an additional non-linear viscosity term, is Kolmogorov-Sivashinsky-Spiegel equation which is given by

$$u_t + u'''' + [(2 - \delta(u')^2)u']' + (u')^2 + \alpha u = 0, \quad (5.2.1)$$

for functions defined on $[0, L]$ and is L-periodic. The parameters α and δ are positive, and $\alpha < 1$ and $L > 1$. The existence of the non-linear viscosity term $\delta((u')^2 u')'$ allows one to show existence of solutions without recourse to the methods used in Kuramoto-Sivashinsky equations. For the sake of completeness, we will give the proofs for the two a priori estimates (from [FNT]) that will be used in the sequel to show the existence of an exponential attractor for (5.2.1). First, we would like to show the existence of an absorbing set of the form

$$B = \{u \in L^2[0, L] : |u'|_{L^2} \leq \rho_1 \text{ and } |u''|_{L^2} \leq \rho_2\}, \quad (5.2.2)$$

where

$$\rho_1 = \delta^{-1/2} L^{3/2} \quad \text{and} \quad \rho_2 = c_0 \rho_1 (1 + \delta^{-1/4} + L). \quad (5.2.3)$$

Consider the following Hilbert spaces,
$$H \doteq L^2[0,L] \quad \text{and} \quad V \doteq \{u \in H^1(0,L) : u \text{ is } L\text{-periodic}\}, \tag{5.2.4}$$
then the local existence theorem guarantees a solution of (5.2.1) with initial value u_0 in V for $t \in [0, t_0)$ with $t_0 > 0$.

Lemma 5.2 [FNT]. *Let u be a solution of (5.2.1) in $V \times [0, t_0)$ then for $t \in [0, t_0)$ $|u'(t)|_{L^2} \geq \rho_1$ implies that*
$$d/dt|u'(t)|_{L^2} < 0. \tag{5.2.5}$$

Proof. Let $v = u'$, then v satisfies
$$v_t + v'''' + 2v'' - \delta(v^3)'' + 2vv' + \alpha v = 0. \tag{5.2.6}$$
Thus
$$\frac{1}{2}\frac{d}{dt}|v|_{L^2}^2 + |v''|_{L^2}^2 + 3\delta(v^2,(v')^2)_{L^2} + \alpha|v|_{L^2}^2 = 2|v'|_{L^2}^2, \tag{5.27}$$
by standard interpolation, $|v'|_{L^2}^2 \leq |v|_{L^2}|v''|_{L^2} \leq \frac{1}{2}|v|_{L^2}^2 + \frac{1}{2}|v''|_{L^2}^2$, hence
$$\frac{1}{2}\frac{d}{dt}|v|_{L^2}^2 + 3\delta(v^2,(v')^2)_{L^2} + \alpha|v|_{L^2}^2 \leq |v|_{L^2}^2. \tag{5.2.8}$$
Since $\alpha < 1$, the contribution of the non-linear term is essential, if for some $t \in [0, t_0)$ $d/dt|v(t)|_{L^2} \geq 0$, then for the same t by (5.2.7) and (5.2.8) we have
$$3\delta(v^2,(v')^2)_{L^2} \leq \min\{2|v'|_{L^2}^2, (1-\alpha)|v|_{L^2}^2\}. \tag{5.2.9}$$
Let
$$v^2 \sim \sum_m c_m w_m, \tag{5.2.10}$$
be the Fourier series expansion of v^2 in $L^2[0, L]$ where
$$w_m(x) = \exp\left\{\frac{2\pi i}{L}mx\right\}. \tag{5.2.11}$$
Then rewriting the left-hand side of the inequality (5.2.9), we obtain
$$3\delta(v^2,(v')^2)_{L^2} = \frac{3\delta}{2}\int_0^L ((v^2)')^2\, dx$$
$$= \frac{3\delta}{2}\left|\sum_{m\neq 0} \frac{2\pi i m}{L} c_m w_m\right|_{L^2}^2$$
$$= \frac{3\delta}{2}\frac{4\pi^2}{L^2}\sum_{m\neq 0} m^2 c_m^2 |w_m|_{L^2}^2 \tag{5.2.12}$$
$$= \frac{6\delta\pi^2}{L^2}\sum_{m\neq 0} m^2 c_m^2 \cdot L = \frac{6\delta\pi^2}{L}\sum_{m\neq 0} m^2 c_m^2$$
$$= \frac{6\delta\pi^2}{L}\sum_{m\neq 0} m^2 c_m^2,$$

combining it with (5.2.9), we obtain

$$\frac{6\delta\pi^2}{L}\sum_{m\neq 0} m^2 c_m^2 \leq \min\{2|v'|_{L^2}^2, (1-\alpha)|v|_{L^2}^2\}. \qquad (5.2.13)$$

On the other hand, since $|v|_{L^2}^2 = |v^2|_{L^1} = Lc_0^2$,

$$\begin{aligned}
\left| v(x)^2 - \frac{1}{L}|v|_{L^2}^2 \right|_{L^\infty} &= \sum_{m\neq 0} c_m \leq \left(\sum_{m\neq 0}\frac{1}{m^2}\right)^{1/2}\left(\sum_{m\neq 0} m^2 c_m^2\right)^{1/2} \\
&\leq \left(\frac{\pi^2}{3}\right)^{1/2} \cdot \left(\frac{L(1-\alpha)}{6\delta\pi^2}\right)^2 |v|_{L^2} \qquad (5.2.14)\\
&= \frac{1}{\sqrt{18}}\left(\frac{L(1-\alpha)}{\delta}\right)^{1/2}|v|_{L^2}
\end{aligned}$$

by (5.2.13). Finally,

$$\begin{aligned}
0 < 2|v'|_{L^2}^2 - 3\delta\int_0^L v^2(v')^2\, dx \\
\leq \int_0^L (v')^2(2-3\delta v^2)\, dx \\
\leq |v'|_{L^2}^2 |2-3\delta v^2|_{L^\infty} \\
\leq |v'|_{L^2}^2 (2-3\delta |v^2|_{L^\infty}) \qquad (5.2.15)\\
\leq |v'|_{L^2}^2 \left(2 - 3\delta\left(\frac{1}{L}|v|_{L^2}^2 - |v^2(x) - \frac{1}{L}|v|_{L^2}^2|_{L^\infty}\right)\right) \\
\leq |v'|_{L^2}^2 \left(2 - \frac{3\delta}{L}|v|_{L^2}^2 + \frac{3\delta}{\sqrt{18}}\left(\frac{L(1-\alpha)}{\delta}\right)^{1/2}|v|_{L^2}\right),
\end{aligned}$$

where we have used (5.2.14) in the last inequality. Now let

$$f(r) = 2 - \frac{3\delta}{L}r^2 + \left(\frac{\delta L(1-\alpha)}{2}\right)^{1/2} r, \qquad (5.2.16)$$

then for $r \geq \delta^{-1/2}L^{3/2}\alpha^a$ with $a \geq \ln\left(\frac{1-\alpha}{18}\right)/2\ln\alpha$,

$$f(r) \leq 0.$$

So that, if $|v|_{L^2} \geq \delta^{-1/2}L^{3/2}\alpha^a$ then the right-hand side of (5.2.15) would be negative, contrary to the assumption. By contradiction, for t such that $|v(t)|_{L^2} \geq \delta^{-1/2}L^{3/2}\alpha^a$, we must have

$$d/dt|v(t)|_{L^2} < 0.$$

□

Remark 5.2. Since $\alpha \in (0,1)$ the apriori estimate we now obtain is slightly better, in particular the set

$$B_a = \{u \in H : |u'|_{L^2} \leq \rho_1 \alpha^a\} \quad (5.2.17)$$

is shown to be absorbing.

By virtue of the above lemma the set

$$B_0 = \{u \in H : |u'|_{L^2} \leq \rho_1\} \quad (5.2.18)$$

is absorbing for the solution operator $\{S(t)\}_{t \geq 0}$, for $t < t_0$, which in turn implies that the solution exists globally. Next, we proceed to show an absorbing ball in $H^2(0,L)$.

Lemma 5.3 [CFNT3]. *Let*

$$B = \{u \in H : |u'|_{L^2} \leq \rho_1 \quad and \quad |u''|_{L^2} \leq \rho_2\} \quad (5.2.19)$$

where ρ_1 and ρ_2 are as given in (5.2.3).

Then B is absorbing for the equation (5.2.1) in H.

Proof. As in Lemma 5.2, we consider the equation for $v = u'$ and also the equation for $w = v' = u''$, whenever it makes sense. First, by (5.2.7) we have

$$\frac{1}{2}\frac{d}{dt}|v|^2 + |v''|^2 + 3\delta|vv'|^2 + \alpha|v|^2 = 2|v'|^2 \leq 2|v||v''|. \quad (5.2.20)$$

Integrating from t_0 to t, and using the fact that $|v| \leq \rho_1$ we deduce that

$$\int_{t_0}^t (|v''(s)|^2 + 3\delta|vv'(s)|^2 + \alpha|v|(s)|^2) ds \leq 2\rho_1 \int_{t_0}^t |v''(s)| ds + \frac{1}{2}\rho_1^2$$

$$\leq 2\rho_1 (t-t_0)^{1/2} \left(\int_{t_0}^t |v''(s)|^2 ds\right)^{1/2} + \frac{1}{2}\rho_1^2 \quad (5.2.21)$$

$$\leq \frac{1}{2}\int_{t_0}^t |v''(s)|^2 ds + 2\rho_1^2(t-t_0) + \frac{1}{2}\rho_1^2.$$

Hence,

$$\int_{t_0}^t (|v''(s)|^2 + 6\delta|vv'(s)|^2 + 2\alpha|v(s)|^2) ds \leq \rho_1^2(4(t-t_0) + 1). \quad (5.2.22)$$

For $t - t_0 \leq 1$, it follows from $|v'|^4 \leq |v|^2|v''|^2$ that

$$\int_{t_0}^t |v'(s)|^4 ds \leq 5\rho_1^4, \quad (5.2.23)$$

hence, there exists $s_0 \in [t_0, t]$ such that $|v'(s_0)| \leq \rho_1 5^{1/4}$.

Next, we consider the equation for $w = v' = u''$, which is
$$w_t + w'''' + 2w'' - 3\delta(v^2 w)' + (2vw)' + \alpha w = 0 \tag{5.2.24}$$

From which, it follows that

$$\begin{aligned}
\frac{1}{2}\frac{d}{dt}|w|^2 + |w''|^2 + \alpha|w|^2 &= 2|w'|^2 - 3\delta(v, w^3) + (w, w^2) \\
&\leq \frac{1}{2}|w''|^2 + 2|w|^2 + (3\delta|v|_{L^\infty} + 1)\left[\int_0^L w^3(x)dx\right] \\
&\leq \frac{1}{2}|w''|^2 + 2|w|^2 + (3\delta|v|^{1/2}|w|^{1/2} + 1)(|w|^2|w'|) \\
&\leq \frac{1}{2}|w''|^2 + 2|w|^2 + (3\delta\rho_1^{1/2}|w|^{1/2} + 1)(|w|^{5/2}|w''|^{1/2}) \\
&\leq |w''|^2 + 2|w|^2 + (3\delta\rho_1^{1/2})^{4/3}|w|^4 + |w|^{10/3}.
\end{aligned} \tag{5.2.25}$$

By (5.2.23) $\int_{t_0}^t |w|^4 \leq 5\rho_1^4$, hence by Uniform Gronwall's lemma (see e.g. [T1]) it follows that $|w(t)|^2$ remains bounded for all time $\geq t_0$. Our goal is to obtain an explicit bound for $|w(t)|^2$ without using Uniform Gronwall's lemma. Consider the functional

$$V(v) = \frac{1}{2}|v'|^2 - |v|^2 + \frac{1}{4}\delta|v^2|^2, \tag{5.2.26}$$

then over a trajectory $\{v(t)\}_{t\geq 0}$, its evolution satisfies

$$\begin{aligned}
\frac{d}{dt}V(v(t)) = \dot{V}(t) &= \left(-v'' - 2v + \delta v^3, \frac{dv}{dt}\right) \\
&= (-v'' - 2v + \delta v^3, (-v'' - 2v + \delta v^3)'' - 2vv' - \alpha v) \\
&= -|(v'' + 2v - \delta v^3)'|^2 + 2(v'', vv') - \alpha|v'|^2 + 2\alpha|v|^2 - \delta\alpha|v^2|^2 \\
&\leq -2\alpha V - \frac{\alpha\delta}{2}|v^2|^2 + 2(v'', vv') \\
&\leq -2\alpha V + 2(v'', vv') \\
&\leq -2\alpha V + 2|v''||vv'| \\
&\leq -2\alpha V + \frac{|v''|^2}{\sqrt{6\delta}} + \sqrt{6\delta}|vv'|^2 \\
&\leq -2\alpha V + \frac{1}{\sqrt{6\delta}}(|v''|^2 + 6\delta|vv'|^2),
\end{aligned} \tag{5.2.27}$$

for $t \geq t_0$. Integrating from t_0 to t, and using (5.2.22), we get

$$\begin{aligned}
V(t) &\leq \exp(2\alpha(t_0 - t))V(t_0) + \exp(-2\alpha t)\frac{1}{\sqrt{6\delta}}5\rho_1^2 \\
&\leq V(t_0) + \left(5\rho_1^2/\sqrt{6\delta}\right) \\
&\leq \frac{1}{2}|v'(t_0)|^2 + \frac{\delta}{4}|v^2(t_0)|^2 + 3\rho_1^2/\delta^{1/2}.
\end{aligned} \tag{5.2.28}$$

On the other hand, applying Poincaré's inequality to the function $u = v^2 - \frac{1}{L}\int_0^L v^2$, which has a vanishing average, one obtains

$$|u|^2 \leq \frac{L^2}{4\pi^2}|u'|^2 = \frac{L^2}{4\pi^2}|(v^2)'|^2 = \frac{L^2}{\pi^2}|vv'|^2.$$

But

$$|u|^2 = |v^2(x) - \frac{1}{L}\int_0^L v^2(y)dy|_{L^2} = |v^2|^2 - \frac{1}{L}|v|^4,$$

hence

$$|v^2|^2 - \frac{1}{L}|v|^4 < \frac{L^2}{\pi^2}|vv'|^2. \tag{5.2.29}$$

Integrating the above inequality from t_0 to t, and using (5.2.22) with $t_0 = t-1$, we get

$$\delta\int_t^{t+1}|v^2(\tau)|_{L^2}^2\, d\tau \leq \frac{\delta}{L}\int_t^{t+1}|v(\tau)|_{L^2}^4\, d\tau + \frac{L^2}{6\pi^2}5\rho_1^2 \tag{5.2.30}$$

$$\leq \frac{\delta}{L}\rho_1^4 + \frac{L^2\rho_1^2}{\pi^2}.$$

Integrating (5.2.28) from $t_0 = t$ to $t_0 = t+1$,

$$V(t) \leq \frac{\sqrt{5}}{2}\rho_1^2 + \frac{\delta\rho_1^4}{4L} + \frac{L^2\rho_1^2}{4\pi^2} + \frac{3\rho_1^2}{\delta^{1/2}} \leq \rho_1^2 c_0'(1 + L^2 + \delta^{-1/2}). \tag{5.2.31}$$

Consequently, for $t \geq t_0$

$$|v'(t)|^2 \leq V(t) + |v(t)|^2 \leq c_0^2\rho_1^2(1 + L + \delta^{-1/4})^2. \tag{5.2.32}$$

$\square$

We now return to the original equation as given in (5.2.1), in the framework given in Chapter 3, we have

$$Au = u'''', \quad R(u) = -2u'' - 3\delta(u')^2 u'' + (u')^2 + \alpha u, \tag{5.2.33}$$

and as for the absorbing set we set:

$$B = \{u \in H : |u'| \leq \rho_1 \text{ and } |u''| \leq \rho_2\}. \tag{5.2.34}$$

Let us first derive the equation for the difference. Setting,

$$w = u_1 - u_2, \tag{5.2.35}$$

where u_1 and u_2 are two solutions of (5.2.1), we deduce that w satisfies

$$w_t + w'''' + 2w'' - 3\delta[(u_1')^2 u_1'' - (u_2')^2 u_2''] + [(u_1')^2 - (u_2')^2] + \alpha w = 0. \tag{5.2.36}$$

5. Applications

Thus, with $\bar{u} = u_1 + u_2$

$$\frac{1}{2}\frac{d}{dt}|w|^2 + |w''|^2 + \alpha|w|^2 = 3\delta(u_1''\bar{u}'w', w) + 3\delta((u_2')^2 w'', w) + (\bar{u}'w', w)$$
$$\leq 3\delta|u_1''|_{L^2}|\bar{u}'|_{L^2}|ww'|_{L^\infty} + 3\delta|w''|_{L^2}|w|_{L^2}|(u_2')^2|_{L^\infty} + |\bar{u}'||w'||w|_{L^\infty}$$
$$\leq 6\delta\rho_2\rho_1|w|_{L^\infty}|w'|_{L^\infty} + 6\delta|w''|\,||w||\,|u_2''|_{L^2}|u_2''|_{L^2} + 2\rho_1|w|^{1/2}|w'|^{3/2}$$
$$\leq 6\delta\rho_2\rho_1|w||w''| + 6\delta\rho_1\rho_2|w||w''| + 2\rho_1|w|^{5/4}|w''|^{3/4} \quad (5.2.37)$$
$$\leq \frac{1}{2}|w''|^2 + c_1(\delta^2\rho_1^2\rho_2^2 + \rho_1^{8/5})|w|^2$$
$$\leq \frac{1}{2}|w''|^2 + c_2[\delta^2\rho_1^2\rho_2^2 + \rho_1^{8/5}]|w|^2.$$

By Gronwall's lemma,

$$|w(t)| \leq \exp\left\{c_2[\delta^2\rho_1^2\rho_2^2 + \rho_1^{8/5}]t\right\}|w(0)|. \quad (5.2.38)$$

So that, $S(t)$ is a Lipschitz map and the Lipschitz constant can be estimated using (5.2.38). Now, we set

$$\lambda(t) = |w''(t)|^2/|w(t)|^2 \quad \text{and} \quad \xi(t) = w(t)/|w(t)|^2, \quad (5.2.39)$$

then the w-inequation becomes,

$$\frac{d}{dt}|w|^2 + \left(\lambda(t) - c_2\left[(\rho_1^{8/5} + \delta^2\rho_1^2\rho_2^2\right]\right)|w|^2 \leq 0, \quad (5.2.40)$$

where we have used the specific values of ρ_1 and ρ_2, combined with the fact $\delta < 1$. Applying Gronwall's lemma once again, we obtain that

$$|w(t)| \leq \delta(t)|w(0)|, \quad (5.2.41)$$

with

$$\delta(t) = -\frac{1}{2}\int_0^t \lambda(\tau)d\tau + \frac{c_2}{2}\left[\rho_1^{8/5} + (\delta\rho_1\rho_2)^2\right]t. \quad (5.2.42)$$

To prove the squeezing property for $S(t_*)$, assume that at $t = t_*$:

$$\lambda_* \doteq \lambda(t_*) \geq \frac{1}{2}\lambda_{N_0+1} = \frac{1}{2}\left(\frac{2\pi}{L}(N_0+1)\right)^4, \quad (5.2.43)$$

and consider the equation for the quotient norm $\lambda(t)$, which is given by

$$\frac{1}{2}\frac{d}{dt}\lambda(t) = \frac{1}{|w|^2}(w_t, (A-\lambda)w)$$
$$= -|(A-\lambda)\xi|^2 + \left(\frac{R(u_2) - R(u_1)}{|w|}, (A-\lambda)\xi\right) \quad (5.2.44)$$
$$\leq -\frac{1}{2}|(A-\lambda)\xi|^2 + \frac{1}{2}\frac{|R(u_1) - R(u_2)|^2}{|w|^2}.$$

Next, we estimate the difference of non-linear terms

$$|R(u_1) - R(u_2)| = |-2w'' - 3\delta[(u')^2 w'' + 2v''\bar{u}'w'] + 2\bar{u}'w'|$$
$$\leq 2|w''| + 3\delta|(u')^2|_{L^\infty}|w''| + 6\delta|v''|\|\bar{u}'\|\|w'|_{L^\infty} + 2|\bar{u}'\|\|w'|_{L^\infty}$$
$$\leq 2\lambda^{1/2}|w| + 3\delta|u'\|\|u''|\lambda^{1/2}|w| + 6\delta\rho_2\rho_1|w'|^{1/2}|w''|^{1/2}$$
$$\quad + 2\rho_1|w|^{1/4}|w''|^{3/4} \hfill (5.2.45)$$
$$\leq (2 + 3\delta\rho_1\rho_2)\lambda^{1/2}|w| + 6\delta\rho_1\rho_2\lambda^{3/8}|w| + 2\rho_1\lambda^{3/8}|w|.$$

Combining (5.2.45) with (5.2.44), and using Young's inequality three times

$$\begin{aligned}\lambda' &\leq c_3\delta^2\rho_1^2\rho_2^2\lambda + c_4(\delta\rho_1\rho_2)^2\lambda^{3/4} + 4\rho_1^2\lambda^{3/4} \\ &\leq c_5\delta^2\rho_1^2\rho_2^2\lambda + c_6\left[(\delta\rho_1\rho_2)^2 + (\delta\rho_2)^{-2}\right] \\ &\leq c_5(\delta\rho_1\rho_2)^2\lambda + c_7\left[(\delta\rho_1\rho_2)^2 + \delta^{-1/2}\right] \\ &\leq c_5(\delta\rho_1\rho_2)^2\lambda + c_8(\delta\rho_1\rho_2)^2\end{aligned} \qquad (5.2.46)$$

By Gronwall's lemma,

$$\lambda(t) \leq e^{\beta_1(t-t_0)}\lambda(t_0) - (1 - e^{\beta_1(t-t_0)})(\beta_2/\beta_1), \qquad (5.2.47)$$

where

$$\beta_1 = c_5(\delta\rho_1\rho_2)^2 \quad \text{and} \quad \beta_2 = c_8(\delta\rho_1\rho_2)^2. \qquad (5.2.48)$$

Reversing (5.2.47) for $0 \leq t_0 < t_*$, and using (5.2.43), we deduce that

$$\lambda(t_0) \geq e^{\beta_1(t_0-t_*)}\lambda_* + \frac{\beta_2}{\beta_1}(e^{\beta_1(t_0-t_*)} - 1). \qquad (5.2.49)$$

Integrating (5.2.49) from $t_0 = 0$ to $t_0 = t_*$,

$$\int_0^{t_*} \lambda(t_0)dt_0 = \frac{1}{\beta_1}(1 - e^{-\beta_1 t_*})\lambda_* - (\beta_2/\beta_1)t_*, \qquad (5.2.50)$$

and setting

$$t_* = \beta_1^{-1} = c_5^{-1}(\delta\rho_1\rho_2)^{-2} = c_5^{-1}L^{-6}(1 + L + \delta^{-1/4})^{-2}, \qquad (5.2.51)$$

we get from (5.2.42) that

$$\delta_* = \delta(t_*) \leq -\frac{1}{4\beta_1}\lambda_* + \beta_2\beta_1^{-2} - \frac{c_2}{2}\left(\rho_1^{8/5} + (\delta\rho_1\rho_2)^2\right)\beta_1^{-1}. \qquad (5.2.52)$$

In order to have $\delta_* < 1/8$, we need

$$\lambda_* \geq c_6 \max\left\{\beta_1, \beta_2\beta_1^{-1}, \rho_1^{8/5} + (\delta\rho_1\rho_2)^2\right\}$$

$$= c_6 \max\left\{(\delta\rho_1\rho_2)^2, 1, \rho_1^{8/5} + (\delta\rho_1\rho_2)^2\right\}$$

$$\geq c_7 \max\left\{\delta^2(\delta^{-1/2}L^{3/2})^4(1 + L^2 + \delta^{-1/2}), 1, (\delta^{-1/2}L^{3/2})^{8/5}\right.$$

$$\left. + L^6(1 + L^2 + \delta^{-1/2})\right\} \tag{5.2.53}$$

$$\geq c_8 \max\left\{1, L^6(1 + L^2 + \delta^{-1/2}) + \delta^{-4/5}L^{12/5}\right\}$$

$$\geq c_9 \max\left\{L^8, L^6\delta^{-1/2}, L^{12/5}\delta^{-4/5}\right\}.$$

Using (5.2.43), we deduce that, if

$$N_0 \geq c_{10} \max\left\{L^3, L^{10/4}\delta^{-1/8}, L^{8/5}\delta^{-1/5}\right\}, \tag{5.2.54}$$

then $\delta_* < 1/8$. On the other hand, the Lipschitz constant for $S(t)$ with $t = t_*$ can be estimated by

$$L_* = \mathrm{Lip}_B(S_*) \leq \exp c_2((\delta\rho_1\rho_2)^2 + \rho_1^{8/5})t_* \tag{5.2.55}$$

$$\leq \exp((c_2/c_5) + c_{11}\delta^{-3/10}),$$

where we have used $\rho_1^{8/5}/\beta_1 \leq c\delta^{-3/10}$. Finally, the estimate on the fractal dimension of the exponential attractor is given by, with $\theta_* = 2\delta_*$

$$d_F(\mathcal{M}) \leq N_0 \frac{\ln\left[\left(\frac{2L_*}{\theta_*}\right) + 1\right]}{\ln(1/\theta_*)} \tag{5.2.56}$$

$$\leq c_{12}\delta^{-3/10} \cdot \max\left\{L^3, L^{10/4}\delta^{-1/8}, L^{8/5}\delta^{-1/5}\right\}.$$

For the comparison with the dimension estimate for the inertial manifold see section 6. Let us summarize the results obtained so far.

Proposition 5.2. *The Kolmogorov-Sivashinsky-Spiegel equation as given in (5.2.1) admits an exponential fractal attractor $\mathcal{M}_0$ in B, as in (5.2.2), whose fractal dimension is estimate by*

$$d_F(\mathcal{M}_0) \leq c_{12}\delta^{-3/10} \max\left\{L^3, L^{10/4}\delta^{-1/8}, L^{8/5}\delta^{-1/5}\right\}, \tag{5.2.57}$$

where c_{12} is an absolute constant that depends on c_0 among other things. Moreover, there exist absolute constants c_{13} and c_{14} such that

$$\mathrm{dist}_{L^2}(S(t)B, \mathcal{M}_0) \leq c_{13}e^{-c_{14}L^6(1+L+\delta^{-1/4})^2 t}. \tag{5.2.58}$$

Proof. The estimate (5.2.57) has already been shown; as for the convergence we use (3.65) and δ_* from (5.2.52) with t_* as in (5.2.51). □

5.3 2D Navier-Stokes Equations

In the functional formulation the Navier-Stokes equations for 2D incompressible viscous fluid flow can be written as an evolution equation as

$$u_t + \nu A u + B(u,u) = f, \qquad (5.3.1)$$
$$u(0) = u_0, \qquad (5.3.2)$$

where $A = -P_H \Delta$ is the Stokes operator, $B(u,u)$ stands for the non-linear term $(u \cdot \nabla)u$ projected to the underlying Hilbert space H, f is the volume force projected to the same Hilbert space and ν is the viscosity of the fluid. The incompressibility condition is taken care of by posing the initial value problem in the following Hilbert spaces

$$H = \{u \in L^2(Q)^2 : \operatorname{div} u = 0, \int_Q u(x) dx = 0, u_i|_{x_i=L} = u_i|_{x_i=0},$$
$$i = 1, 2\}, \qquad (5.3.3)$$

and

$$V = \{u \in H^1(Q)^2 : u \in H\}, \qquad (5.3.4)$$

where Q is the square $[0, L] \times [0, L]$ and the boundary conditions are assumed to be periodic. In this case, the domain of the Stokes operator A is given by

$$D(A) = H^2(Q)^2 \cap V. \qquad (5.3.5)$$

Corresponding to the inner products $(u,v) = (u,v)_{L^2(Q)^2}$ and $((u,v)) = (\nabla u, \nabla v)_{L^2(Q)^2}$, one has the following norms

$$|u| \doteq |u|_H = |u|_{L^2(Q)^2} \quad \text{and} \quad \|u\| = |u|_V = |\nabla u|_{L^2(Q)^2}. \qquad (5.3.6)$$

By Sobolev imbedding theorem, V is compactly imbedded in H, and as a simple consequence of

$$(Au, v) = ((u,v)) \quad \text{for} \quad u \in D(A), v \in V \qquad (5.3.7)$$

one obtains that A is a self-adjoint, positive operator which has a compact inverse. Hence, H has an orthonormal basis consisting of eigenvectors of A corresponding to the positive eigenvalues of A, namely $A w_n = \lambda_n w_n$ and

$$0 < \lambda_1 \leq \lambda_2 \leq \cdots \leq \lambda_n \to \infty. \qquad (5.3.8)$$

Moreover, for the periodic boundary conditions the asymptotic behaviour of the eigenvalues can be determined more precisely since (see [CF], prop. 4.14)

$$\lim_{n \to \infty} \frac{1}{n} \left(\frac{\lambda_n}{\lambda_1} \right) = \omega_0, \qquad (5.3.9)$$

so one has $\lambda_n \sim \omega_0 \lambda_1 n$, in two space dimension. As for the non-linear term, in addition to the standard continuity properties (see [CF], [T1–4])

$$|(B(u,v),w)| \leq c_1 \begin{cases} |u|^{1/2}\|u\|^{1/2}\|v\|^{1/2}|Av|^{1/2}|w|, & u \in V, v \in D(A), w \in H \\ |u|^{1/2}|Au|^{1/2}\|v\|\|w|, & u \in D(A), v \in V, w \in H \\ |u|\|v\|\|w|^{1/2}|Aw|^{1/2}, & u \in H, v \in V, w \in D(A) \\ |u|^{1/2}\|u\|^{1/2}\|v\|\|w|^{1/2}\|w\|^{1/2}, & v, u, w \in V \end{cases}$$
(5.3.10)

we will also need the orthogonality relations, that hold for 2D periodic case, namely,

$$(B(u,v), v) = 0 \quad , \quad \text{for} \quad u, v \in V \tag{5.3.11}$$

$$(B(u,u), Au) = 0 \quad , \quad \text{for} \quad u \in D(A) \tag{5.3.12}$$

and finally,

$$(B(u,u), A^2 u) = (B(Au, u), Au) \quad , \quad \text{for} \quad u \in D(A^2). \tag{5.3.13}$$

The orthogonality properties (5.3.11) and (5.3.12) allow one to obtain, directly, apriori estimates on the solutions of (5.3.1) and (5.3.2), using these estimates it is easy to show that the set

$$B_0 = \{u \in V : |u| \leq 2\rho_0 \quad \text{and} \quad \|u\| \leq 2\rho_1\} \tag{5.3.14}$$

with

$$\rho_0 = 2|f|/\nu\lambda_1 \quad \text{and} \quad \rho_1 = 2|f|/\nu\lambda_1^{1/2}, \tag{5.3.15}$$

absorbs all bounded subsets of H in finite time. In terms of the Grashoff number

$$G \doteq |f|/\nu^2 \lambda_1, \tag{5.3.16}$$

the set B_0 can be rewritten as

$$B_0 = \{u \in V : |u| \leq 4G\nu \quad \text{and} \quad \|u\| \leq 4G\nu\lambda_1^{1/2}\}. \tag{5.3.17}$$

In order to obtain the estimate (3.11) on the non-linear term, it is necessary to restrict our attention to a subset of B_0, that is bounded in $D(A)$. At this point, we must assume that f is in V, in place of the normal assumption that f is in H.

Lemma 5.3. *Let $u(t)$ be a solution of (5.3.1) such that $u_0 \in B_0$, then for $t \geq 1/\nu\lambda_1$,*

$$|Au(t)| \leq c_2 G^2 \nu \lambda_1, \tag{5.3.18}$$

where c_2 is a constant that depends on c_1, from (5.3.10), and the shape factor of f, $S_f = \|f\|/(\sqrt{\lambda_1}|f|)$.

Proof. Since the solution operator $S(t)$ maps H into $D(A)$, for $t > 0$, when f is in H and maps V into $D(A^{3/2})$ when $f \in V$, we can take the inner product of (5.3.1) with $A^2 u$ to deduce that

$$\frac{1}{2}\frac{d}{dt}|Au|^2 + \nu|A^{3/2}u|^2 = -(B(u,u), A^2 u) + (f, A^2 u)$$

$$= -(B(Au, u), Au) + (A^{1/2}f, A^{3/2}u)$$

$$\leq c_1|Au|\|Au\|\|u\| + |A^{1/2}f|\|A^{3/2}u| \quad (5.3.19)$$

$$\leq c_1\rho_1|Au|\|A^{3/2}u| + \|f\|\|A^{3/2}u|$$

$$\leq \frac{\nu}{2}|A^{3/2}u|^2 + \frac{c_1^2\rho_1^2}{\nu}|Au|^2 + \frac{1}{\nu}\|f\|^2$$

where we have used the facts that $|A^{1/2}v| = \|v\|$, the fourth of the estimates in (5.3.10) and Young's inequality twice. We define the shape factor S_f of the volume force f by

$$S_f \doteq \frac{\|f\|}{\sqrt{\lambda_1}|f|}, \quad (5.3.20)$$

then combined with (5.3.16), (5.3.19) simplifies to

$$\frac{d}{dt}|Au|^2 \leq 8c_1^2 G^2 \nu \lambda_1 |Au|^2 + S_f^2 \nu^3 \lambda_1^3 G^2. \quad (5.3.21)$$

Integrating this inequality from t_0 to t, we obtain

$$|Au(t)|^2 \leq |Au(t_0)|^2 + 8c_1^2 G^2 \nu \lambda_1 \int_{t_0}^{t} |Au(s)|^2 ds + S_f^2 \nu^3 \lambda_1^3 G^2(t-t_0), \quad (5.3.22)$$

but a simple estimate of $\int_{t_0}^{t}|Au(s)|^2 ds$ can be obtained by multiplying (5.3.1) with Au and using the orthogonality property (5.3.12), as

$$\frac{d}{dt}\|u\|^2 + \nu|Au|^2 \leq \frac{|f|^2}{\nu} = G^2 \nu^3 \lambda_1^2, \quad (5.3.23)$$

implies that

$$\int_{t_0}^{t} |Au(s)|^2 ds \leq \frac{1}{\nu}\|u(t_0)\|^2 + \frac{|f|^2}{\nu^2}(t-t_0)$$

$$\leq \frac{1}{\nu} 16 G^2 \nu^2 \lambda_1 + (G\nu\lambda_1)^2 (t-t_0) \quad (5.3.24)$$

$$\leq 16 G^2 \nu \lambda_1 + (G\nu\lambda_1)^2 (1/\nu\lambda_1)$$

$$\leq 17 G^2 \nu \lambda_1,$$

where we have assumed that $t - t_0 = (\nu\lambda_1)^{-1}$. Returning back to (5.3.22)

$$|Au(t)|^2 \leq |Au(t_0)|^2 + 8c_1^2 G^2 \nu \lambda_1 (17 G^2 \nu \lambda_1) + S_f^2 \nu^3 \lambda_1^3 G^2 \left(\frac{1}{\nu\lambda_1}\right)$$

$$\leq |Au(t_0)|^2 + c'c_1^2 (G^2\nu\lambda_1)^2 + S_f^2 \nu^2 \lambda_1 G^2 \quad (5.2.25)$$

and integrating from $t_0 = t - 1/\nu\lambda_1$ to $t_0 = t$ once again, we have

$$\frac{1}{\nu\lambda_1}|Au(t)|^2 \leq \int_{t-1/\nu\lambda_1}^{t} |Au(t_0)|^2 dt_0 + c'c_1^2 G^4(\nu\lambda_1) + S_f^2\nu\lambda_1 G^2$$

$$\leq 17G^2\nu\lambda_1 + c'c_1^2 G^4(\nu\lambda_1) + S_f^2\nu\lambda_1 G^2 \qquad (5.3.26)$$

hence

$$|Au(t)|^2 \leq G^2(\nu\lambda_1)^2 \left[17 + c'c_1^2 G^2 + S_f^2\right]$$
$$\leq c''(G\nu\lambda_1)^2 \left[1 + G^2 + S_f^2\right]. \qquad (5.3.27)$$

□

Starting with the absorbing set B_0, as given in (5.3.14), we form

$$B \doteq \overline{\bigcup_{t \geq 1/(\nu\lambda_1)} S(t)B_0}. \qquad (5.3.28)$$

Then B is a compact subset of B_0 that is invariant under the flow, moreover by Lemma 5.3, if u is in B then by (5.3.18),

$$|Au| \leq c_2 G^2(\nu\lambda_1). \qquad (5.3.29)$$

Next, we consider the solution operator $S(t)$ as a map from B into B and estimate its Lipschitz constant L. Let u_1 and u_2 be two solutions of (5.3.1) that is in B, setting

$$w(t) = u_1(t) - u_2(t) \quad \text{and} \quad \bar{u}(t) = \frac{1}{2}(u_1(t) + u_2(t)), \qquad (5.3.30)$$

we see that w satisfies

$$\frac{d}{dt}w + \nu Aw + B(\bar{u}, w) + B(w, \bar{u}) = 0, \qquad (5.3.31)$$

$$w(0) = u_1(0) - u_2(0). \qquad (5.3.32)$$

Taking the inner product of (5.3.31) with w in H and using the orthogonality property (5.3.11), we obtain that

$$\frac{1}{2}\frac{d}{dt}|w|^2 + \nu\|w\|^2 = -(B(w,\bar{u}), w)$$
$$\leq c_1|w|\|w\|\|\bar{u}\| \qquad (5.3.33)$$
$$\leq \frac{\nu}{2}\|w\|^2 + \frac{c_1^2}{2\nu}|w|^2\|\bar{u}\|^2$$
$$\leq \frac{\nu}{2}\|w\|^2 + 8c_1^2(G^2\nu\lambda_1)|w|^2.$$

Consequently,
$$\frac{d}{dt}|w|^2 + \nu\|w\|^2 \le 16c_1^2(G^2\nu\lambda_1)|w|^2, \qquad (5.3.34)$$

and neglecting $\nu\|w\|^2$ and utilizing Gronwall's lemma, we have
$$|w(t)|^2 \le \exp(8c_1^2 G^2 \nu\lambda_1 t)|w(0)|^2. \qquad (5.3.35)$$

Hence,
$$\mathrm{Lip}_B(S(t)) \le \exp(4c_1^2 G^2 \nu\lambda_1 t). \qquad (5.3.36)$$

Once, again, setting $\lambda(t) = \|w(t)\|^2/|w(t)|^2$ and using the second line in (5.3.33), we get that

$$\frac{1}{2}\frac{d}{dt}|w|^2 + \nu\lambda(t)|w|^2 \le c_1\lambda^{1/2}(t)|w|^2\|\bar{u}\| \le (4c_1 G\nu\lambda_1^{1/2})\lambda^{1/2}(t)|w|^2. \quad (5.3.37)$$

By Gronwall's lemma,
$$|w(t)| \le \delta(t)|w(0)|, \qquad (5.3.38)$$
where
$$\delta(t) = \exp\left\{-\nu\int_0^t (\lambda(\tau) - (2c_1 G\nu\lambda_1^{1/2})\lambda^{1/2}(\tau))d\tau\right\}. \qquad (5.3.39)$$

In order to prove the squeezing property, we take
$$t_* \doteq \left[c_3 G^2 \nu\lambda_1 \log(G^4\nu^2\lambda_1 + 1)\right]^{-1} \qquad (5.3.40)$$
and assume that
$$\lambda_* \doteq \lambda(t_*) > \frac{1}{2}\lambda_{N_0+1}. \qquad (5.3.41)$$

Next, we consider the equation for the quotient norm $\lambda(t)$, which is given by

$$\frac{1}{2}\frac{d}{dt}\lambda(t) = \frac{1}{|w|^2}(w_t, (A - \lambda(t))w) \qquad (5.3.42)$$
$$= -\nu|(A - \lambda(t))\xi|^2 - (B(\xi,\bar{u}) + B(\bar{u},\xi), (A - \lambda(t))\xi)$$
$$\le -\frac{\nu}{2}|(A - \lambda(t))\xi| + \frac{1}{\nu}(|B(\xi,\bar{u})|^2 + |B(\bar{u},\xi)|^2)$$

where we have denoted $w(t)/|w(t)|$ by $\xi(t)$. The two terms involving the non-linearity are estimated by

$$|B(\xi,\bar{u})| \le c_1|\xi|^{1/2}\|\xi\|^{1/2}\|\bar{u}\|^{1/2}|A\bar{u}|^{1/2} \le c_1\lambda^{1/4}(2\rho_1)^{1/2}|A\bar{u}|^{1/2} \qquad (5.3.43)$$

and

$$|B(\bar{u},\xi)| \le |\bar{u}|_{L^\infty}\|\xi\| \le c_2\left(\log\frac{|A\bar{u}|^2}{\lambda_1\|\bar{u}\|^2} + 1\right)^{1/2}\|\bar{u}\|\lambda^{1/2}, \qquad (5.3.44)$$

where in addition to (5.3.10) an L^∞-estimate is utilized in the above inequality (see [CFT2]). Using the last two estimates in the λ-inequation, one has

$$\frac{d}{dt}\lambda(t) \leq \frac{2}{\nu}\left(2c_1^2\rho_1|A\bar{u}|\lambda(t)^{1/2} + \frac{c_2^2}{2}\left(\log\frac{|A\bar{u}|^2}{\lambda_1\|\bar{u}\|^2} + 1\right)\|\bar{u}\|^2\lambda(t)\right). \quad (5.3.45)$$

We set

$$g(t) \doteq \frac{4c_1^2\rho_1}{\nu}|A\bar{u}(t)| \quad \text{and} \quad f(t) = \frac{c_2^2}{\nu}\left(\log\frac{|A\bar{u}(t)|^2}{\lambda_1\|\bar{u}\|^2} + 1\right)\|\bar{u}\|, \quad (5.3.46)$$

then, after dividing (5.3.45) through by $\sqrt{\lambda(t)}$ we obtain that

$$\frac{d}{dt}\left(\sqrt{\lambda(t)}\right) \leq g(t) + f(t)\left(\sqrt{\lambda(t)}\right). \quad (5.3.47)$$

Using Gronwall's inequality, from t_0 to t,

$$\sqrt{\lambda(t)} \leq \sqrt{\lambda(t_0)}\exp\left(\int_{t_0}^t f(s)ds\right) + \int_{t_0}^t \exp\left(\int_s^t f(\tau)d\tau\right)g(s)ds$$

$$\leq \exp\left(\int_{t_0}^t f(s)ds\right)\left[\sqrt{\lambda(t_0)} + \int_{t_0}^t g(s)ds\right]. \quad (5.3.48)$$

Setting $t = t_*$, and using $\lambda(t_*) = \lambda_*$, we obtain by reversing the inequality (5.3.48),

$$\sqrt{\lambda(t_0)} \geq \exp\left(-\int_{t_0}^t f(s)ds\right)\sqrt{\lambda_*} - \int_{t_0}^t g(s)ds. \quad (5.3.49)$$

In order to get a lower estimate on $\int_0^{t_*}\lambda(\tau)d\tau$, we note that

$$E \doteq \int_0^{t_*}\lambda(t_0)dt_0 \geq \frac{1}{t_*}\left[\int_0^{t_*}\sqrt{\lambda(t_0)}dt_0\right]^2 \quad (5.3.50)$$

$$\geq \frac{1}{t_*}\left[\int_0^{t_*}\exp\left(-\int_{t_0}^{t_*}f(s)ds\right)\sqrt{\lambda_*}dt_0 - \int_0^{t_*}\int_{t_0}^{t_*}g(s)dsdt_0\right]^2,$$

hence it remains to estimate the integral involving g from above and the exponential term from below. On the one hand,

$$\int_0^{t_*}\int_{t_0}^{t_*}g(s)dsdt_0 = \frac{4c_1^2\rho_1}{\nu}\int_0^{t_*}\int_{t_0}^{t_*}|A\bar{u}(s)|dsdt_0$$

$$\leq \frac{4c_1^2\rho_1}{\nu}\int_0^{t_*}(t^* - t_0)^{1/2}\left(\int_{t_0}^{t_*}|A\bar{u}(s)|^2ds\right)^{1/2}dt_0 \quad (5.3.51)$$

$$\leq \frac{4c_1^2\rho_1}{\nu}\int_0^{t_*}(t^* - t_0)^{1/2}(17G^2\nu\lambda_1)^{1/2}dt_0$$

$$\leq c'c_1^2G^2\nu^{1/2}\lambda_1\int_0^{t_*}(t_* - t_0)^{1/2}dt_0 = \frac{3}{2}c'c_1^2G^2\nu^{1/2}\lambda_1 t_*^{3/2}.$$

On the other hand,

$$\lambda_*^{1/2} \int_0^{t_*} \exp\left(-\int_{t_0}^{t_*} f(s)ds\right) dt_0$$

$$\geq \lambda_*^{1/2} \int_0^{t_*} \exp\left(-\frac{c_2^2}{\nu} \int_{t_0}^{t_*} \left(\log \frac{|A\bar{u}(s)|^2}{\lambda_1 \|\bar{u}(s)\|^2} + 1\right) \|\bar{u}(s)\|^2 ds\right) dt_0$$

$$\geq \lambda_*^{1/2} \int_0^{t_*} e^{-\beta(t_*-t_0)} dt_0 = \frac{\lambda_*^{1/2}}{\beta}(1 - e^{-\beta t_*}), \quad (5.3.52)$$

where the constant β is defined by

$$\beta \doteq \frac{c_2^2}{\nu} \sup_{u \in B} \|u\|^2 \left(\log \frac{|Au|^2}{\lambda_1 \|u\|^2} + 1\right). \quad (5.3.53)$$

The estimate on β will be obtained by using the facts that $\|u\|^2 \leq 16G^2\nu^2\lambda_1$ and $|Au|^2 \leq (c_2 G^2 \nu \lambda_1)^2$ for u in B. To this end, let us consider the function

$$\phi(x,y) = x\left(\log \frac{y}{x} + 1\right), \quad (5.3.54)$$

on the domain

$$0 \leq x \leq 16G^2\nu^2\lambda_1 \quad \text{and} \quad 0 \leq y \leq c_2^2 G^4 \nu^2 \lambda_1. \quad (5.3.55)$$

If $x \geq (G^4\nu^2\lambda_1)^{-1}$, then

$$\phi(x,y) \leq 16G^2\nu^2\lambda_1(\log c_2(G^4\nu^2\lambda_1)^2 + 1) \leq c_3 G^2\nu^2\lambda_1(\log G^4\nu^2\lambda_1 + 1).$$

On the other hand, if $x < (G^4\nu^2\lambda_1)^{-1} \leq 1$ then

$$\phi(x,y) \leq x\left(\log y + \log\frac{1}{x} + 1\right) \leq (\log y + 1) + x\log 1/x \&(5.3.56)$$

$$\leq (\log c_2 G^4 \nu^2 \lambda_1 + 1) + 1/2 \leq c_3 G^2 \nu^2 \lambda_1 (\log G^4 \nu^2 \lambda_1 + 1).$$

Hence, in both cases β as given in (5.3.53) can be estimated by

$$\beta \leq c_3 G^2 \nu \lambda_1 (\log G^4 \nu^2 \lambda_1 + 1). \quad (5.3.57)$$

Finally, combining (5.3.51), (5.3.52) and (5.3.57) into (5.3.50) we obtain that

$$E = \int_0^{t_*} \lambda(t_0) dt_0 \geq \frac{1}{t_*}\left[\frac{\lambda_*^{1/2}}{\beta}(1 - e^{-\beta t_*}) - c''c_1^2 G^2 \nu^{1/2} \lambda_1 t_*^{3/2}\right]^2. \quad (5.3.58)$$

Returning back to (5.3.39), by definition

$$\delta_* = \delta(t_*) = \exp\left\{-\nu \int_0^{t_*} [\lambda(\tau) - (2c_1 G \nu \lambda_1^{1/2}) \lambda^{1/2}(\tau)] d\tau\right\}$$

By Young's inequality, applied to $a = (\lambda(\tau)\nu)^{1/2}$ and $b = c_1 G(\nu\lambda_1)^{1/2}$

$$\delta_* \leq \exp\left\{-\nu \int_0^{t_*} \lambda(\tau)d\tau + 2c_1^2 G^2 \nu \lambda_1 t_*\right\}$$

$$\leq \exp\left\{-\frac{\nu}{2t_*}\left[\frac{\lambda_*^{1/2}}{\beta}(1 - e^{-\beta t_*}) - c'' c_1^2 G^2 \nu^{1/2} \lambda_1 t_*^{3/2}\right]^2 + 2c_1^2 G^2 \nu \lambda_1 t_*\right\}$$

$$\leq \exp\left\{-c_4 \nu \beta \left[\frac{\lambda_*}{2\beta^2} - c_5 G^4 \nu \lambda_1^2 (1/\beta)^3\right] + 2c_1^2 G^2 \nu \lambda_1 \beta^{-1}\right\}$$

where we have set $t^* = 1/\beta$, so that

$$\delta_* \leq \exp\left\{-\frac{c_4}{2}\nu \lambda_* \beta^{-1} + c_6 G^4 \nu^2 \lambda_1^2 \beta^{-2} + 2c_1^2 G^2 \nu \lambda_1 \beta^{-1}\right\}. \tag{5.3.59}$$

Recall that $\lambda_* \geq \frac{1}{2}\lambda_{N_0+1} \sim \omega_0 N_0 \lambda_1$, hence to guarantee $\delta_* < 1/8$ we need to choose N_0 such that

$$N_0 \geq c_7 \max\left\{\beta/\nu\lambda_1, \frac{G^4 \nu^2 \lambda_1^2}{\beta^2} \cdot \frac{\beta}{\nu\lambda_1}, \frac{G^2 \nu \lambda_1}{\beta} \cdot \frac{\beta}{\nu\lambda_1}\right\}$$

$$\geq c_7 \max\left\{\beta/\nu\lambda_1, \frac{G^4 \nu \lambda_1}{\beta}, G^2\right\} \tag{5.3.60}$$

$$\geq c_8 G^2 (\log G^4 \nu \lambda_1 + 1).$$

Furthermore, for $t = t_* = \beta^{-1}$, the Lipschitz constant for $S_* = S(t_*)$ can be estimated, via (5.3.36) by

$$L_* = \operatorname{Lip}_B(S_*) \leq \exp(8c_1^2 G^2 \nu \lambda_1 t_*) \tag{5.3.61}$$
$$\leq \exp c_9 [\log(G^4 \nu^2 \lambda_1 + 1)]^{-1} \leq e^{c_{10}}.$$

Finally, summarizing the results:

Proposition 5.3. *The 2D Navier-Stokes equations, with periodic boundary conditions and $f \in V$, admits an exponential fractal attractor $\mathcal{M}$ in B, whose dimension can be estimated by*

$$d_F(\mathcal{M}) \leq c_8 G^2 (\log G^4 \nu \lambda_1 + 1), \tag{5.3.62}$$

where G is the Grashoff number given by $|f|/\nu^2 \lambda_1$, and c_8 is a constant that depends on the shape factor S_f, as given in (5.3.20), the constants c_1 and ω_0, given in (5.3.10) and (5.3.9), respectively.

Moreover, the rate of convergence to the exponential attractor can be estimated by

$$\operatorname{dist}(S(t)B, \mathcal{M}_0) \leq c_{11} e^{-c_{12}\beta t}, \tag{5.3.63}$$

where

$$\beta = c_3 G^2 \nu \lambda_1 (\log G^4 \nu^2 \lambda_1 + 1). \tag{5.3.64}$$

Remark 5.3. In the proof, we have implicitly assumed that $G^2 \nu^2 \lambda_1 > 1$, by definition of the Grashoff number it is easy to see that this would be assured if $\min\{G, |f|\} > 1$.

The relevance to turbulence of exponential attractors for Navier-Stokes is discussed in [EFNS].

5.4 3D Navier-Stokes Equations

For 3D Navier-Stokes equations even the global existence of solutions is an unresolved problem, yet when one can overcome this problem it is possible to consider the existence of an exponential attractor. In particular, following Constantin et al. ([CFT1]), we will consider functional invariant sets X that are bounded in V and closed in H and show that the fractal dimension of the exponential attractor, obtained by restricting the flow on X, is a function of the Grashoff's number and a Reynolds number. Again we start from the functional formulation of 3D Navier-Stokes equations

$$u_t + \nu A u + B(u, u) = f, \tag{5.4.1}$$
$$u(0) = u_0, \tag{5.4.2}$$

where u_0 is coming from a bounded set X in V that is invariant under the flow. We will assume that f is in $H^1(\Omega)^3$ to guarantee, at least locally, that u will remain in $\mathcal{C}^1(\Omega)^3$. In such a case, the Reynolds number defined by

$$\overline{\mathrm{Re}} = \frac{1}{\nu \lambda_1^{1/2}} \sup_{u \in X} \sup_{x \in \Omega} |u(x)| \tag{5.4.3}$$

is finite. Moreover, the Grashoff number is defined by

$$G = \frac{|f|}{\nu^2 \lambda_1^{3/4}} \tag{5.4.4}$$

is dimensionless. From the usual computations it follows that for $t \geq t_0(X)$

$$|u(t)|_H \leq 4 G \nu \lambda_1^{-1/4}. \tag{5.4.5}$$

On the other hand, taking inner product of (5.4.1) in H with $2Au$, and using the standard techniques

$$\begin{aligned}
\frac{d}{dt}\|u\|^2 + 2\nu |Au|^2 &\leq 2|(f, Au)| + 2|(B(u,u), Au)| \\
&\leq 2|f||Au| + 2|B(u,u)||Au| \\
&\leq 2|f||Au| + 2|u|_{L^\infty(\Omega)^3}\|u\||Au| \\
&\leq 2|f||Au| + 2\overline{\mathrm{Re}}(\nu \lambda_1^{1/2})|u|^{1/2}|Au|^{3/2} \\
&\leq \nu|Au|^2 + \frac{2}{\nu}|f|^2 + c_1 (\overline{\mathrm{Re}})^4 \nu \lambda_1^2 |u|^2.
\end{aligned} \tag{5.4.6}$$

Hence,

$$\frac{d}{dt}\|u\|^2 + \nu|Au|^2 \leq 2G^2\nu^3\lambda_1^{3/2} + c_1(\overline{Re})^4 G^2\nu^3\lambda_1^{3/2}$$
$$\leq G^2\nu^3\lambda_1^{3/2}(2 + c_1(\overline{Re})^4) \doteq K. \tag{5.4.7}$$

Since $|Au|^2 \geq \lambda_1\|u\|^2$, by Gronwall's inequality it follows that for any $t > 0$,

$$\|u(t)\|^2 \leq \frac{K}{\nu\lambda_1}(1 - e^{-\nu\lambda_1 t}) + \|u_0\|^2 e^{-\nu\lambda_1 t}. \tag{5.4.8}$$

Consequently, since X is bounded in V, there exists $t_1 = t_1(X)$ such that for $t \geq t_1$,

$$\|u(t)\|^2 \leq \frac{2K}{\nu\lambda_1} = 2G^2\nu^2\lambda_1^{1/2}(2 + c_1(\overline{Re})^4). \tag{5.4.9}$$

Set $t_2 = \max\{t_0, t_1\}$ and

$$X_1 \doteq \overline{\bigcup_{t \geq t_2} S(t)X}, \tag{5.4.10}$$

then X_1 is a closed invariant set such that for any u in X_1

$$|u| \leq 4G\nu\lambda_1^{-1/4} \quad \text{and} \quad \|u\| \leq \left(\frac{2K}{\nu\lambda_1}\right)^{1/2}. \tag{5.4.11}$$

Next, we consider the equation satisfied by the difference of two solutions that are in X_1. Namely, let u and v be in X, then the equation that $w = u - v$ satisfies is

$$w_t + \nu Aw + B((u+v)/2, w) + B(w, (u+v)/2) = 0. \tag{5.4.12}$$

Setting $\bar{u} = (u+v)/2$ and taking the inner product with $2w$, it follows from (5.4.12) that

$$\frac{d}{dt}|w|^2 + 2\nu\|w\|^2 = (B(w, \bar{u}), 2w) = 2(B(w, w), \bar{u})$$
$$\leq 2(\overline{Re})(\nu\lambda_1^{1/2})|w|\|w\| \tag{5.4.13}$$
$$\leq \frac{(\overline{Re})^2}{2}(\nu\lambda_1)|w|^2 + \nu\|w\|^2$$

After simplification, and letting as before $\lambda(t) = \|w(t)\|^2/|w(t)|^2$ we obtain

$$\frac{d}{dt}|w(t)|^2 + \left[\nu\lambda(t) - \left(\frac{\nu\lambda_1}{2}\right)(\overline{Re})^2\right]|w(t)|^2 \leq 0. \tag{5.4.14}$$

Hence by Gronwall's inequality

$$|w(t)|^2 \leq \delta(t)|w(0)|^2, \qquad (5.4.15)$$

where

$$\delta(t) \doteq \exp\left\{-\nu \int_0^t \lambda(t_0)dt_0 + \frac{\nu\lambda_1}{2}(\overline{\mathrm{Re}})^2 t\right\}. \qquad (5.4.16)$$

In order to show that the squeezing property holds, we assume that at $t = t_*$

$$\lambda(t_*) \geq \frac{1}{2}\lambda_{N_0+1} = c_0\lambda_1(N_0+1)^{2/3} \qquad (5.4.17)$$

and analyze the past behaviour of the quotient norm via the equation that $\lambda(t)$ satisfies. Clearly, with $\xi = w/|w|$

$$\frac{d}{dt}\lambda(t) \leq \frac{2}{\nu}(|B(\xi,\bar{u})|^2 + |B(\bar{u},\xi)|^2), \qquad (5.4.18)$$

and the nonlinear terms are estimated as follows:

$$|B(\bar{u},\xi)|^2 \leq |\bar{u}|^2_{L^\infty(\Omega)^3}\|\xi\|^2 \leq (\overline{\mathrm{Re}})^2\nu^2\lambda_1\|\xi\|^2, \qquad (5.4.19)$$

and

$$|B(\xi,\bar{u})|^2 \leq c_1\|\xi\|^2\|u\||A\bar{u}| \leq \left(\frac{2c_1K}{\nu\lambda_1}\right)^{1/2}|A\bar{u}|\|\xi\|^2. \qquad (5.4.20)$$

Hence, using $\lambda(t) = \|\xi\|^2$

$$\frac{d}{dt}\lambda(t) \leq \frac{2}{\nu}\left(\left(\frac{2c_1K}{\nu\lambda_1}\right)^{1/2}|A\bar{u}(t)| + (\overline{\mathrm{Re}})^2\nu^2\lambda_1\right)\lambda(t). \qquad (5.4.21)$$

Letting

$$f(t) \doteq \left(\frac{8c_1K}{\nu^3\lambda_1}\right)^{1/2}|A\bar{u}(t)| + 2(\overline{\mathrm{Re}})^2\nu\lambda_1, \qquad (5.4.22)$$

and using Gronwall's inequality we obtain from (5.4.21) that

$$\int_0^{t_*} \lambda(t_0)dt_0 \geq \lambda_* \int_0^{t_*} \exp\left\{-\int_{t_0}^{t_*} f(t)dt\right\} dt_0$$

$$\geq c_0\lambda_1 N_0^{2/3} \int_0^{t_*} \exp\left\{-\left(\frac{8c_1K}{\nu^3\lambda_1}\right)^{1/2}\left(\int_{t_0}^{t_*}|A\bar{u}(t)|dt\right)\right.$$

$$\left. - 2(\overline{\mathrm{Re}})^2\nu\lambda_1(t_*-t_0)\right\} dt_0 \qquad (5.4.23)$$

$$\geq c_0\lambda_1 N_0^{2/3} \int_0^{t_*} \exp\left\{-\left(\frac{8c_1K}{\nu^3\lambda_1}\right)^{1/2}\left(\int_{t_0}^{t_*}|A\bar{u}(t)|^2 dt_0\right)^{1/2}\right.$$

$$\left. \times (t_*-t_0)^{1/2} - 2(\overline{\mathrm{Re}})^2\nu\lambda_1(t_*-t_0)\right\} dt_0$$

But it follows from (5.4.7) and (5.4.11) that

$$\int_{t_0}^{t_*} |A\bar{u}(t)|^2 dt \leq 2K/\nu^2 \lambda_1. \qquad (5.4.24)$$

Hence,

$$\int_0^{t_*} \lambda(t_0) dt_0 \geq c_0 \lambda_1 N_0^{2/3} \int_0^{t_*} \exp\left\{ -\left(\frac{8c_1 K}{\nu^3 \lambda_1}\right)^{1/2} \left(\frac{2K}{\nu^2 \lambda_1}\right)^{1/2} (t_* - t_0)^{1/2} \right.$$
$$\left. - 2(\overline{\text{Re}})^2 (\nu \lambda_1)(t_* - t_0) \right\} dt_0, \qquad (5.4.25)$$

assuming that $t_* < [2(\overline{\text{Re}})^2 \nu \lambda_1]^{-1}$, the above inequality simplifies to

$$\int_0^{t_*} \lambda(t_0) dt_0 \geq c_2 \lambda_1 N_0^{2/3} \int_0^{t_*} \exp\left\{ -\frac{4c_1^{1/2} K}{\nu^{5/2} \lambda_1} (t_* - t_0)^{1/2} \right\} dt_0$$
$$= \alpha \int_0^{t_*} \exp\left\{ -\beta (t_* - t_0)^{1/2} \right\} dt_0, \qquad (5.4.26)$$

where

$$\alpha \doteq c_2 \lambda_1 N_0^{2/3} \quad \text{and} \quad \beta \doteq 4c_1^{1/2} K / \nu^{5/2} \lambda_1. \qquad (5.4.27)$$

Integrating the right-hand side, we get

$$\int_0^{t_*} \lambda(t_0) dt_0 \geq \alpha \left(\frac{2\sqrt{t_*}}{-\beta} e^{-\beta\sqrt{t_*}} - \frac{2}{\beta^2}(e^{-\beta\sqrt{t_*}} - 1) \right). \qquad (5.4.28)$$

Now we choose t_* such that $\beta\sqrt{t_*} = 1$, that is

$$t_* = 1/\beta^2 = \frac{\nu^5 \lambda_1^2}{16 c_1 K^2} = \left[c_3 G^4 \nu \lambda_1 (1 + (\overline{\text{Re}})^8) \right]^{-1}, \qquad (5.4.29)$$

then after simplification

$$\int_0^{t_*} \lambda(t_0) dt_0 \geq \alpha / c_3 \beta^2 \qquad (5.4.30)$$

and substituting into (5.4.16)

$$\delta_* \doteq \delta(t_*) \leq \exp\left\{ -\frac{\nu \alpha}{c_3 \beta^2} + \frac{\nu \lambda_1}{2} (\overline{\text{Re}})^2 \frac{1}{\beta^2} \right\}. \qquad (5.4.31)$$

In order to assure $\delta_* < 1/8$, we need to assume that

$$\alpha \geq c_4 \max \left\{ \frac{\beta^2}{\nu}, \lambda_1 (\overline{\text{Re}})^2 \right\}, \qquad (5.4.32)$$

hence
$$N_0 \geq c_5 \max\left\{G^6(1+(\overline{Re})^{12}),(\overline{Re})^3\right\}. \tag{5.4.33}$$

Under the above condition on N_0 the existence of an exponential attractor is assured. Clearly, for $t = t_*$ the Lipschitz constant for the flow $S(t_*)$ on X_1 can be estimated via (5.4.14) as

$$L_* = \text{Lip}_{X_1}(S(t_*)) \leq \exp\left\{\frac{\nu\lambda_1}{2}(\overline{Re})^2 t_*\right\}$$

$$\leq \exp\left\{c_6 G^{-4}(\overline{Re})^{-6}\right\}, \tag{5.4.34}$$

whence the fractal dimension of the exponential attractor is proportional to N_0, with N_0 being estimated by (5.4.33). Moreover, the convergence to the exponential attractor is easily estimated by

$$\text{dist}(S(t)X_1,\mathcal{M}) \leq c_7 \exp\left\{-c_8 G^4 \nu\lambda_1(1+(\overline{Re})^8)t\right\}. \tag{5.4.35}$$

We summarize the above arguments in the following proposition.

Proposition 5.4. *Let X_1 be the functional invariant set defined by (5.4.10) then the solution operator for the 3D Navier-Stokes equations restricted to X_1, admits an exponential fractal attractor $\mathcal{M}$ whose fractal dimension can be estimated by*

$$d_F(\mathcal{M}) \leq c \ G^6(1+(\overline{Re})^{12}), \tag{5.4.36}$$

where G is the Grashoff's number given in (5.4.4) and $\overline{Re}$ is a Reynolds number defined in (5.4.3).

Moreover, the convergence to the exponential attractor is estimated by

$$\text{dist}\,(S(t)X_1,\mathcal{M}) \leq c\exp\left\{cG^4\nu\lambda_1(1+(\overline{Re})^8)t\right\}. \tag{5.4.37}$$

Remark 5.4. Clearly, the same arguments would yield similar results for 3D MHD equations, see [ST] for the mathematical formulation and [EL] for the method that can be utilized.

5.5 The Original Burgers Equations

Here we will consider the original Burgers equations with Dirichlet boundary values and show the existence of an exponential attractor. It is worth mentioning that for this type of boundary condition, the existence of inertial manifold is not known even in the simpler case of the standard Burgers equation with dissipation.

The Burgers' original equations are of the form

$$b\frac{dU}{dt} = P - \frac{\nu}{b}U - \frac{1}{b}\int_0^b v^2(t,y)dy, \tag{5.5.1}$$

$$\frac{\partial v}{\partial t} = \frac{1}{b}Uv + \nu\frac{\partial^2 v}{\partial y^2} - 2v\frac{\partial v}{\partial y}, \tag{5.5.2}$$

where b, ν are positive real constants and P is any real number. For more information about these equations see [B1], [B2] and [E]. By a simple change of variables, the equations (5.5.1) and (5.5.2) can be reduced to the dimensionless form

$$U_t = R - U - \int_0^1 v^2(t,y)dy, \qquad (5.5.3)$$

$$v_t = Uv + v_{yy} - 2vv_y, \qquad (5.5.4)$$

where

$$R \doteq \frac{Pb^2}{\nu^2} \qquad (5.5.5)$$

will be taken as a Reynolds number. The equations (5.5.3) and (5.5.4) are supplemented with Dirichlet boundary conditions

$$v(t,0) = v(t,1) = 0 \quad \text{for every} quad t \geq 0. \qquad (5.5.6)$$

The corresponding initial value problem can be posed on the following Hilbert spaces; let

$$H = \mathbf{R} \times L_d^2(0,1) \quad \text{and} \quad V = \mathbf{R} \times H_0^1(0,1), \qquad (5.5.7)$$

where $L_d^2(0,1)$ consists of functions with only sine Fourier modes. Then the usual bilinear forms on $u_i = (U_i, v_i)$ for $i = 1, 2$,

$$[u_1, u_2]_H = U_1 U_2 + (v_1, v_2)_{L^2(0,1)}, \qquad (5.5.8)$$

and

$$\langle u_1, u_2 \rangle_V = U_1 U_2 + \left(\frac{\partial v_1}{\partial y}, \frac{\partial v_2}{\partial y}\right)_{L^2(0,1)}, \qquad (5.5.9)$$

defines inner-products on H and V respectively. Then the problem (5.5.3), (5.5.4) and (5.5.6) have the following reformulation, for $u = (U, v)$ in H,

$$\left.\begin{array}{r}\dfrac{du}{dt} + Au + R(u) = 0, \\ u(0) = u_0,\end{array}\right\} \qquad (5.5.10)$$

where the linear unbounded operator A is defined on H by

$$A = \begin{bmatrix} I & 0 \\ 0 & -\frac{\partial^2}{\partial y^2} \end{bmatrix} \qquad (5.5.11)$$

with $D(A) = V \cap (\mathbf{R} \times H^2(0,1))$, and the non-linear part is given by

$$R(u) = (-R + |v|_{L^2(0,1)}^2, -Uv + 2vv_y), \qquad (5.5.12)$$

and finally the initial value u_0 is coming from H. It was shown in [E] that (5.5.10) has an attractor that is bounded in $H_0^1(0,1)$ whose dimension is of the order $\sqrt{R}$. Here, we will derive the apriori H and V estimates once again, in the latter case making the estimate more explicit.

Going back to the basic equations (5.5.3) and (5.5.4) and multiplying the first by $U(t)$, the second by $v(t,y)$ and integrating from 0 to 1, we obtain

$$\frac{1}{2}\frac{d}{dt}|u(t)|_H^2 + \|u(t)\|_V^2 = R \cdot U(t), \qquad (5.5.13)$$

where

$$|u|_H^2 = U^2 + |v|_{L^2(0,1)}^2 \quad \text{and} \quad \|u\|_V^2 = U^2 + |v_y|_{L^2(0,1)}^2. \qquad (5.5.14)$$

As an immediate consequence of Poincaré's inequality for functions in $H_0^1(0,1)$, i.e. $|v|_{L^2(0,1)} \leq \frac{1}{\pi}|v_y|_{L^2(0,1)}$, we obtain that

$$|u|_H \leq \|u\|_V. \qquad (5.5.15)$$

Now, the H-norm estimates for the solutions of (5.5.10) can be derived very easily, since

$$RU \leq \frac{R^2}{2} + \frac{U^2}{2} \leq \frac{R^2}{2} + \frac{1}{2}\|u\|_V^2 \qquad (5.5.16)$$

implies, in conjunction with (5.5.13) and (5.5.15), that

$$\frac{d}{dt}|u(t)|_H^2 + |u(t)|_H^2 \leq \frac{d}{dt}|u(t)|_H^2 + \|u(t)\|_V^2 \leq R^2. \qquad (5.5.17)$$

Then, by Gronwall's lemma we have

$$|u(t)|^2 \leq |u_0|^2 e^{-t} + R^2(1 - e^{-t}). \qquad (5.5.18)$$

Hence, given $u_0 \in H$, there exists $t_0 = t_0(|u_0|)$ such that for $t \geq t_0$

$$|u(t)|^2 \leq 2R^2. \qquad (5.5.19)$$

Integrating (5.5.17) from t_0 to t, we get that

$$\int_{t_0}^{t} \|u(s)\|_V^2 ds \leq R^2(t - t_0) + |u(t_0)|^2 \leq R^2[(t - t_0) + 2]. \qquad (5.5.20)$$

Next, we would like to derive apriori estimates in the V-norm. The standard method of multiplying (5.5.2) with $-v_{yy}$ and integrating would only give an estimate of the form

$$\|v\| \leq cR^5. \qquad (5.5.21)$$

Here, in contrast to 2D Navier-Stokes equations with periodic boundary conditions where the nonlinear term is orthogonal to Au as well as to u, see

(5.3.12), the nonlinear term does not disappear. Still, it is possible to estimate the nonlinear term in a different way. To this end, we first multiply (5.5.2) with v^3 and integrate to get

$$\frac{1}{4}\frac{d}{dt}|v|_{L^4}^4 = U|v|_{L^4}^4 + (v_{yy}, v^3)_{L^2} - ((v^2)_y, v^3)_{L^2}. \tag{5.5.22}$$

Note, however, that the last term will disappear and the second term simplifies to

$$(v_{yy}, v^3)_{L^2} = -(v_y, 3v^2 v_y)_{L^2} = -\frac{3}{4}|(v^2)_y|^2. \tag{5.5.23}$$

Setting
$$a(t, x) = v^2(t, x), \tag{5.5.24}$$

and observing that

$$|a|^2 = |v|_{L^4}^4 \quad \text{and} \quad |a|_{L^1} = |v|^2, \tag{5.5.25}$$

we obtain from (5.5.22) that

$$\frac{d}{dt}|a|^2 + 3\|a\|^2 = 4U|a|^2. \tag{5.5.26}$$

From this equality one can deduce via uniform Gronwall's inequality that $|a(t)|^2$ is bounded uniformly in time. We will proceed a little differently and use the fact that we have already derived good apriori estimates for $|v|^2$ that will transfer to $|a|^2$. Since

$$|a|^2 \leq |a|_{L^1}|a|_{L^\infty} \leq |v|^2|a|^{1/2}\|a\|^{1/2}, \tag{5.5.27}$$

we have
$$|a|^2 \leq |v|^{8/3}\|a\|^{2/3}. \tag{5.5.28}$$

Returning back to (5.5.26),

$$\frac{d}{dt}|a|^2 + 3\|a\|^2 \leq 4|U|\|v\|^{8/3}\|a\|^{2/3} \leq \frac{1}{3}\|a\|^2 + \frac{2}{3}[4|U|\|v|^{8/3}]^{3/2}. \tag{5.5.29}$$

Consequently, by (5.5.19),

$$\frac{d}{dt}|a|^2 + \frac{8}{3}\|a\|^2 \leq \frac{16}{3}[|U|\|v\|\|v|^{5/3}]^{3/2}$$
$$\leq \frac{16}{3}[\frac{1}{2}(2R^2)(2R^2)^{5/6}]^{3/2} \tag{5.5.30}$$
$$\leq 13R^{11/2}.$$

After a simple application of Poincaré's inequality and of Gronwall's inequality, one obtains

$$|a(t)|^2 \leq |a(0)|^2 e^{-(8/3)t} + 5R^{11/2}(1 - e^{-(8/3)t}). \tag{5.5.31}$$

Hence, the set
$$B_1 = \{v \in L^4 : |v|_{L^4}^4 \leq 10 R^{11/2}\} \tag{5.5.32}$$
is an absorbing set. Moreover, if $v(0) = v_0$ is in B_1, then one also has
$$\frac{8}{3} \int_{t_0}^{t_0+1} \|a(\tau)\|^2 \, d\tau \leq 16 R^{11/2}. \tag{5.5.33}$$

It is interesting to write the above estimate in terms of v:
$$\int_{t_0}^{t_0+1} \|a(\tau)\|^2 \, d\tau = \int_{t_0}^{t_0+1} |(v^2(\tau))_y|_{L^2}^2 \, d\tau \leq 5 R^{11/2}, \tag{5.5.34}$$

observe that this is nothing but the high order nonlinear term in (5.5.2). Next, we turn our attention to the V-norm, multiplying (5.5.2) by $-v_{yy}$ and integrating we obtain that

$$\begin{aligned}
\frac{1}{2}\frac{d}{dt}\|v\|^2 + \|v_y\|^2 &= U\|v\|^2 + ((v^2)_y, v_{yy}) \\
&\leq |U|\|v\|\|v_y\| + \|a\|\|v_y\| \\
&\leq (R^2 + \|a\|)\|v_y\| \\
&\leq R^4 + \|a\|^2 + \frac{1}{2}\|v_y\|^2
\end{aligned} \tag{5.5.35}$$

Consequently,
$$\frac{d}{dt}\|v\|^2 + \|v_y\|^2 \leq 2R^4 + 2\|a\|^2; \tag{5.5.36}$$
hence, it follows that
$$\begin{aligned}
\|v(t)\|^2 &\leq \|v_0\|^2 e^{-t} + 2R^4(1-e^{-t}) + 2\int_0^t e^{-s}\|a(s)\|^2 \, ds \\
&\leq \|v_0\|^2 e^{-t} + 2R^4(1-e^{-t}) + 20 R^{11/2},
\end{aligned} \tag{5.5.37}$$

where we have used the fact that, if $t \leq N+1$, then
$$\int_0^t e^{-s}\|a(s)\|^2 \, ds \leq \sum_{n=0}^{N} e^{-n} \int_n^{n+1} \|a(s)\|^2 \, ds \leq \sum_{n=0}^{N} e^{-n}(5R^{11/2})$$
$$\leq \frac{1}{1-e^{-1}}(5R^{11/2}) \leq 10 R^{11/2}. \tag{5.5.38}$$

As an easy consequence of (5.5.37) we obtain that the set
$$B = \{u \in V : |u|_H \leq \sqrt{2}R \quad \text{and} \quad \|u\|_V \leq 30 R^{11/4}\} \tag{5.5.39}$$

is an absorbing set for (5.5.10); moreover, one also has

$$\int_{t_0}^{t_0+1} |v_{yy}(\tau)|^2 \, d\tau \leq cR^{11/2}. \tag{5.5.40}$$

Next, we restrict the solution operator $S(t)$ of the problem (5.5.10) to the invariant set B given in (5.5.39) and proceed to show that $(S(t), B)$ enjoys an exponential attractor.

In order to guarantee the squeezing property we consider the equation satisfied by the difference of two solutions. Let u_1 and u_2 be two solutions of (5.5.10) with initial values u_{10} and u_{20}, respectively. Then we set $w(t)$ to be the difference of these solutions; $w(t) \doteq (W(t), z(t))$. Let us consider the second of the equations satisfied by $w(t)$:

$$\begin{aligned} z_t &= U_1 v_1 - U_2 v_2 + z_{yy} - (v_1^2 - v_2^2)_y \\ &= U_1 z + W v_2 + z_{yy} - (z(v_1 + v_2))_y. \end{aligned} \tag{5.5.41}$$

Multiplying through by z and integrating from 0 to 1,

$$\frac{1}{2} \frac{d}{dt} |z|^2 = U_1 |z|^2 + W(v_2, z) - \|z\|^2 + (z(v_1 + v_2), z_y). \tag{5.5.42}$$

On the other hand, the first equation satisfied by $W(t)$ multiplied by $W(t)$ gives

$$\frac{1}{2} \frac{d}{dt} W^2 = -W^2 - (|v_1|^2 - |v_2|^2) W \tag{5.5.43}$$

Adding the last two equations, we obtain, with $\bar{v} = \frac{v_1 + v_2}{2}$,

$$\frac{1}{2} \frac{d}{dt} |w(t)|_H^2 + \|w(t)\|_V^2 = U_1 |z|^2 + W(v_2, z) - (\bar{v}_y, z^2) + (|v_2|^2 - |v_1|^2). \tag{5.5.44}$$

If u_1 and u_2 are in the absorbing set B then

$$|v_1|^2 - |v_2|^2 \leq |v_1 - v_2|(|v_1| + |v_2|) \leq |z|(2\sqrt{2}R) \leq 3R|z| \tag{5.5.45}$$

and

$$U_1 |z|^2 + W(v_2, z) \leq \sqrt{2} R |z|^2 + W |v_2| |z| \leq \sqrt{2} R (|z|^2 + W |z|) \tag{5.5.46}$$
$$\leq 3R |w|_H^2,$$

$$-(\bar{v}_y, z^2) = 2(\bar{v}, z z_y) \leq 2|\bar{v}|_{L^\infty} |z| |z_y| \leq 2|\bar{v}|^{1/2} \|\bar{v}\|^{1/2} |w|_H \|w\|_V \tag{5.5.47}$$
$$\leq 2R^{1/2} \|\bar{v}\|^{1/2} |w|_H \|w\|_V.$$

With the help of these inequalities

$$\frac{1}{2} \frac{d}{dt} |w|_H^2 + \|w\|_V^2 \leq 3R |w|_H^2 + 2R^{1/2} \|\bar{v}\|^{1/2} |w|_H \|w\|_V 3R |z| W \tag{5.5.48}$$
$$\leq 3R |w|_H^2 + 2R^{1/2} \|\bar{v}\|^{1/2} |w|_H \|w\|_V + \frac{3}{2} R |w|_H^2$$

Exponential Attractors for Dissipative Evolution Equations

Letting $\lambda(t) = \|w(t)\|_V^2/|w(t)|_H^2$, and rearranging

$$\frac{d}{dt}|w(t)|_H^2 + (\lambda(t) - 5R - 2R^{1/2}\|\bar{v}\|^{1/2}\lambda(t)^{1/2})|w(t)|_H^2 \leq 0. \quad (5.5.49)$$

Hence, by Gronwall's inequality

$$|w(t)|_H^2 \leq \delta(t)|w(0)|_H^2, \quad (5.5.50)$$

where

$$\delta(t) = \exp\left\{-\int_0^t (\lambda(s) - 5R - 2R^{1/2}\|\bar{v}\|^{1/2}\lambda(s)^{1/2})ds\right\}. \quad (5.5.51)$$

In order to estimate $\delta(t)$, we need to consider the equation for $\lambda(t)$ which reads as, see (3.40),

$$\frac{1}{2}\frac{d}{dt}\lambda(t) = \frac{1}{|w|_H}(w_t, (A - \lambda)\xi) \quad (5.5.52)$$

$$= \frac{1}{|w|_H}(-Aw - (R(u_1) - R(u_2)), (A - \lambda)\xi)$$

where $\xi(t) = w(t)/|w(t)|_H$. As in (3.41), we have $[\lambda\xi, (A - \lambda)\xi]_H = 0$, hence $|(A - \lambda)\xi|_H^2 = \frac{1}{|w|}[Aw, (A - \lambda)\xi]_H$. So that

$$\frac{1}{2}\frac{d}{dt}\lambda(t) + |(A - \lambda(t))\xi|_H^2 = \frac{1}{|w|_H}[R(u_1) - R(u_2), (A - \lambda)\xi]_H \quad (5.5.53)$$

$$\leq \frac{1}{|w|_H}|R(u_1) - R(u_2)|_H|(A - \lambda)\xi|_H,$$

using Young's inequality and simplifying

$$\frac{d}{dt}\lambda(t) \leq \frac{2}{|w|_H^2}|R(u_1) - R(u_2)|_H^2. \quad (5.5.54)$$

So it remains to estimate the difference of the nonlinear terms.

$$|R(u_1) - R(u_2)|_H^2 = (|v_1|^2 - |v_2|^2)^2 + |U_1v_1 - (v_1^2)_y - U_1v_2 + (v_2^2)_y|^2$$
$$\leq 4|z|^2|\bar{v}|^2 + 4|U_1 - U_2|^2|v_1|^2$$
$$+ 4|U_2|^2|z|^2 + 4|z\bar{v}_y|^2 + 4|z_y\bar{v}|^2$$
$$\leq 16R^2|w|_H^2 + 4|z|_{L^\infty}^2\|\bar{v}\|^2 + 4\|z\|^2|\bar{v}|_{L^\infty}^2 \quad (5.5.55)$$
$$\leq 16R^2|w|_H^2 + 4|w|_H\|w\|_V\|\bar{v}\|^2 + 6R\|w\|_V^2\|\bar{v}\|$$
$$\leq (16R^2 + 4\lambda^{1/2}\|\bar{v}\|^2 + 6R\lambda\|\bar{v}\|)|w|_H^2.$$

5. Applications

Hence, by Young's inequality

$$\frac{2}{|w|_H^2}|R(u_1) - R(u_2)|_H^2 \le 32R^2 + 8\lambda^{1/2}\|\bar{v}\|^2 + 12R\lambda\|\bar{v}\| \quad (5.5.56)$$

$$\le 13R\|\bar{v}\|\lambda + (32R^2 + \frac{4}{R}\|\bar{v}\|^3).$$

Returning back to (5.5.54), we see that it is of the form

$$\frac{d}{dt}\lambda(t) \le f(t)\lambda(t) + g(t) \quad (5.5.57)$$

where

$$f(t) = 13R\|\bar{v}(t)\| \quad \text{and} \quad g(t) = 32R^2 + \frac{4}{R}\|\bar{v}(t)\|^3. \quad (5.5.58)$$

By Gronwall's inequality, it follows from (5.5.57) that

$$\lambda(t) \le \exp\left(\int_{t_0}^t f(\tau)d\tau\right)\left[\lambda(t_0) + \int_{t_0}^t g(\tau)d\tau\right]. \quad (5.5.59)$$

If we assume that at $t = t_*$, $\lambda(t_*) \ge \frac{1}{2}\lambda_{N_0+1}$, then the above inequality gives

$$\lambda(t_0) \ge \exp\left(-\int_{t_0}^{t_*} f(\tau)d\tau\right)\frac{1}{2}\lambda_{N_0+1} - \int_{t_0}^{t_*} g(\tau)d\tau. \quad (5.5.60)$$

Integrating both sides from $t_0 = 0$ to $t_0 = t_*$ we obtain that

$$\int_0^{t_*} \lambda(t_0)dt_0 \ge \frac{1}{2}\lambda_{N_0+1}\int_0^{t_*} \exp\left(-\int_0^{t_*} f(\tau)d\tau\right)dt_0 - \int_0^{t_*}\int_{t_0}^{t_*} g(\tau)d\tau dt_0. \quad (5.5.61)$$

Next we set $t_* = cR^{-15/4}$, then by (5.5.39)

$$\int_{t_0}^{t_*} f(\tau)d\tau = 13R\int_{t_0}^{t_*}\|\bar{v}(\tau)\|d\tau \le 13R(30R^{11/4})(t_* - t_0) = cR^{15/4}(t_* - t_0); \quad (5.5.62)$$

hence,

$$\int_0^{t_*} \exp\left(-\int_{t_0}^{t_*} f(\tau)d\tau\right)dt_0 \ge \int_0^{t_*} \exp(-cR^{15/4}(t_* - t_0))dt_0$$

$$\ge \frac{1}{cR^{15/4}}(1 - e^{-cR^{15/4}t_*}) \quad (5.5.63)$$

$$\ge \frac{1}{2cR^{15/4}}.$$

At the same time,

$$\int_0^{t_*}\int_{t_0}^{t_*} g(\tau)d\tau \leq 32R^2 t_*^2 + \frac{4}{R}(30R^{11/4})(2R^2)t_* \quad (5.5.64)$$
$$\leq 32c^2 R^{-11/2} + 240c.$$

Consequently, (5.5.61) combined with (5.5.63) and (5.5.64) imply that

$$\int_0^{t_*} \lambda(t_0)dt_0 \geq \frac{N_0^2}{4cR^{15/4}} - 32c^2 R^{-11/2} - 240c. \quad (5.5.65)$$

Returning back to the w-inequality (5.5.49) and the estimate of the Lipschitz constant δ_* for the squeezing property, we deduce from (5.5.51) that

$$\delta_* = \delta(t_*) = \exp\left\{-\int_0^{t_*} [\lambda(t_0) - 5R - 2R^{1/2}\|\bar{v}\|^{1/2}\lambda(t_0)^{1/2}]dt_0\right\}$$
$$\leq \exp\left\{\left(-\frac{1}{2}\int_0^{t_*}\lambda(t_0)dt_0\right) + 5Rt_* + 2R\int_0^{t_*}\|\bar{v}(t_0)\|dt_0\right\}$$
$$\leq \exp\left\{\left(-\frac{N_0^2}{8cR^{15/4}} + 16c^2 R^{-11/2} + 120c\right) + 5cR^{-11/4}\right. \quad (5.5.66)$$
$$\left. + 2R(30R^{11/4})(cR^{-15/4})\right\}$$
$$\leq \exp\left\{-\frac{N_0^2}{8cR^{15/4}} + 180c + 16c^2 R^{-11/2} + 5cR^{-11/4}\right\}.$$

There exists a constant c_1, such that if

$$N_0 > c_1 \max\{R^{15/8}, R^{-7/8}, R^{1/2}\}, \quad (5.5.67)$$

then $\delta_* < 1/8$ and the squeezing property holds. As for the Lipschitz constant for the full equation, we have from (5.5.49)

$$L_* = \text{Lip}(S(t_*)) \leq \exp\left\{5Rt_* + 2R\int_0^{t_*}\|\bar{v}(t_0)\|dt_0\right\} \quad (5.5.68)$$
$$\leq c_2 e^{R^{-11/2} + R^{-11/4}}.$$

Clearly, if $R > 1$, then $L_* \leq c_2 e^2$.

Proposition 5.5. *The Burger's equations (5.5.1) and (5.5.2) with Dirichlet boundary conditions admit an exponential fractal attractor $\mathcal{M}_0$ such that, if $R > 1$, then*

$$d_F(\mathcal{M}_0) \leq c_4 N_0 \leq c_4 R^{15/8}. \quad (5.5.69)$$

Moreover, the rate of convergence to the exponential attractor is estimated by

$$\text{dist}_H(S(t)u_0, \mathcal{M}_0) \leq c_5 \exp(-c_6 R^{15/4} t), \quad (5.5.70)$$

where c_4, c_5, c_6 are absolute positive constants.

Remark 5.5. It is possible to improve, slightly, the estimates found in this section. The basic idea is to take the L^2-inner product of (5.5.2) with v^7 and estimate the L^8-norm of v, as it was done for the L^4-norm of v. This computation gives $|v|_8 \sim R^{19/16}$, which implies by interpolation that $|v|_4 \sim R^{17/16}$. Now using this estimate in (5.5.26) results in a better estimate for the integral term. Consequently, the estimate for the fractal dimension takes the form $R^{7/4}$. Note, however, that since the dimension of the attractor is $R^{1/2}$, there is still room for improvement (see [E]). However, when we do not insist on the explicit control of the exponential rate of convergence, the Lyapunov construction outlined in Chapter 7 gives optimal dimension for the exponential attractor.

5.6 Chaffee-Infante Reaction-Diffusion Equations

We consider the Chaffee-Infante equations as given in [CI], [He], [CFNT2], these equations enjoy the existence of an inertial manifold (see [MS]; [CFNT2], [Mr]) even in higher space dimensions. Yet the estimates that are used in the proof of the existence involve a non-constructive result hence does not give explicit estimates on the dimension of the inertial manifold. Here we are able to show that these equations have, in any space dimension, exponential fractal attractors and furthermore the estimates that we obtain for its fractal dimension is of the same order as the one that is obtained for its attractor by [Mp] using the Constantin-Foias theory of Lyapunov exponents. In view of the fact that the present theory is much simpler to develop than the theory of Lyapunov exponents and gives the same estimate for the attractor (see Lemma 2.2) suggests that the mechanism that gives rise to the attractor in these equations is quite different form the ones considered so far.

Let Ω be an open, bounded subset of $\mathbf{R}^d$, the Chaffee-Infante equation is given by

$$\left. \begin{array}{l} \dfrac{\partial u}{\partial t} - \Delta u + \lambda(u^3 - u) = 0 \qquad \text{on} \quad \Omega \times [0, T], \\[6pt] u(0, x) = u_0(x) \quad \text{on } \Omega. \end{array} \right\} \qquad (5.6.1)$$

Depending on the boundary conditions one wants to impose, the underlying Hilbert spaces would either be

$$H = L^2(\Omega) \quad , \quad V = H_0^1(\Omega) \qquad (5.6.2)$$

or

$$H = L^2(\Omega) \quad , \quad V = H^1(\Omega) \qquad (5.6.3)$$

or

$$H = L^2(\Omega) \quad , \quad V = \{v \in H^1(\Omega) : v \text{ is } L\text{-periodic}\} \qquad (5.6.4)$$

where in the last case Ω has the special form $[0, L]^d$. These spaces correspond to Dirichlet, Neumann and finally to periodic type boundary values, respectively. For simplicity, we will consider the Dirichlet boundary problem, noting however that most of the arguments would still be valid without change for the other boundary conditions as well. The initial value problem, on H, then is given by

$$u_t + Au + R(u) = 0 \qquad (5.6.5)$$

$$u(0) = u_0$$

where $Au = -\Delta u$ with $D(A) = H_0^1(\Omega) \cap H^2(\Omega)$ and the nonlinear term by $R(u) = \lambda(u^3 - u)$. The existence of an absorbing set in $L^p(\Omega) \cap V$ for $p \geq 2$ is well-known (see [M]); moreover, it is known the solution operator $\{S(t)\}_{t \geq 0}$ is uniformly compact in H, i.e., for any bounded set B, there exists $t_0 = t_0(B)$ such that

$$B_1 = \overline{\bigcup_{t \geq t_0} S(t)B} \text{ is compact in } H. \qquad (5.6.6)$$

Clearly, B_1 is a positively invariant set, and therefore can be used as X in Theorem 3.1, here the proper choice of t_0 and B will play an important role. Moreover, it is known that there exists an absorbing ball in $L^\infty(\Omega)$. Here, we would like to start by obtaining explicit apriori L^∞-estimates for the solutions of (5.6.5). The fact that these estimates do not depend on the particular initial value one starts with has already been observed (see, e.g., [CFNT2]) by many authors, still the fact that the estimate does not depend either on λ or the size of the domain $|\Omega|$ was not explicitly stated (see [T] for a proof of: $u \in \mathcal{A}$ implies $|u|_{L^\infty} \leq 1$, $c_2 = 1/2$ in his notation, also comparison principles would work).

Lemma 5.6. *Let $u(t)$ be a solution of the Chaffee-Infante equation such that u_0 belongs to the absorbing set in V, which is bounded in $L^\infty(\Omega)$, then*

$$t > 1/\lambda \text{ implies that } |u(t)|_{L^\infty(\Omega)} \leq \sqrt{2}. \qquad (5.6.7)$$

Proof. Since u_0 is in the absorbing set in V, $u(t)$ will remain in V and will also be $L^\infty(\Omega)$. Hence, it is allowed to multiply the equation pointwise with $|u(t)|^k u(t)$ and integrate over Ω, for any positive k. If we denote the norm in $L^p(\Omega)$ by $|\ |_p$, then using the boundary conditions on $u(t)$, it follows from (5.6.1) that

$$\frac{1}{k+2}\frac{d}{dt}|u(t)|_{k+2}^{k+2} + (k+1)\int_\Omega |u(t,x)|^k |\nabla u(t,x)|^2 dx +$$
$$\lambda |u(t)|_{k+4}^{k+4} - \lambda |u(t)|_{k+2}^{k+2} = 0 \qquad (5.6.8)$$

where we have used

$$(u_t, |u|^k u)_{L^2(\Omega)} = \frac{1}{k+2}\frac{d}{dt}\int_\Omega |u(t,x)|^{k+2} dx, \qquad (5.6.9)$$

and

$$(Au, |u|^k u)_{L^2(\Omega)} = (k+1)\int_\Omega |u(t,x)|^k |\nabla u(t,x)|^2 dx. \qquad (5.6.10)$$

Now we set,

$$a(t) = \int_\Omega |u(t,x)|^{k+2} dx = |u(t)|_{k+2}^{k+2}, \qquad (5.6.11)$$

then, by a simple application of Hölder's inequality

$$a(t) \leq \left(\int_\Omega |u(t,x)|^{k+4} dx\right)^{\frac{k+2}{k+4}} \cdot |\Omega|^{\frac{2}{k+4}}, \qquad (5.6.12)$$

therefore,

$$|u(t)|_{k+4}^{k+4} \geq \left(a|\Omega|^{-\frac{2}{k+4}}\right)^{\frac{k+4}{k+2}} = a^{\frac{k+4}{k+2}} |\Omega|^{-\frac{2}{k+2}}. \qquad (5.6.13)$$

Substituting it into (5.6.8), neglecting the positive term involving $|\nabla u(t)|$ and finally multiplying through by $(k+2)$, one deduces that

$$\frac{da}{dt} + \lambda(k+2) a^{\frac{k+4}{k+2}} |\Omega|^{-\frac{2}{k+2}} - \lambda(k+2)a \leq 0. \qquad (5.6.14)$$

Setting,

$$p = \frac{k+4}{k+2} \quad \text{and} \quad q = \frac{k+4}{2}, \qquad (5.6.15)$$

one obtains after simplification that

$$\frac{da}{dt} + \frac{\lambda(k+2)}{|\Omega|^{2/k+2}} a^p \leq \lambda(k+2)a = \left[\frac{\lambda(k+2)}{2|\Omega|^{2/k+2}}\right]^{1/p} a(2|\Omega|^{2/k+2})^{1/p}(\lambda(k+2))^{1/q}$$

$$\leq \frac{1}{p} \frac{\lambda(k+2)}{2|\Omega|^{2/k+2}} a^p + \frac{1}{q}[2|\Omega|^{2/k+2}]^{q/p}\lambda(k+2) \qquad (5.6.16)$$

$$\leq \frac{\lambda(k+2)}{2|\Omega|^{2/k+2}} a^p + \frac{2}{k+4} 2^{k+2/2} |\Omega|\lambda(k+2)$$

where we have used Young's inequality with p and q as given in (5.6.15) and the fact that $1/p < 1$. Clearly, (5.6.16) reduces to

$$\frac{da}{dt} + \frac{\lambda(k+2)}{2|\Omega|^{2/k+2}} a^p \leq \frac{2^{k+4/2}}{k+4} |\Omega|\lambda(k+2) \qquad (5.6.17)$$

which is of the form

$$\frac{da}{dt} + \gamma a^p \leq \delta \qquad (5.6.18)$$

with

$$p = \frac{k+4}{k+2}, \quad \gamma = \lambda(k+2)/2|\Omega|^{2/k+2} \quad \text{and} \quad \delta = \frac{2^{\frac{k+4}{2}}}{k+4} |\Omega|\lambda(k+2). \qquad (5.6.19)$$

Let us recall a non-linear version of the Gronwall's lemma due to J. M. Ghidaglia (see [T1], p. 163).

Lemma 5.7. *Let $a(t)$ be a positive absolutely continuous function on $(0, \infty)$ that satisfies*

$$\frac{da}{dt} + \gamma a^p \leq \delta, \tag{5.6.20}$$

for some $p > 1$ and $\delta, \gamma > 0$. Then, for $t \geq 0$

$$a(t) \leq \left(\frac{\delta}{\gamma}\right)^{1/p} + \frac{1}{(\gamma(p-1)t)^{1/p-1}}. \tag{5.6.21}$$

Proof. If $a(0) \leq (\delta/\gamma)^{1/p}$ then from (5.6.20) it follows that $da/dt \leq 0$, hence $a(t) \leq (\delta/\gamma)^{1/p}$ for $t > 0$. If, on the other hand, $a(0) > (\delta/\gamma)^{1/p}$ then there exists $t_0 > 0$ such that

$$a(t) > \left(\frac{\delta}{\gamma}\right)^{1/p} \quad \text{for} \quad 0 \leq t < t_0, \tag{5.6.22}$$

and $a(t_0) \leq (\delta/\gamma)^{1/p}$. By the first argument, $a(t) \leq (\delta/\gamma)^{1/p}$ for $t \geq t_0$. So, we only need to consider the interval $[0, t_0]$, setting

$$b(t) \doteq a(t) - \left(\frac{\delta}{\gamma}\right)^{1/p}, \tag{5.6.23}$$

we see that $b(t) \geq 0$, on $[0, t_0]$ and

$$a(t)^p = \left(b(t) + \left(\frac{\delta}{\gamma}\right)^{1/p}\right)^p \geq b(t)^p + \frac{\delta}{\gamma}. \tag{5.6.24}$$

Hence, the inequality (5.6.20) takes the form

$$\frac{db}{dt} + \gamma b^p + \delta \leq \delta, \tag{5.6.25}$$

integrating from 0 to t, gives

$$\frac{1}{1-p} \frac{1}{b(t)^{p-1}} \leq \frac{1}{1-p} \frac{1}{b(0)^{p-1}} - \gamma t, \tag{5.6.26}$$

which after simplification reduces to

$$b(t)^{p-1} \leq \frac{1}{b(0)^{p-1} + \gamma(p-1)t} \leq \frac{1}{\gamma(p-1)t}. \tag{5.6.27}$$

Finally, substituting in the value of $b(t)$ from (5.6.23) for $t < t_0$, the desired conclusion follows. $\square$

Returning back to (5.6.17) and applying the above Lemma, we obtain that, for $t \geq 1/\lambda$

$$a(t) \leq \left[2^{\frac{k+4}{2}} \frac{|\Omega|\lambda(k+2)}{k+4} \cdot \frac{2|\Omega|^{2/k+2}}{\lambda(k+2)}\right]^{\frac{k+2}{k+4}} + \left[\frac{2|\Omega|^{2/k+2}}{\lambda(k+2) \cdot \frac{2}{k+2} \cdot t}\right]^{\frac{k+2}{2}}$$

$$\leq \left[\frac{2^{k+6/2}}{k+4}|\Omega|^{k+4/k+2}\right]^{\frac{k+2}{k+4}} + \frac{|\Omega|}{(\lambda t)^{k+2/2}} \qquad (5.6.28)$$

$$\leq |\Omega|\left[\left(\frac{2^{\frac{k+6}{2}}}{k+4}\right)^{\frac{k+2}{k+4}} + 1\right].$$

where we have used $\frac{1}{p} = \frac{k+2}{k+4}$, $\frac{1}{p-1} = \frac{k+2}{2}$ and the fact that $(\lambda t)^{-\frac{k+2}{2}} \leq 1$.
Since

$$|u(t)|_\infty \leq \overline{\lim_{k\to\infty}} |u(t)|_k \leq \overline{\lim_{k\to\infty}} a(t)^{1/k+2}, \qquad (5.6.29)$$

from (5.6.28) and (5.6.29) one obtains that $|u(t)|_\infty \leq \sqrt{2}$ for $t \geq 1/\lambda$. □

As a simple corollary to the Lemma 5.6, we can obtain a compact positively invariant set B with a uniform, in λ and $|\Omega|$ too, estimate on the L^∞-norm of its elements. Namely, let B_0 be the absorbing ball of the solution operator in V that is bounded in L^∞, then the set defined by

$$X \doteq \overline{\bigcup_{t \geq 1/\lambda} S(t)B_0}, \qquad (5.6.30)$$

is a compact subset of H by (5.6.6); moreover, by Lemma 5.6, if $u \in X$ then $|u|_\infty \leq \sqrt{2}$.

Let us consider the solution operator $S(t)$ for (5.6.5) restricted to X as given in (5.6.30) and try to apply the Theorem 3.1 to this particular case. In order to prove the squeezing property for $S_* = S(t_*)$, with t_* suitably chosen, let us first consider the equation that the difference of two solutions satisfy, that is if

$$w(t) = u(t) - v(t) \qquad (5.6.31)$$

then $w(t)$ satisfies

$$w_t - \Delta w + \lambda(u^3 - v^3) - \lambda w = 0. \qquad (5.6.32)$$

In order to avoid the confusion between the quotient norm $\lambda(t)$ and the constant λ, we will set $\lambda = \alpha$ from now on. Then multiplying by w, gives

$$\frac{1}{2}\frac{d}{dt}|w|^2 + \|w\|^2 + \alpha(u^2 + uv + v^2, w^2) - \alpha|w|^2 = 0. \qquad (5.6.33)$$

Letting $\lambda(t) = \frac{\|w(t)\|^2}{|w(t)|^2}$, and noting that $u^2 + uv + v^2$ is always positive, (5.6.33) implies that

$$\frac{d}{dt}|w(t)|^2 + (2\lambda(t) - 2\alpha)|w(t)|^2 \leq 0. \tag{5.6.34}$$

By Gronwall's inequality,

$$|w(t)| \leq \delta(t)|w(0)|, \tag{5.6.35}$$

where

$$\delta(t) = \exp\left\{-\int_0^t \lambda(\tau)d\tau + \alpha t\right\}. \tag{5.6.36}$$

In particular, we deduce that

$$\text{Lip } (S(t)) \leq e^{\alpha t}. \tag{5.6.37}$$

On the other hand, to show the squeezing property for $S(t_*) = S_*$, we set

$$t_* = 1/\alpha, \tag{5.6.38}$$

note that $\alpha = \lambda$ is the bifurcation parameter, and, as in (3.23), assume that at $t = t_*$

$$\lambda_* = \lambda(t_*) \geq \frac{1}{2}\lambda_{N_0+1} \geq \frac{1}{2}c_0|\Omega|^{-2/d}N_0^{2/d} \tag{5.6.39}$$

where we have used the asymptotic properties of the eigenvalues of $-\Delta$ (see (5.3.9)).

We choose N_0 such that

$$N_0 = c_1|\Omega|\alpha^{d/2} \tag{5.6.40}$$

where c_1 is an absolute constant to be specified later. Next we consider the equation that $\lambda(t)$, the quotient norm, satisfy,

$$\frac{1}{2}\frac{d}{dt}\lambda(t) = \frac{1}{|w|^2}(w_t, (A - \lambda(t))w)_{L^2(\Omega)}$$
$$= (-A\xi - \alpha\xi(u^2 + uv + v^2) + \alpha\xi, (A - \lambda(t))\xi)_{L^2(\Omega)} \tag{5.6.41}$$
$$= -|(A - \lambda(t))\xi|^2 - \alpha(\xi(u^2 + uv + v^2), (A - \lambda(t))\xi)_{L^2(\Omega)},$$

where we have used the fact that $(\xi, (A - \lambda(t))\xi)_{L^2(\Omega)} = 0$ twice, with $\xi(t) \doteq w(t)/|w(t)|_2$. Since u and v are in X, by Lemma 5.6

$$|u^2 + uv + v^2|_\infty \leq 2(|u|_\infty^2 + |v|_\infty^2) \leq 8, \tag{5.6.42}$$

hence, after an application of Schwarz inequality and Young's inequality and neglecting a negative term on the right-hand side, (5.6.41) implies that

$$\frac{d}{dt}\lambda(t) \leq \alpha^2|\xi|_2^2|u^2 + uv + v^2|_\infty^2 \leq 64\alpha^2. \tag{5.6.43}$$

By Gronwall's inequality,
$$\lambda(t) \le 64\alpha^2(t-t_0) + \lambda(t_0) \tag{5.6.44}$$
setting $t = t_*$ and integrating from $t_0 = 0$ to $t_0 = t_*$, we obtain that
$$\int_0^{t_*} \lambda(t_0)dt_0 \ge t_*\lambda_* - 64\alpha^2 t_*^2$$
$$\ge t_*\left(\frac{1}{2}c_0|\Omega|^{-2/d}N_0^{2/d}\right) - 64\alpha^2 t_*^2 \tag{5.6.45}$$
$$\ge \frac{1}{\alpha}\left(\frac{c_0}{2}|\Omega|^{-2/d}\left(c_1|\Omega|\alpha^{d/2}\right)^{2/d}\right) - 64$$
$$\ge \frac{c_0}{2}c_1^{2/d} - 64,$$
where we have used (5.6.38), (5.6.39), (5.6.40) combined with (5.6.44). Hence by (5.6.36)
$$\delta_* = \delta(t_*) = \exp\left\{-\int_0^{t_*}\lambda(t_0)dt_0 + \alpha t_*\right\}$$
$$\le \exp\left\{-\frac{c_0 c_1^{2/d}}{2} + 64 + \alpha \cdot \frac{1}{\alpha}\right\}, \tag{5.6.46}$$
but then $\delta_* < 1/8$ if $c_1 = (136/c_0)^{d/2}$, and with this choice of c_1, the squeezing property is satisfied. Moreover,
$$L_* = \mathrm{Lip}_X(S_*) \le e^{\alpha t_*} = e. \tag{5.6.47}$$
So we have obtained:

Proposition 5.6. *The Chaffee-Infante equations with Dirichlet boundary conditions admit an exponential fractal attractor $\mathcal{M}$ whose fractal dimension can be estimated by*
$$d_F(\mathcal{M}) \le c_2|\Omega|\lambda^{d/2}, \tag{5.6.48}$$
where c_2 is a constant that depends only on d and the shape of Ω.

Moreover, there exist positive constants c_3 and c_4 such that
$$\mathrm{dist}_{L^2(\Omega)}(S(t)X, \mathcal{M}) \le c_3 e^{-c_4\lambda t}. \tag{5.6.49}$$

Proof. The estimate on the fractal dimension follows from Theorem 3.1 and Theorem 2.1 where N_0 is chosen as in (5.6.40), whereas the convergence follows from (3.65) with $t_* = 1/\lambda$. □

Remark 5.6. Various generalizations are possible at this stage, the easiest possible being to other boundary conditions mentioned at the beginning, including the periodic case where the operator A is no longer coercive. It is worth mentioning that we did not make use of Poincaré's inequality during our arguments. In the framework of Chapter 3, the non-linearity satisfies the Lipschitz condition, i.e.,
$$|R(u) - R(v)|_2 \le c_0|u-v|_2 \tag{5.6.50}$$
for u, v in X.

Chapter 6
Exponential Attractors for Second Order Evolution Equations with Damping and Applications

The construction of the exponential attractor outlined in the first chapters did not refer to any specific type of dynamical system. Rather, the key property of the dynamical system under question was the discrete squeezing property. Therefore, any dynamical system that can be put in the same framework is a good candidate for applying the same construction. In this chapter, we will show that for a general class of damped semilinear wave equations the discrete squeezing property still holds for the dynamical systems that arise from such equations. Our treatment here will be brief and we will refer to other works for some technical but vital facts.

The significance of the following construction is twofold. First, the method of verification of DSP is almost trivial and depends heavily on the Lipschitzianity of the nonlinearity under different norms. Second, there are well-known examples of damped wave equations that have global attractors but generically fail to admit C^1-inertial manifolds (see [MSM]). Hence, the following examples would put more weight to our claim that the exponential attractors are as common as attractors (at this point we do not know any example where a global attractor exists in some strong sense, caveat the KdV (see [G]), yet there cannot be an exponential attractor.)

Our treatment of the material basically follows the one given in [EMN] where it was first exposed. The only important difference is that the condition assumed on the nonlinearity is slightly more general. We start with introducing the functional set-up and recall the basic results that assure the existence of a solution semigroup $\{S(t)\}_{t \geq 0}$.

6.1. Functional Set-up for Second Order Evolution Equations

Let H be a separable Hilbert space on which the following initial value problem is posed:

$$\epsilon u_{tt} + u_t + Au + g(u) = f; \qquad (H^\epsilon)$$

$$u(0) = u_0 \text{ and } u_t(0) = u_1; \qquad (IV)$$

where $\epsilon > 0$, A is a positive, self-adjoint operator with compact inverse and g is a C^1-nonlinearity from $D(A^{1/2})$ into H. Set $V = D(A^{1/2})$ and denote the norms in V, H and V' (dual of V) by $\|\cdot\|_V$, $|\cdot|_H$ and $\|\cdot\|_*$, respectively. We further denote the inner product on H by $(\cdot,\cdot)$ and the duality pairing between V' and V by $\langle\cdot,\cdot\rangle$. Let $\{w_n : n = 1, 2, \ldots\}$ be a complete set of eigenvectors for A and let

$$0 < \lambda_1 \leq \lambda_2 \leq \cdots \leq \lambda_n \to \infty \qquad (6.1.1)$$

be the corresponding eigenvalues of A. Since A has a complete set of eigenvectors, we can define $D(A^\sigma)$ for $\sigma \in \mathbf{R}$. Note that $D(A^0) = H$ and $D(A^{1/2}) = V$. We assume that the nonlinearity $g(u)$ satisfy a Lipschitz condition $(L^{\sigma,\gamma})$ of the following type

$$(L^{\sigma,\gamma}): \qquad (L^{\sigma,\gamma})\|g(u) - g(v)\|_{D(A^\sigma)} \leq L(\sigma,\gamma)\|u - v\|_{D(A^{\sigma+\gamma})}$$

for all $u, v \in B^{D(A^{\sigma+1/2})}(0; R)$, where $\gamma \geq 0$ and σ is any real number and $L(\sigma,\gamma)$ depends on R as well as σ and γ.

Note that the norm on $D(A^\sigma)$ is simply given by

$$\|u\|_{D(A^\sigma)} = |A^\sigma u|_H. \qquad (6.1.2)$$

Typically, we will take $\gamma = 0$ and $\sigma = 1/2$, then $(L^{1/2,0})$ reads as

$$\|g(u) - g(v)\|_V \leq L\|u - v\|_V \quad \forall u, v \in B^{D(A)}(0; R). \qquad (6.1.3)$$

We introduce the product spaces on which the initial value problem will be well posed: let $w = (u, v)$ and

$$E_0 = V \times H \text{ furnished with the norm } \|w\|_{E_0}^2 = \|u\|_V^2 + \epsilon|v|_H^2, \quad (6.1.4)$$

$$E_1 = D(A) \times V \text{ furnished with the norm } \|w\|_{E_1}^2$$
$$= \|u\|_{D(A)}^2 + \epsilon\|v\|_V^2, \qquad (6.1.5)$$

and

$$E_{-1} = H \times V' \text{ furnished with the norm } \|w\|_{E_{-1}}^2 = |u|_H^2 + \epsilon\|v\|_*^2 \quad (6.1.6)$$

The following existence and uniqueness results are standard and can be found, among other places, in [T1] and [BV1].

Theorem 6.1. (i) *If $\epsilon > 0$ and $f \in C_b(\mathbf{R}^+; H)$, then for every (u_0, u_1) in E_0 there exists a unique solution $u(t)$ for the initial value problem (H^ϵ) and (IV) such that*
$$u(\cdot) \in C_b(\mathbf{R}^+; V) \cap C_b^1(\mathbf{R}^+; H).$$

(ii) *If $f \in C_b^1(\mathbf{R}^+; H)$ and $(u_0, u_1) \in E_1$, then the unique solution $u(t)$ belongs to*
$$C_b(\mathbf{R}^+; D(A)) \cap C_b^1(\mathbf{R}^+; V) \cap C_b^2(\mathbf{R}^+; H).$$

Remark 6.2. The global time existence of solutions and time independent apriori estimates for different norms are obtained via a decomposition of the solution operator $S^\epsilon(t)$. An important difference between the global attractor and the exponential attractor we will construct is the requirements of the smoothness for the admissible initial values. It is well known that the global attractor, whenever it exists, will attract all solutions in E_0 with the E_0-norm and will be a bounded subset of E_1. In contrast, we are only able to show that the exponential attractor contains the global attractor, attracts all *bounded initial values in E_1 exponentially with respect to E_0-norm*. Hence, we are not able to conclude that all solutions in E_0 are exponentially attracted to the exponential attractor. This remains an interesting open question. Compared with the existing theories of inertial manifolds, E_1-boundedness requirement is not unusual, since the inertial manifolds are also constructed inside a bounded subset of E_1 (see [CL], [MSM], [BV]). Let us finally remark that to ensure the right Lipschitz condition on the nonlinearity $g(u)$ we need to restrict the solutions to a more regular domain, e.g., need u, v in $D(A)$ to show that g is Lipschitz from V to V in most of the applications we have in mind.

6.2. Discrete Squeezing Property for Second Order Evolution Equations with Damping

Let us recall that for dissipative evolution equations that were discussed in the third section the discrete squeezing property was a consequence of the fact that the linear dissipation of the difference of two trajectories was controlled by the quotient norm $\lambda(t)$. More precisely, if w denotes the difference of two trajectories, then w satisfied an equation of the type

$$\frac{d}{dt}w + \nu\lambda w = F(u,v) (= (R(u) - R(v), w)). \tag{6.2.1}$$

Hence, as long as the contribution of the nonlinear term, i.e., F, were controllable, see (3.28), the squeezing of w depended on the estimation of

$$\nu \int_0^t \lambda(\tau)\, d\tau \tag{6.2.2}$$

from below. This was achieved, in turn, by showing that if at a time $t = t_*$ the q-modes dominate the p-modes, then $\lambda(t_*) > 1/2\lambda_{N_0+1}$, see (3.23), and, furthermore, the differential equation satisfied by $\lambda(t)$ gave grounds for estimating the integral (6.2.2) by a constant multiple of $\nu t_* \lambda(t_*)$. The situation for the damped equations is quite different. There is no natural candidate to replace the quotient norm; if one writes the second order evolution equation as a first order evolution equation in either E_0 or E_1, then the linear part is no longer self-adjoint (see [Mo], [MSM]) and, hence, does not quantitatively control the damping. Another way of explaining the same phenomenon passes through the properties of the semigroup $S^\epsilon(t)$ that take the initial values in E_0 (or E_1) into E_0 (or E_1). In contrast to the case described in Chapter 3, $S^\epsilon(t)$ is a homeomorphism of E_i onto itself (see [T1]). Therefore, one has to contend with studying the semigroup both in E_0 and in E_1 at the same time. Recall that in the parabolic case $S(t)$ mapped H into $D(A)$ and an initial value in H entered into an absorbing set in V in finite time.

The method of proof that will be described below can be summarized as follows. Starting with two solutions u and v, we consider $W = (w, w_t)$ with $w = u - v$ and proceed to verify the DSP on the Hilbert space E_0. In the case where the q-modes dominate, we only consider the equation satisfied by the q-modes and use suitable renorming of the space to control these modes. The effect of damping is increased by jumping from H to V norms, which is achieved by considering the equation on H-norm first.

Let us proceed to show the DSP for the solution operator $\{S^\epsilon(t)\}$ of the initial value problem (H^ϵ) and (IV). As the invariant compact set in which the exponential attractor will live, we choose a bounded, invariant subset of E_1. For all the applications that will be considered, the existence of such a set is assured. On the other hand, we will work with the topology of E_0, hence consider

$$S^\epsilon(t) : E_0 \to E_0. \qquad (6.2.3)$$

In order to describe the class of orthogonal projections that will be used in the process, we introduce

$$H_N = \text{linear span } \{w_1, w_2, \ldots, w_N\} \qquad (6.2.4)$$

where $w_1, \ldots, w_N$ are the eigenvectors of A that correspond to the first N eigenvalues, i.e., $Aw_i = \lambda_i w_i$ for $i = 1, 2, \ldots, N$. Let us set p_N and q_N be the orthogonal projections onto H_N and $H \ominus H_N$ respectively, i.e.,

$$p_N : H \to H_N \text{ and } q_N = I - P_N. \qquad (6.2.5)$$

Note also that p_N and q_N are orthogonal both in H and V. Moreover, from the definition of the projection, we obtain that

$$|u|_H^2 \le \lambda_{N+1}^{-1} \|u\|_V^2 \text{ for all } u \in q_N V. \qquad (6.2.6)$$

Now we are ready to define the projections we will be using. Let

$$P_N : E_0 \to (p_N V) \times (p_N H) \text{ and } Q_N = I - P_N \qquad (6.2.7)$$

be defined by

$$P_N(u, v) = (p_N u, p_N v) \text{ for } (u, v) \in E_0. \qquad (6.2.8)$$

Then P_N and Q_N are orthogonal projections and the DSP will be verified via these projections.

Besides the usual norm on E_0 given in (6.1.4), various other norms can be considered, among these we will consider the following two: given as squares of norms

$$N^\epsilon(z) = \frac{1}{2\epsilon}|u|_H^2 + (u,v) + \|z\|_{E_0}^2 = \frac{1}{2\epsilon}|u|_H^2 + (u,v) + \epsilon|v|_H^2 + \|u\|_V^2$$
$$\text{for } z = (u,v) \in E_0 \tag{6.2.9}$$

and

$$M^\epsilon(z) = \|u\|_V^2 + (u,v) + \epsilon|v|_H^2 = (u,v) + \|z\|_{E_0}^2 \text{ for } z = (u,v) \in E_0. \tag{6.2.10}$$

The first of these "norms" will help us to obtain the Lipschitz constant for the solution operator $S^\epsilon(t)$ on E_0, whereas the second one will be instrumental in the verification of the DSP. Note that both of these "norms" are equivalent to the usual E_0-norm on the suitable subspaces of E_0. More specifically,

Lemma 6.3. (i) $N^\epsilon(-)$ *induces a norm equivalent to the norm on E_0, in fact*

$$\|u\|_V^2 \leq N^\epsilon(z) \text{ and } \frac{1}{2}\|z\|_{E_0}^2 \leq N^\epsilon(z) \leq k\|z\|_{E_0}^2 \tag{6.2.11}$$

where $k = \max\{1 + 1/\epsilon\lambda_1, 3/2\}$.

(ii) $M^\epsilon(\cdot)$ *induces a norm equivalent to the E_0-norm on the space $Q_N E_0$, where N is large enough such that $\lambda_{N+1} \geq (2/\epsilon)$, in fact*

$$\|z\|_{E_0}^2 \leq 4M^\epsilon(z) \leq 8\|z\|_{E_0}^2, \text{ for } z = (u,v) \in Q_N E_0. \tag{6.2.12}$$

Proof. (i) By the Schwarz inequality

$$|(u,v)| \leq |u|_H |v|_H \leq \frac{1}{2\epsilon}|u|_H^2 + \frac{\epsilon}{2}|v|^2.$$

Hence,

$$N^\epsilon(z) \leq \frac{1}{\epsilon}|u|_H^2 + \frac{3}{2}\epsilon|v|_H^2 + \|u\|_V^2 \leq (\frac{1}{\epsilon\lambda_1} + 1)\|u\|_V^2 + \frac{3}{2}\epsilon|v|_H^2 \leq k\|z\|_{E_0}^2.$$

Also,

$$N^\epsilon(z) \geq \frac{\epsilon}{2}|v|_H^2 + \|u\|_V^2 \geq \max\{\frac{1}{2}\|z\|_{E_0}^2, \|u\|_V^2\}.$$

(ii) Note that $M^\epsilon(z) = N^\epsilon(z) - \frac{1}{2\epsilon}|u|_H^2$, hence one only needs to control the H-norm of u. Since $z = (u,v) \in Q_N E_0$, u is in $q_N V$; therefore, by (6.2.6),

$$\frac{1}{2\epsilon}|u|_H^2 \leq \frac{1}{2\epsilon\lambda_{N+1}}\|u\|_V^2 \leq \frac{1}{4}\|u\|_V^2 \leq \frac{1}{4}\|z\|_{E_0}^2.$$

Consequently,
$$\frac{1}{4}\|z\|_{E_0}^2 \le M^\epsilon(z).$$

On the other hand,
$$M^\epsilon(z) = (u,v) + \|z\|_{E_0}^2 \le |u|_H|v|_H + \epsilon|v|_H^2 + \|u\|_V^2$$
$$\le \frac{\epsilon}{2}|v|_H^2 + \frac{2}{\epsilon}|u|_H^2 + \epsilon|v|_H^2 + \|u\|_V^2 \le \frac{3}{2}\epsilon|v|_H^2 + (\frac{2}{\lambda_{N+1}\epsilon} + 1)\|u\|_V^2$$
$$\le \frac{3}{2}\epsilon|v|_H^2 + 2\|u\|_V^2 \le 2\|z\|_{E_0}^2.$$

□

Next we use the "norms" to control the difference of two solutions.

Proposition 6.4. Let u and $\bar{u}$ be two solutions of (H^ϵ) and let $w = u - \bar{u}$ and $W = (w, w_t)$ so that $W \in C_b(\mathbf{R}^+; E_0)$.

(i) Set as before $k = \max\{1 + (1/\epsilon\lambda_1), 3/2\}$ and also set $\alpha = 2(L_0^2 + L_0/2\epsilon\lambda_1)$, where $L_0 = L(0, 1/2)$ is as given in $(L^{\sigma,\gamma})$ with $\sigma = 0$, $\gamma = 1/2$, then for all $t \ge 0$,
$$\|W(t)\|_{E_0}^2 \le 2k e^{\alpha t}\|W(0)\|_{E_0}^2. \qquad (6.2.13)$$

(ii) Let N be large enough so that $\epsilon\lambda_{N+1} \ge 2$ and set
$$\varphi = q_N w \quad \text{and} \quad \Phi = (\varphi, \varphi_t) = Q_N W. \qquad (6.2.14)$$
Then, for all $t \ge 0$, $M^\epsilon(\Phi(t))$ satisfies the differential inequality
$$\frac{d}{dt}M^\epsilon(\Phi(t)) + \frac{1}{2\epsilon}M^\epsilon(\Phi(t)) \le \frac{c_1}{\lambda_{N+1}^{2\sigma}}\|W(t)\|_{E_0}^2, \qquad (6.2.15)$$
where c_1 is a constant that depends on only $\sigma, \gamma, \epsilon, \lambda$, and $L(\sigma, \gamma)$, not on Φ and W.

Proof. To prove (i) we note that w satisfies the equation
$$\epsilon w_{tt} + w_t + Aw = g(u) - g(\bar{u}) \qquad (6.2.16)$$

Multiplying the above equation with $2w_t + \frac{1}{\epsilon}w$ in H we obtain that
$$\epsilon\frac{d}{dt}|w_t|_H^2 + 2|w_t|_H^2 + \frac{d}{dt}\|w\|_V^2 + (w_{tt}, w) + \frac{1}{2\epsilon}\frac{d}{dt}|w|_H^2 + \frac{1}{\epsilon}\|w\|_V^2 =$$
$$= (g(u) - g(\bar{u}), 2w_t + \frac{1}{\epsilon}w). \qquad (6.2.1)$$

Using the fact that $d/dt(w_t, w) = (w_{tt}, w) + |w_t|_H^2$ and regrouping the terms in (6.2.17) we have
$$\frac{d}{dt}\left\{\epsilon|w_t|_H^2 + \|w\|_V^2 + (w_t, w) + \frac{1}{2\epsilon}|w|_H^2\right\} + |w_t|_H^2 + \frac{1}{\epsilon}\|w\|_V^2$$
$$= (g(u) - g(\bar{u}), 2w_t + \frac{1}{\epsilon}w) \le |g(u) - g(\bar{u})|_H(2|w_t|_H + \frac{1}{\epsilon}|w|_H)$$
$$\le L_0\|w\|_V(2|w_t|_H + \frac{1}{\epsilon}|w|_H) \le (L_0^2 + \frac{L_0}{2\lambda_1\epsilon^2})\|w\|_V^2 + |w_t|_H^2.$$

Note, however, that the expression inside the time derivative is nothing but the norm $N^\epsilon(W)$, hence using also the equivalent of norms given in (6.2.11) we get

$$\frac{d}{dt}N^\epsilon(W(t)) + |w_t|_H^2 + \frac{1}{\epsilon}\|w\|_V^2 \leq \frac{\alpha}{2}\|W\|_{E_0}^2 \leq \alpha N^\epsilon(W(t)). \quad (6.2.18)$$

Omitting the positive terms on the left-hand side and using Gronwall's inequality,

$$N^\epsilon(W(t)) \leq e^{2\alpha t} N^\epsilon(W(0)). \quad (6.2.19)$$

On the other hand, by (6.2.11) applied twice the desired result, (6.2.13) follows.

As for the differential inequality satisfied by $M^\epsilon(\Phi(t))$, we consider once again the equation (6.2.16) and apply q_N to it, using the fact that q_N commutes with A $\varphi = q_N w$ satisfies

$$\epsilon \varphi_{tt} + \varphi_t + A\varphi = q_N(g(u) - g(\bar{u})) \equiv \Gamma. \quad (6.2.20)$$

Multiplying as before with $2\varphi_t + \frac{1}{\epsilon}\varphi$ in H, we deduce that

$$\epsilon \frac{d}{dt}|\varphi_t|_H^2 + |\varphi_t|_H^2 + \frac{d}{dt}\|\varphi\|_V^2 + \frac{d}{dt}(\varphi_t, \varphi) + \frac{1}{\epsilon}(\varphi_t, \varphi) + \frac{1}{\epsilon}\|\varphi\|_V^2$$

$$= (\Gamma, 2\varphi_t + \frac{1}{\epsilon}\varphi). \quad (6.2.21)$$

Now, by the definition of M^ϵ, given in (6.2.10),

$$\frac{d}{dt}M^\epsilon(\Phi(t)) + \frac{1}{\epsilon}M^\epsilon(\Phi(t))$$

$$= (\Gamma, 2\varphi_t + \frac{1}{\epsilon}\varphi)_H$$

$$\leq \|\Gamma\|_{D(A^\sigma)}\|2\varphi_t + \frac{1}{\epsilon}\varphi\|_{D(A^{-\sigma})}$$

$$\leq L(\sigma, \gamma)\|w\|_{D(A^{\sigma+\gamma})}\|2\varphi_t + \frac{1}{\epsilon}\varphi\|_{D(A^{-\sigma})} \quad (6.2.22)$$

At the same time, φ and φ_t belong to $q_N V$, hence,

$$\|\varphi_t\|_{D(A^{-\sigma})} \leq \lambda_{N+1}^{-\sigma}|\varphi_t|_H \text{ and } \|\varphi\|_{D(A^{-\sigma})} \leq \lambda_{N+1}^{-\sigma}|\varphi|_H \quad (6.2.23)$$

Combining the above inequalities with $\|w\|_{D(A^{\sigma+\gamma})} \leq \lambda_1^{-\frac{1}{2}+(\sigma+\gamma)}\|w\|_V$, and returning back to (6.2.22)

$$\frac{d}{dt}M^\epsilon(\Phi(t)) + \frac{1}{\epsilon}M^\epsilon(\Phi(t))$$

$$\leq L(\sigma, \gamma)\lambda_1^{-\frac{1}{2}+(\sigma+\gamma)}\|w\|_V \lambda_{N+1}^{-\sigma}(2|\varphi_t|_H + \frac{1}{\epsilon}|\varphi|_H)$$

$$\leq \frac{c_0}{\lambda_{N+1}^\sigma}\|w\|_V(2|\varphi_t|_H + \frac{1}{\epsilon \lambda_1^{1/2}}\|\varphi\|_V)$$

$$\leq \max\left\{\frac{2c_0^2}{\lambda_{N+1}^{2\sigma}}, \frac{c_0^2}{\epsilon \lambda_1 \lambda_{N+1}^{2\sigma}}\right\}\|w\|_V^2 + \frac{1}{2\epsilon}(\epsilon|\varphi_t|_H^2 + \|\varphi\|_V^2)$$

$$\leq \frac{c_1}{\lambda_{N+1}^{2\sigma}}\|W\|_{E_0}^2 + \frac{1}{2\epsilon}M^\epsilon(\Phi(t)) \quad (6.2.24)$$

where we have set

$$c_0 = L(\sigma,\gamma)\lambda_1^{-\frac{1}{2}+(\sigma+\gamma)} \quad \text{and} \quad c_1 = c_0^2 \max\left\{2, \left(\frac{1}{\epsilon\lambda_1}\right)\right\}. \tag{6.2.25}$$

Simplifying (6.2.24), we finally obtain (6.2.15). $\square$

Remark 6.5. Let us remark that typically we will take $\gamma = 0$ and $\sigma = 1/2$ and the condition $(L^{\sigma,\gamma})$ takes the form

$$\|g(u) - g(\bar{u})\|_V \leq L_2 \|u - \bar{u}\|_V \text{ for } u, v \in B^{D(A)}(0, R), \tag{6.2.26}$$

that is, the condition will only be satisfied for a bounded subset of E_1, in which case u and $\bar{u}$ are both bounded in $D(A)$.

Corollary 6.6. *Under the conditions of Proposition 6.4, we also have*

$$\frac{d}{dt} M^\epsilon(\Phi(t)) + \frac{1}{\epsilon} M^\epsilon(\Phi(t)) \leq \frac{2c_1 k e^{\alpha t}}{\lambda_{N+1}^{2\sigma}} \|W(0)\|_{E_0}^2. \tag{6.2.27}$$

Proof. Just combine (6.2.13) and (6.2.14) together. $\square$

To complete the verification of the DSP, we need to show that $\|W(t_*)\|_{E_0}^2$ is squeezed when $Q_N W(t_*)$ dominates. The germ of the idea is in the inequality (6.2.27), by chosing first $t = t_*$ so that the contraction of $M^\epsilon(\Phi(t))$ is controlled. Next, we will choose N large enough that the right-hand side of (6.2.27) is also small.

Theorem 6.7. *Let t_* and N_0 be chosen according to*

$$16 e^{-t_*/\epsilon} = \frac{1}{2}(1/8)^2, \tag{6.2.28}$$

$$\lambda_{N_0+1}\epsilon \geq 2 \text{ and } \frac{16 k c_1}{(\alpha+1/\epsilon)} \lambda_{N_0+1}^{-2\sigma} e^{\alpha t_*} \leq 1/2(1/8)^2. \tag{6.2.29}$$

Then the solution operator $\{S^\epsilon(t) : t \geq 0\}$ on a bounded subset of E_1, on which $(L^{\sigma,\gamma})$ is satisfied, satisfies the DSP. More explicitly, letting $t = t_*$ and P_{N_0} and Q_{N_0} chosen as in (6.2.7) with N_0 large enough, so that (6.2.29) are satisfied, one has: if

$$\|P_{N_0} W(t_*)\|_{E_0} \leq \|Q_{N_0} W(t_*)\|_{E_0} \tag{6.2.30}$$

then

$$\|W(t_*)\|_{E_0}^2 \leq \left(\frac{1}{8}\right)^2 \|W(0)\|_{E_0}^2. \tag{6.2.31}$$

where $W(t) = S^\epsilon(t)U - S^\epsilon(t)\bar{U}$, with $U = (u_0, u_1)$ and $\bar{U} = (\bar{u}_0, \bar{u}_1)$.

Proof. We start from (6.2.27) and apply Gronwall's inequality to that inequation to get

$$M^\epsilon(\Phi(t)) \leq M^\epsilon(\Phi(0))e^{-t/\epsilon} + \frac{2c_1 k e^{\alpha t}}{\lambda_{N+1}^{2\sigma}} \|W(0)\|_{E_0}^2 e^{-t/\epsilon} \int_0^t e^{(\alpha+1/\epsilon)s} \, ds$$

$$\leq M^\epsilon(\Phi(0))e^{-t/\epsilon} + \frac{2c_1 k}{\lambda_{N+1}^{2\sigma}} \|W(0)\|_{E_0}^2 \frac{e^{2\alpha t}}{(\alpha + 1/\epsilon)}$$

$$\leq \|W(0)\|_{E_0}^2 \left(2e^{-t/\epsilon} + \frac{2c_1 k e^{2\alpha t}}{(\alpha + 1/\epsilon)} \frac{1}{\lambda_{N+1}^{2\sigma}} \right). \tag{6.2.32}$$

It follows from (6.2.28) and (6.2.29) that $2e^{-t_*/\epsilon} = \frac{1}{16}\left(\frac{1}{8}\right)^2$ and $2c_1 k e^{2\alpha t_*}(\alpha + 1/\epsilon)^{-1} \lambda_{N+1}^{-2\sigma} \leq \frac{1}{16}\left(\frac{1}{8}\right)^2$. Now using (6.2.12), since $\epsilon \lambda_{N_0+1} \geq 2$ is satisfied, we obtain that

$$\|Q_N W(t_*)\|_{E_0}^2 \leq 4M^\epsilon(\Phi(t_*)) \leq \frac{1}{2}\left(\frac{1}{8}\right)^2 \|W(0)\|_{E_0}^2.$$

Hence,

$$\|W(t_*)\|_{E_0}^2 = \|P_{N_0} W(t_*)\|_{E_0}^2 + \|Q_{N_0} W(t_*)\|_{E_0}^2$$

$$\leq 2\|Q_{N_0} W(t_*)\|_{E_0}^2 \leq \left(\frac{1}{8}\right)^2 \|W(0)\|_{E_0}^2,$$

which is the desired result. $\square$

6.3. Applications to Damped Semilinear Wave Equations

As applications we will consider sine-Gordon and Klein-Gordon equations in various space dimensions and systems of sine-Gordon equations. In all the cases the dimension of space will influence the sharpness of the estimates tremendously. Most of the examples described below are studied in [T1], as for the Klein-Gordon in 3D we refer the reader to [BV2].

6.3.1. Sine-Gordon Equations

We consider the equation

$$\epsilon u_{tt} + u_t - \Delta u + \beta \sin u = f \tag{6.3.1}$$

with Dirichlet boundary conditions on a bounded, open subset Ω of $\mathbf{R}^d$ with $d \leq 4$, with smooth boundary $\partial \Omega$, say, C^2 for example. We choose $H = L^2(\Omega)$; $V = H_0^1(\Omega)$ and $D(A) = H_0^1(\Omega) \cap H^2(\Omega)$ where obviously $A = -\Delta$ and $g(u) = \beta \sin u$. It can be shown that the sets

$$B_0 = \{(u,v) \in V \times H = E_0 : \|u\|_V^2 + \epsilon |v|_H^2 \leq \rho_0^2\} \tag{6.3.2}$$

and

$$B_1 = \{(u,v) \in D(A) \times V = E_1 : \|u\|_{D(A)}^2 + \epsilon\|v\|_V^2 \leq \rho_1^2\}, \quad (6.3.3)$$

are invariant absorbing sets in E_0 and E_1, respectively, with suitably chosen ρ_0 and ρ_1. Now, using the set $B = B_0 \cap B_1$ as the invariant compact set on which the flow $\{S^\epsilon(t)\}_{t>0}$ is defined we verify the condition $(L^{\sigma,\gamma})$, which is the only nonobvious one. First, for L_0, i.e., with $\sigma = 0$, $\gamma = 1/2$, we have

$$\|g(u) - g(\bar{u})\|_{D(A^0)} = |g(u) - g(\bar{u})|_H = |\beta|\|\sin u - \sin v|_{L^2(\Omega)}$$
$$\leq |\beta|\|u - v|_{L^2(\Omega)} = |\beta|\|w|_H \leq \frac{|\beta|}{\lambda_1^{1/2}}\|w\|_V, \quad (6.3.4)$$

Hence, $L_0 \leq |\beta|\lambda_1^{-1/2}$. On the other hand, for $(L^{\sigma,\gamma})$ with $\sigma = 1/2$ and $\gamma = 0$,

$$\|g(u) - g(\bar{u})\|_{D(A^{1/2})}^2 = \|g(u) - g(\bar{u})\|_{H_0^1(\Omega)}^2 \leq |\beta|^2 \int_\Omega |\nabla u|^2 |u - \bar{u}|^2 \, dx$$
$$+ |\beta|^2 \int_\Omega |\cos u|^2 |\nabla w|^2 \, dx$$
$$\leq |\beta|^2 \|w\|_V^2 + |\beta|^2 |w|_{L^4}^2 |\nabla u|_{L^4}^2$$
$$\leq c|\beta|^2 (1 + c\rho_0\rho_1)\|w\|_V^2. \quad (6.3.5)$$

Therefore, $L(1/2, 0) \leq c|\beta|(1 + (\rho_0\rho_1)^{1/2})$ where ρ_0 and ρ_1 are as given in (6.3.2) and (6.3.3). Note that in the estimate above we have considered the case where $d = 4$. For $d < 4$, the estimate (6.3.5) can be improved to reduce the effect of ρ_1 in the calculation; this is especially the case when $d = 1$.

6.3.2. Klein-Gordon Type Equations

For $d = 3$, the equations of the type

$$\epsilon u_{tt} + u_t - \Delta u + u^3 + p(u) = f \quad (6.3.6)$$

where $p(u)$ is a quadratic polynomial. Again, we consider the Dirichlet boundary conditions on an open, bounded domain Ω in $\mathbf{R}^3$ and take the same Hilbert space setting. In this case, to obtain an invariant absorbing set of the form $B_0 \cap B_1$ as given in (6.3.2) and (6.3.3) is more involved, we refer the reader to [BV] for the general case and to [EM] for the case where ϵ is small. We only check the Lipschitz conditions, for $\sigma = 0$, $\gamma = 1/2$ and $\sigma = 1/2$, $\gamma = 0$. In both cases, it suffices to show that $g(u) = u^3$ satisfies the desired properties since it is the leading term. Clearly,

$$|u^3 - \bar{u}^3|_H \leq |u - \bar{u}|_{L^6}|u^2 + u\bar{u} + \bar{u}^2|_{L^3} \leq 3\rho_0^2\|u - \bar{u}\|_V = 3\rho_0^2\|w\|_V \quad (6.3.7)$$

follows from the standard Sobolev imbedding theorems in $\mathbf{R}^3$ with $V = H_0^1(\Omega) \hookrightarrow L^6(\Omega)$. At the same time,

$$\|u^3 - \bar{u}^3\|_V \leq 3|(u^2 - \bar{u}^2)\nabla u|_H + 3|\bar{u}^2(\nabla(u - \bar{u}))|_H$$
$$\leq 6\max\{|u|_{L^\infty}, |\bar{u}|_{L^\infty}\}|\nabla u|_{L^3}|w|_{L^6} + |\bar{u}|_{L^\infty}^2\|w\|_V$$
$$\leq 6\rho_1\|\nabla u\|_V\|w\|_V + \rho_1^2\|w\|_V \leq 7\rho_1^2\|w\|_V, \quad (6.3.8)$$

where we have used the imbedding $H^2(\Omega) \hookrightarrow L^\infty(\Omega)$.

6.3.3. Systems of Sine-Gordon Equations

The abstract theory introduced in this section is general enough to apply to systems of sine-Gordon equations as well. Again, the existence of absorbing sets of the form B_0 and B_1 as given in (6.3.2) and (6.3.3) is crucial, see [T1].
The following two systems of equations:

$$\text{(I)} \quad \begin{cases} \epsilon u_{tt} + u_t - \Delta u + \sin u + (u - v) = f_1 \\ \epsilon v_{tt} + v_t - \Delta v + \sin v + (v - u) = f_2 \end{cases} \quad (6.3.9)$$

and

$$\text{(II)} \quad \begin{cases} \epsilon u_{tt} + u_t - \Delta u + \sin(u + v) = f_1 \\ \epsilon v_{tt} + vt - \Delta v + \sin(u - v) = f_2 \end{cases} \quad (6.3.10)$$

with dirichlet boundary conditions can be put into the same framework. In both cases, $V = (H_0^1(\Omega))^2$ and $H = (L^2(\Omega))^2$. As for the operators A and g, we take

$$A = \begin{bmatrix} -\Delta & 0 \\ 0 & -\Delta \end{bmatrix}, \quad (6.3.11)$$

and

$$g_1 \begin{pmatrix} u \\ v \end{pmatrix} = \begin{pmatrix} \sin u + (u - v) \\ \sin v + (v - u) \end{pmatrix}, \quad (6.3.12)$$

$$g_2 \begin{pmatrix} u \\ v \end{pmatrix} = \begin{pmatrix} \sin(u + v) \\ \sin(u - v) \end{pmatrix}. \quad (6.3.13)$$

Similar computations give

$$L(0, 1/2) = L_0 \leq 6\lambda_1^{-1/2} \;;\; L(1/2, 0) \leq c(1 + (\rho_0 \rho_1)^{1/2}) \quad (6.3.14)$$

for (I); and

$$L(0, 1/2) \leq 4\lambda_1^{-1/2} \;;\; L(1/2, 0) \leq c(1 + (\rho_0 \rho_1)^{1/2}) \quad (6.3.15)$$

for (II), where λ_1 is the first eigenvalue of A.

Chapter 7
Alternative Construction of Exponential Attractors for Evolution Equations

In Chapters 2 and 3, we have constructed exponentially attracting sets of finite fractal dimension. In the process, we were able to control both the fractal dimension of the underlying set and the exponential rate at which all solutions converge to this set, *explicitly*. In particular, a critical reading of the proof of Proposition 3.1 reveals that one can either try to choose the rank N_0 of the projection P_{N_0} optimally, i.e., as small as possible, or try to get the fastest exponential convergence possible by readjusting t_*. The former of these approaches is the one actually carried out in the proof of Proposition 3.1, since the aim there was to get the smallest possible dimension for the exponential attractor. If one is willing to sacrifice the optimality of N_0, another set of choices is revealed. Returning back to (3.49) and fixing $\delta_* = 1/8$, we see that since $\lambda_{N_0} \to \infty$ as $N_0 \to \infty$, the left hand side of (3.49) can be made as small as one likes; e.g., if $N_0(t_*)$ is so large so that

$$\lambda_{N_0+1} \geq \frac{1}{1-e^{-c_3 t_*}}\{(6\ln 2)c_3 + (c_2 + c_1 c_3)t_*\} = f(t_*) \qquad (7.1)$$

then $\delta_* \leq 1/8$. Consequently, choosing t_* arbitrarily and $N_0(t_*) = N_0$ to satisfy the above inequality, it follows from (3.49) that $\delta_* \leq 1/8$. Moreover, (3.31) gives

$$L_* = \mathrm{Lip}\,_X(S(t_*)) \leq e^{c_1 t_*} \qquad (7.2)$$

and (3.65) implies that

$$\mathrm{dist}\,(S(t)X, \mu) \leq cL_* \left[\left(\frac{1}{8}\right)^{1/t_*}\right]^t = cL_* \exp\{-\alpha t\}, \qquad (7.3)$$

where $\alpha = \frac{3}{t_*}|\ln 2|$. Therefore, α can be made arbitrarily large by taking t_* small enough. The price is paid through (7.1), where as $t_* \to 0$, $N_0 \to \infty$. The moral therefore is:

Exponential attractors of higher fractal dimension may attract solutions much faster.

There are various ways of relaxing the two controls mentioned above. In the coming paragraphs, we will try to obtain
  1) Exponential attractors of almost optimal Hausdorff dimension and arbitrarily fast rate of convergence;
  2) Exponential attractors of almost optimal Lyapunov dimension but somewhat evasive exponential rate of convergence.

7.1. Exponential Attractors of Optimal Hausdorff Dimension

The former of these goals is achieved very easily due to the strong properties of Hausdorff dimension, whereas the second one will be realized by the introduction of Lyapunov exponents. We start with the easy task. Let us first note that Hausdorff dimension of a countable set of points is zero, hence if C is a countable set then

$$d_H(\mathcal{A} \cup C) = d_H(\mathcal{A}) \tag{7.1.1}$$

(see Appendix A). This fact allows us to obtain any countable set of points to the global attractor without changing its Hausdorff dimension. It remains, therefore, to choose these points so as the resulting object is exponentially attracting.

We start with our continuous semiflow $\{S(t) : t \geq 0\}$ that leaves the compact set X invariant and set

$$S = S(1), \tag{7.1.2}$$

then

$$S : X \to X, \tag{7.1.3}$$

and we know that

$$\mathcal{A} = \bigcap_{n \geq 0} S^n X \tag{7.1.4}$$

is the global attractor. Basically, we will follow the outline of the construction given in Chapter 2; however, we no longer utilize DSP. As before, $X \subseteq B_R(a)$ and the first generation of points are chosen so that

$$E^{(1)} = \{a_1, a_2, \ldots, a_{N_1}\} \subseteq SX \tag{7.1.5}$$

consists of centers of a minimal θR covering of SX, i.e.,

$$S(X \cap B_R(a)) \subseteq \bigcup_{j_1=1}^{N_1} (B_{\theta R}(a_{j_1}) \cap SX). \tag{7.1.6}$$

Here, $\theta < 1$ is any arbitrary number; this fact will give an arbitrary exponential convergence at the end.

At the next stage, we introduce for each j_1 a set of points

$$E_{2;j_1} = \{a_{j_1,j_2} : j_2 = 1, 2, \ldots, N_{2;j_1}\} \subseteq S^2 X \tag{7.1.7}$$

consisting of centers of a minimal $\theta^2 R$ covering of $S(B_{\theta R}(a_{j_1}) \cap SX)$, i.e.,

$$S(SX \cap B_{\theta R}(a_{j_1})) \subseteq \bigcup_{j_2=1}^{N_{2,j_1}} (B_{\theta^2 R}(a_{j_1,j_2}) \cap S^2 X). \tag{7.1.8}$$

We then set $E^{(2)}$ to denote all the second generation points:

$$E^{(2)} = \bigcup_{j_1=1}^{N_1} E_{2,j_1} \subseteq S^2 X. \tag{7.1.9}$$

Note that $E^{(2)}$ is still finite, although we do not have any control on the number of points in $E^{(2)}$. We continue this way to construct k^{th} generation of these, almost generic, points (see Definition 2.3) with the following two simple properties:

$$E^{(k)} = \bigcup_{j_i} E_{k;j_1,\ldots,j_{k-1}} \subseteq S^k X \quad \text{is finite,} \tag{7.1.10}$$

and

$$S^{k+1} X \subseteq \bigcup_{j_{k-1}} B_{\theta^k R}(a_{j_1,j_2,\ldots,j_{k-1}}) \cap S^k X. \tag{7.1.11}$$

Lemma 7.1. *Set $E^{(\infty)} = \bigcup_{k=1}^{\infty} E^{(k)}$, then $E^{(\infty)}$ is countable and $\overline{E^{(\infty)}} \subseteq \mathcal{A} \cup E^{(\infty)} \doteq \mathcal{E}_0$.*

Proof. The countability of $E^{(\infty)}$ is clear. Let $\{a_n\} \subseteq E^{(\infty)}$ and $a_n \to a$, then there exists k_n such that $a_n \in E^{(k_n)}$. If $\sup k_n = k < +\infty$, then $\{a_n\} \subseteq E^{(k)}$ and the latter being a finite set implies automatically that $a \in E^{(k)}$. On the other hand, if $\sup k_n = +\infty$, then $a_n = S^{k'_n} x_n$ with $x_n \in X$ and $k'_n \to \infty$ for some suitably chosen sequence $\{k'_n\}$ of $\{k_n\}$. By the characterization of global attractors, this in turn implies that $a \in \mathcal{A}$. □

As a simple corollary to Lemma 7.1, we see that $\mathcal{A} \cup E^{(\infty)}$ is closed. However, the new set need not be invariant under the map S, in order to fix that problem we define a larger set by adding on all the images:

$$\mathcal{E} \doteq \mathcal{A} \cup \bigcup_{j=0}^{\infty} S^j(E^{(\infty)}), \tag{7.1.12}$$

then $\mathcal{E}$ is a compact, closed subset of X and

$$d_H(\mathcal{E}) = d_H(\mathcal{A}). \tag{7.1.13}$$

Since $E^{(\infty)} \subseteq SX \subseteq X$, it follows that $\mathcal{E} \subseteq X$. Note also that countable union of countable sets is countable hence (7.1.13) follows from (7.1.1). We have already proved in (2.78) that $\mathcal{E}$ is closed. However one has more:

Proposition 7.2. *The set $\mathcal{E}$ defined in (7.1.12) is an exponential attractor for S on X; moreover,*

$$d_H(\mathcal{E}) = d_H(\mathcal{A}) \tag{7.1.14}$$

and

$$h(S^k X, \mathcal{E}) \leq R\theta^k. \tag{7.1.15}$$

Proof. We have already stated (7.1.14). As for (7.1.15), we proceed as in Lemma 2.6. Let $x \in X$, then there exists $a_{j_1,\ldots,j_k}$ in $E^{(k)}$ such that

$$|S^k x - a_{j_1,\ldots,j_k}| \leq R\theta^k, \tag{7.1.16}$$

since $E^{(k)} \subseteq E^{(\infty)} \subseteq \mathcal{E}$, it follows that

$$\text{dist}\,(S^k x, \mathcal{E}) \leq R\theta^k, \tag{7.1.17}$$

and by definition of the pseudo-distance h, (7.1.15) follows.

Remark 7.3. Note that throughout the construction θ remains arbitrary, hence the convergence rate given in (7.1.15) is arbitrarily fast. The only surprising part is that the Hausdorff dimension remains the same throughout. This again supports the idea that the Hausdorff dimension is not a good measure of complexity.

Let us try to realize the simple goal of constructing an exponentially attracting set for the map we will obtain from solving the initial value problem

$$\frac{dx}{dt} = -x^2, \qquad x(0) = x_0 \quad \text{with} \quad 0 \leq x_0 \leq 1. \tag{7.1.18}$$

Here the global attractor is $\{0\}$ and it is not attracting exponentially. We consider the solution operator on $[0,1]$; it is given by

$$S(t)x_0 = \frac{x_0}{tx_0 + 1} \tag{7.1.19}$$

and the rate of convergence of $S(t)x_0$ to zero is like $1/t$. The argument given above for obtaining an exponentially attracting set can be made very explicit for the case of the map

$$Sx = S(1)x = \frac{x}{x+1}. \tag{7.1.20}$$

Clearly, $S^n x = S(n)x = \frac{x}{nx+1}$ converges to zero, as $n \to \infty$. Therefore, the global attractor of $(S, [0,1])$ is the singleton $\{0\}$. A natural choice for the exponential attractor is

$$\mathcal{E}_0 = \{0\} \cup \left\{ \frac{k}{2^m} : \text{ for all } m \text{ and all } k \text{ such that } k \leq \frac{2^m}{m} \right\}. \qquad (7.1.21)$$

It is straightforward to verify that $\mathcal{E}_0$ is closed and its only limit point is zero. Moreover, the basic observation that

$$0 \leq S^n x \leq \frac{1}{n+1} \leq \frac{1}{n} \qquad (7.1.22)$$

allows one to select $k = k(x)$ such that

$$\frac{k}{2^n} \leq S^n x \leq \frac{k+1}{2^n}. \qquad (7.1.23)$$

Therefore,

$$\operatorname{dist}(S^n x, \mathcal{E}_0) \leq \frac{1}{2^n} = \left(\frac{1}{2}\right)^n. \qquad (7.1.24)$$

Also, since $\mathcal{E}_0$ is still countable, $d_H(\mathcal{E}_0) = 0$. Unfortunately, $\mathcal{E}_0$ is not invariant under the map S, so it has to be further expanded. Let

$$\mathcal{E} = \bigcup_{k=0}^{\infty} S^k \mathcal{E}_0. \qquad (7.1.25)$$

Then $\mathcal{E}$ is a closed subset of $[0,1]$ that is invariant under S. $\mathcal{E}$ is the desired exponential attractor.

Note that $1/2$ played no particular role in the proof, hence could have been replaced by any $\theta < 1$ which would have resulted in an arbitrary rate of convergence. On the other hand, the set that is constructed in (7.1.25) does not have a good fractal dimension since by its definition any covering of $\mathcal{E}$ will need to cover $\mathcal{E}_0$ also, and the latter has fractal dimension equal to 1.

As the previous example suggests, constructing an exponentially attracting set that also has the same fractal dimension as the global attractor is not a simple task. In the Appendix we give examples of various sets in infinite dimensions with differing Hausdorff and fractal dimension; an instructive example in one space dimension is the set $\mathcal{E}_0$ considered in (7.1.21). Its Hausdorff dimension is zero, whereas its fractal dimension is one. Hence, in order to control the fractal dimension of a countable set (as in the easy construction of exponential attractors) one also needs to control the finite number of points one adds at each stage. We follow a similar construction, however, introducing new tools that give us a better control on the number of points added at each stage. From here on we will follow the exposition given in [EFT].

7.2. Exponential Attractors of Optimal Outer Lyapunov Dimension

The best known estimates for the dimension of the attractor are obtained by estimating various Lyapunov exponents of the nonlinear semigroup $\{S(t) : t \geq 0\}$ on the compact absorbing set X. Inspired by the Kaplan-Yorke formula, they were first utilized by Constantin and Foias [CF], to obtain a better dimension estimate for the fractal dimension of the global attractor of the 2D Navier-Stokes equations. Later on they were used for a variety of *dissipative evolution equations* (see [T1]). The estimates obtained through the Lyapunov exponents are more accurate when the dynamics of the k-volume elements is close to the dynamics of the attractors. However, when the system is a damped perturbation of a Hamiltonian system, like sine-Gordon equation, then the estimates are quite crude. Already, through the theory of Lyapunov exponents, various optimal dimension estimates are obtained (for 2D Navier-Stokes equations see Constantin et al. ([CF1], [CFT]) for Ginzburg-Landau equations see [DGHN] and for the original Burgers' equations see [E]). Let us briefly recall their definitions.

Let $\{S(t) : t \geq 0\}$ be a continuous semi-group of operators acting on a separable Hilbert space H. Let X be a compact subset of H such that $S(t)X \subseteq X$ for every $t \geq 0$. We further assume that for all u_0 in X, there exists a compact linear operator $S'(t; u_0)$ on H satisfying

$$|S(t)u - S(t)u_0 - S'(t,u_0)(u - u_0)|_H \leq c(t)|u - u_0|_H^{1+\gamma} \qquad (7.2.1)$$

for some fixed $\gamma > 0$, and $c(t)$ depends on t exponentially (see [CF2], [CFT1] and [T1]). The linear operator $S'(t, u_0)$ need not be defined on all H', for our purpose it suffices to be defined for each $t > 0$ and u_0 in X.

In this set-up X plays the role of a compact invariant absorbing set and the global attractor is uniquely defined as

$$\mathcal{A} = \bigcap_{t>0} S(t)X. \qquad (7.2.2)$$

In order to estimate the fractal dimension of the global attractor, we need to develop the notion of Lyapunov exponents. Instead of the measure theoretic Lyapunov exponents that is more commonly recognized, we will use a topological version introduced in [CF1]. The latter concept, due to its uniform nature, allows a natural control of fractal dimension.

Let us first decompose the linear, compact operator $S'(t, u_0)$ as

$$S'(t, u_0) = U(t; u_0)M(t; u_0) \qquad (7.2.3)$$

where $U(t, u_0)$ is a unitary operator and $M(t, u_0)$ is given by

$$M(t; u_0) = [S'(t; u_0)^* S'(t; u_0)]^{1/2} \qquad (7.2.4)$$

is the positive part of $S'(t, u_0)$. Since the latter operator is compact, $M(t; u_0)$ is a compact, self-adjoint, positive operator on the separable Hilbert space H. Therefore, there exists a complete orthonormal set of eigenvectors

$$\{\varphi_j = \varphi_j(t; u_0) : j = 1, 2, \ldots\} \qquad (7.2.5)$$

such that
$$M(t, u_0)\varphi_j = m_j(t; u_0)\varphi_j, \quad j = 1, 2, \ldots, \quad (7.2.6)$$
where we arrange these positive eigenvalues $m_j = m_j(t, u_0)$, so that
$$m_1(t; u_0) \geq m_2(t; u_0) \geq \cdots \geq m_j(t; u_0) \geq \cdots \geq 0. \quad (7.2.7)$$

Let us denote by
$$P_K(t, u_0) = m_1(t, u_0) m_2(t, u_0) \cdots m_K(t, u_0) \quad (7.2.8)$$
and
$$\pi_K(t) \doteq \sup\{P_K(t, u_0) : u_0 \in X\} \quad (7.2.9)$$

Note that we have deviated slightly from the standard definitions already. The supremum in (7.2.9) is taken over the absorbing set X, rather than the global attractor $\mathcal{A}$. In terms of practical applications, this will cause no harm, since most of the estimates are evaluated over the absorbing set X. However, in the implementation of these quantities we will have to be careful since the supremums are taken over a set that is only positively invariant.

For comparison, let us recall the more usual definition of (7.2.9).
$$P_K(t) = \sup\{P_K(t; u_0) : u_0 \in \mathcal{A}\} \quad (7.2.10)$$
since $\mathcal{A} \subseteq S(t)X$ for all $t \geq 0$, we have
$$P_K(t) \leq \pi_K(t). \quad (7.2.11)$$

On the other hand, noting that $S(s)X \subseteq X$, from the well-known flow properties of $S'(t, u_0)$ it follows that
$$P_K(t + s, u_0) \leq P_K(t, S(s)u_0) P_K(s, u_0); \quad (7.2.12)$$
hence, taking supremum over $u_0 \in X$, we deduce that
$$\pi_K(t+s) \leq \sup\{P_K(t, S(s)u_0) : u_0 \in X\} \cdot \sup\{P_K(s, u_0) : u_0 \in X\}. \quad (7.2.13)$$

Now, noting that $S(s)X \subseteq X$ and that the first supremum is taken over $v_0 \in S(s)X$ and will only get larger if taken over X, we get
$$\pi_K(t+s) \leq \sup\{P_K(t, v_0) : v_0 \in X\} \cdot \sup\{P_K(s, u_0) : u_0 \in X\}$$
$$\leq \pi_K(t) \cdot \pi_K(s). \quad (7.2.14)$$

These multiplicative nets have the following remarkable property
$$\lim_{t \to \infty} \frac{1}{t} \ln \pi_K(t) = t \geq 1 \to \inf \tfrac{1}{t} \ln \pi_K(t) = k \to \inf \tfrac{1}{k} \ln \pi_K(k) \quad (7.2.15)$$

[EFT] Lemma 2.2. Consequently, we can define

$$\mu_1^0 + \mu_2^0 + \cdots + \mu_K^0 \doteq \lim_{t\to\infty} \frac{1}{t} \ln \pi_K(t) \qquad (7.2.16)$$

and

$$\bar{\mu}_K^0 \doteq \limsup_{t\to\infty} \frac{1}{t} \ln \left[\sup_{u_0 \in X} m_K(t; u_0) \right] \qquad (7.2.17)$$

Again, at the cost of being overrepetitive, let us mention that both quantities are larger than the usual ones obtained by taking supremums over the attractor. However, the basic estimate that relates (7.2.16) to (7.2.17) still holds since (7.2.7) implies that

$$m_K(t, u_0) \leq [m_1(t; u_0) m_2(t; u_0) \ldots m_K(t; u_0)]^{1/K} = P_K(t, u_0)^{1/K} \qquad (7.2.18)$$

hence taking the supremum over u_0 in X

$$\bar{m}_K(t) \doteq \sup\{m_K(t, u_0) : u_0 \in X\} \leq \pi_K(t)^{1/K} \qquad (7.2.19)$$

and passing to lim sup as $t \to \infty$, after operating both sides by $\frac{1}{t} \ln$, we easily get

$$\bar{\mu}_K^0 \leq \frac{1}{K}\{\mu_1^0 + \mu_2^0 + \cdots + \mu_K^0\}. \qquad (7.2.20)$$

The numbers defined in (7.2.16) will be called outer-global Lyapunov exponents and the ones defined in (7.2.17) will be called outer-upper Lyapunov exponents. We then define the Outer Lyapunov Dimension as

$$d_{oL}(\mathcal{A}) \doteq \max_{1 \leq k_0 \leq K} \left\{ k_0 + \frac{\mu_1^0 + \cdots + \mu_{k_0}^0}{|\bar{\mu}_{K+1}^0|} \right\} \qquad (7.2.21)$$

where K is any integer such that $\bar{\mu}_{K+1}^0 < 0$. As we have already mentioned several times,

$$\mu_1 + \cdots + \mu_k \leq \mu_1^0 + \cdots + \mu_k^0, \qquad (7.2.22)$$

and

$$\bar{\mu}_{K+1} \leq \bar{\mu}_{K+1}^0 < 0. \qquad (7.2.23)$$

Consequently, $|\bar{\mu}_{K+1}^0| \leq |\bar{\mu}_{K+1}|$ and $\frac{1}{|\bar{\mu}_{K+1}|} \leq \frac{1}{|\bar{\mu}_{K+1}^0|}$, therefore the outer Lyapunov dimension is greater than the usual Lyapunov dimension: at least in the case where $\bar{\mu}_{K+1}^0 < 0$:

$$d_{FL}(\mathcal{A}) \doteq \max_{1 \leq k \leq K} \left\{ k + \frac{\mu_1 + \cdots + \mu_k}{|\bar{\mu}_{K+1}|} \right\} \leq d_{oL}(\mathcal{A}). \qquad (7.2.24)$$

In terms of the practical estimates of the fractal dimension of $\mathcal{A}$, the two dimensions above are hard to distinguish. Since the way to estimate the sum $\mu_1 + \cdots + \mu_K$ passes through the application of the trace formula and taking supremums over, in effect, the absorbing set X (instead of the global attractor). On the other hand, if K is such that

$$\mu_1^0 + \mu_2^0 + \cdots + \mu_{K+1}^0 < 0 \qquad (7.2.25)$$

then automatically $\mu_1 + \cdots + \mu_{K+1} < 0$ and it follows from [CFT1] that $d_F(\mathcal{A}) \leq d_{FL}(\mathcal{A})$. Combining this with (7.2.24), we obtain a, possibly, coarser estimate of the fractal dimension of the attractor, namely

$$d_F(\mathcal{A}) \leq d_{0L}(\mathcal{A}). \qquad (7.2.26)$$

The construction of an exponential attractor with finite fractal dimension will follow from an iterative definition where at each generation of points the number (which is really finite) of new points added to the attractor is a fixed multiple of the number added in the previous generation.

Assume for the moment that we have already determined $t = T$ and we are considering the map

$$S = S(T) : X \to X \qquad (7.2.27)$$

the choice of T will be made at the end. The first generation of points are the easiest to find. Since X is bounded in H, there exists a in X and $R > 0$ such that

$$X \subseteq B_R(a). \qquad (7.2.28)$$

Next, we consider the image of X under S, SX, being a compact set in H can be covered by finitely many balls of radius $r = \tilde{\theta} R$. Here $\tilde{\theta}$ is a number less than 1 and the specific value for it will also be determined at the end. Through this covering, we see that

$$S(X \cap B_R(a)) = SX \subseteq \bigcup_{i=1}^{\tilde{N}} (B_r(a_i) \cap SX). \qquad (7.2.29)$$

The first generation of points consists of the centers of these r-balls:

$$E^{(1)} = \{a_1, a_2, \ldots, a_{\tilde{N}}\} \subseteq SX. \qquad (7.2.30)$$

In order to choose the second generation of points, we consider

$$S(B_r(a_i) \cap SX), \qquad i = 1, 2, \ldots, \tilde{N}, \qquad (7.2.31)$$

and would like to cover these images more carefully now. Let

$$N_r(A) = \text{ the minimum number of } r\text{-balls necessary to cover } A; \qquad (7.2.32)$$

we would like to obtain an iterative estimate of the form

$$N_{\theta r}(S(B_r(a_i) \cap SX)) \leq \beta(T) N_r(B_r(a_i) \cap SX) \qquad (7.2.33)$$

from which it will follow, by adding up all i's, that

$$N_{\theta r}(S^2 X) \leq \beta(T) N_r(SX) \leq \tilde{N}\beta(T), \qquad (7.2.34)$$

where $\theta = \theta(T) < 1$; hence, S, θ, β all depend on T. Let $B_r(u_0)$ stand for one of the balls $B_r(a_i)$, i.e., $u_0 = a_i$ for some i. Notice that since the centers belong to SX so is u_0, i.e., $u_0 \in S(T)X$. Next we try to cover

$$S(B_r(u_0) \cap SX) \text{ with balls of radius } \theta r, \qquad (7.2.35)$$

where $\theta = \theta(T) < 1$ willl also be given at the end. Proceeding as in [EFT], we write an arbitrary element of H as

$$h = \sum_{j=1}^{\infty} (h, \varphi_j) \varphi_j \qquad (7.2.36)$$

where $\varphi_j = \varphi_j(T, u_0)$ is as in (7.2.5). Using the polar decomposition of $S'(T, u_0)$ given in (7.2.3), we obtain that

$$S'(T, u_0)h = \sum_{j=1}^{\infty} (h, \varphi_j) \psi_j \quad \text{where} \quad \psi_j = m_j U \varphi_j. \qquad (7.2.36)$$

The differentiability condition (7.2.1) with $h = u - u_0$ transforms into

$$|S(T)u - S(T)u_0 - \sum_{j=1}^{K} (u - u_0, \varphi_j) \psi_j|_H$$

$$\leq \left| \sum_{j=K+1}^{\infty} (u - u_0, \varphi_j) \psi_j \right| + c(T) |u - u_0|_H^{1+\gamma}. \qquad (7.2.37)$$

On the other hand, utilizing (7.2.7) and the fact that $U = U(T, u_0)$ is unitary

$$\left| \sum_{j=K+1}^{\infty} (u - u_0, \varphi_j) \psi_j \right|_H^2 \leq m_{K+1}^2(T; u_0) \sum_{j=K+1}^{\infty} |(u - u_0, \varphi_j)|^2 |U \varphi_j|_H^2$$

$$\leq m_{K+1}^2(T, u_0) |u - u_0|_H^2 \qquad (7.2.38)$$

which reduces (7.2.37) to

$$|S(T)u - S(T)u_0 - \sum_{j=1}^{K} (u - u_0, \varphi_j) \psi_j|_H$$

$$\leq m_{K+1}(T, u_0) |u - u_0|_H + c(t) |u - u_0|_H^{1+\gamma} \qquad (7.2.39)$$
$$\leq (m_{K+1}(T, u_0) + c(T) r^\gamma) r$$

Exponential Attractors for Dissipative Evolution Equations

where we have assumed that $u \in B_r(u_0)$. Consequently, for $S = S(T)$, we have

$$\text{dist}\,(Su, \sum_K^r) \leq m_{K+1}(T, u_0)r + c(T)r^{1+\gamma} \leq \bar{m}_{K+1}(T)r + c(T)r^{1+\gamma} \quad (7.2.40)$$

where

$$|u - u_0| \leq r = \tilde{\theta}R \quad \text{and} \quad u_0 \in S(T)X, \quad (7.2.41)$$

and the set $\sum_K^r$ is the ellipsoid defined by

$$\sum_K^r \doteq \sum_K^r(T, u_0) = \{S(T)u_0 + \sum_{i=1}^{K}(h, \varphi_i)\psi_i : \psi_i = m_i U\varphi_i, |h| \leq r\} \quad (7.2.42)$$

where m_i and φ_i are as defined in (7.2.6) and (7.2.7) with $t = T$. In order to pursue the idea of iterated coverings and estimate the number of θr-balls necessary to cover $S(B_r(u_0) \cap SX)$, it suffices to cover the set $\sum_K^r$ with balls of radius smaller than the error given by (7.2.40). The set $\sum_K^r$ is an ellipsoid centered at $S(T)u_0$ and is isometric to the K dimensional ellipsoid in $\mathbf{R}^K$ given by

$$\sum \doteq \{\zeta \in \mathbf{R}^K : \sum_{i=1}^{K}\zeta_i^2/m_i^2 \leq r^2\} \quad (7.2.43)$$

under the correspondence $m_j(h, \varphi_j)_H$ to ζ_j. The ellipsoid $\sum$ is included in the rectangular box

$$\prod \doteq \prod_{i=1}^{K}[-m_i r, m_i r]. \quad (7.2.44)$$

The latter can be covered with cubes in the form

$$Q = Q(j_1, j_2, \ldots, j_k) = \prod_{k=1}^{K}[-m_k r + j_k \frac{\mu r}{\sqrt{K}}, -m_k r + (j_k + 1)\frac{\mu r}{\sqrt{K}}] \quad (7.2.45)$$

where $j_k \in \mathbf{N}$ satisfies

$$0 \leq j_k \leq 2(\sqrt{K}m_k/\mu) + 1, \quad k = 1, 2, \ldots, K. \quad (7.2.46)$$

Each cube Q can be imbedded into a ball of radius $(\mu r/\sqrt{K})(\sqrt{K}/2) = \mu r/2$. Then the minimum number of balls of radius less than or equal to $\mu r/2$ that is necessary to cover $\sum$, albeit $\sum_K^r$, can be estimated by

$$N_{\mu r/2}(\sum_K^r) \leq \prod_{k=1}^{K}(2m_k\sqrt{K}/\mu) + 1. \quad (7.2.47)$$

Setting
$$\mu \doteq \bar{m}_{k+1}(T), \qquad (7.2.48)$$
it follows from (7.2.7) and $\mu \geq m_{k+1}(T, u_0)$ that for every u_0 in X, there exists j_0 such that
$$m_{j_0}(T, u_0) > \mu \geq m_{j_0+1}(T, u_0), \qquad 1 \leq j_0 \leq K. \qquad (7.2.49)$$
Therefore,
$$2 m_k \sqrt{K}/\mu \leq \begin{cases} (2\sqrt{K}+1) m_k/\mu & \text{for } k=1,\ldots,j_0 \\ 2\sqrt{K}+1 & \text{for } h = j_0+1,\ldots,K \end{cases} \qquad (7.2.50)$$
consequently,
$$N_{\mu r/2}\left(\sum_K^r\right) \leq C_k m_1 \ldots m_{j_0} \cdot \mu^{-j_0} \quad \text{with} \quad C_K = (2\sqrt{K}+1)^K. \qquad (7.2.51)$$
In order to simplify we set
$$\beta(T) \doteq C_K \max_{1 \leq j_0 \leq K} \frac{(m_1 \cdots m_{j_0})(T)}{\mu^{j_0}} = C_K \max_{1 \leq j_0 \leq K} \frac{\pi_{j_0}(T)}{\mu^{j_0}} \qquad (7.2.52)$$
since $\beta(T)$ is independent of u_0, the estimate
$$N_{\mu r/2}\left(\sum_K^r\right) \leq \beta(T) \qquad (7.2.53)$$
holds independent of the center of the ellipsoid $\sum_K^r$, but depends only on T and K.

Choose $\tilde{\theta}$ small enough such that $r = \tilde{\theta} R$ satisfies:
$$\max\{r, r^{1+\gamma}\} \leq \mu/2c(T). \qquad (7.2.54)$$
Returning back to (7.2.40), it follows from the fact that $\mu = \bar{m}_{K+1}(T)$
$$\text{dist}\,(S(T)u, \sum_K^r) \leq \mu r + \frac{1}{2}\mu r = \frac{3}{2}\mu r, \qquad (7.2.55)$$
hence, by enlarging the radii from $\mu r/2$ to $2\mu r$, the cover of $\sum_K^r$ transforms into a cover of (7.2.35). Therefore, with
$$\theta = \theta(T) = 2\mu = 2\bar{m}_{K+1}(T) \qquad (7.2.56)$$
we obtain (7.2.33). Notice, however, that the assumption
$$\limsup_{t \to \infty} \frac{1}{t} \ln \bar{m}_{K+1}(t) = \bar{\mu}^0_{K+1} < 0 \qquad (7.2.57)$$

implies for large T, $\theta(T) = 2\bar{m}_{K+1}(T)$ can be made arbitrarily small.

From (7.2.33) it follows that at each point a_{i_1}, one can choose a set of centers

$$E_{2;i_1} = \{a_{i_1,i_2} : i_2 = 1,\ldots,[\beta(T)]+1\} \subseteq S(2T)X \qquad (7.2.58)$$

such that

$$S(B_r(a_{i_1}) \cap SX) \subseteq \bigcup \{B_{\theta r}(a_{i_1,i_2}) \cap S^2 X : i_2 = 1,\ldots,\nu(T)\} \qquad (7.2.59)$$

where for convenience we have set

$$\nu(T) \doteq [\beta(T)] + 1. \qquad (7.2.60)$$

The second generation of points are defined by these centers

$$E^{(2)} = \bigcup \{E_{2;i_1} : i_1 = 1,\ldots,\tilde{N}\}, \qquad (7.2.61)$$

by (7.2.30)

$$\text{card}(E^{(1)}) = \tilde{N}, \qquad (7.2.62)$$

whereas, by (7.2.61),

$$\text{card}(E^{(2)}) \leq \tilde{N}\nu(T). \qquad (7.2.63)$$

Next, we attempt to repeat this procedure for

$$S(B_{\theta r}(a_{i_1,i_2}) \cap S^2 X) \subseteq \bigcup \{B_{\theta^2 r}(a_{i_1,i_2,i_3}) \cap S^3 X : i_3 = 1,\ldots,\nu(T)\}. \qquad (7.2.64)$$

Now however there is an important difference since the centers a_{i_1,i_2} are from $S^2 X$, we only need to take supremums over $S(2T)X = S^2 X$, therefore $\beta(T)$ defined on (7.2.40) can still be used

$$\beta(2T) \leq \beta(T) \qquad (7.2.65)$$

since the supremum is taken over a smaller set $S^2 X \subseteq SX$. It follows from the previous arguments that, similar to (7.2.53),

$$N_{\theta^2 r}(S(B_{\theta r}(a_{i_1,i_2}) \cap S^2 X)) \leq \beta(T) N_{\theta r}(B_{\theta r}(a_{i_1,i_2}) \cap S^2 X) \qquad (7.2.66)$$

and, consequently, forming the union of all these balls and utilizing (7.2.66),

$$N_{\theta^2 r}(S^3 X) \leq \beta(2T) N_{\theta r}(S^2 X) \leq \beta(2T)\beta(T) N_r(SX) \qquad (7.2.67)$$

which in turn can be simplified to, via (7.2.65),

$$N_{\theta^2 r}(S^3 X) \leq \beta(T)^2 N_r(SX). \qquad (7.2.68)$$

This procedure can be extended by induction to develop a kth generation of centers in $S^k X$ such that

$$E^{(k)} = \bigcup \{E_{k;i_1,i_2,\ldots,i_{k-1}} : i_1 = 1,\ldots,\tilde{N}, i_m = 1,\ldots,\nu(T), m = 2,\ldots,k-1\}$$
$$\subseteq S^k X \quad (7.2.69)$$

and

$$S^{k+1} X \subseteq \bigcup \{B_{\theta^k r}(a) \cap S^k X : a \in E^{(k)}\} \quad (7.2.70)$$

where $\nu(mT) = [\beta(mT)] + 1 \leq [\beta(T)] + 1 = \nu(T)$. Also we have

$$N_{\theta^k r}(S^{k+1} X) \leq \beta(T)^k N_r(SX). \quad (7.2.71)$$

Clearly,

$$\operatorname{card}(E^{(k)}) \leq \tilde{N} \nu(T)^{k-1}, \quad (7.2.72)$$

in agreement with (7.2.62) and (7.2.63).

The exponential attractor for the map $S = S(T)$ is defined as (7.1.12) by

$$\mathcal{E}_F = \mathcal{A} \cup \bigcup \{S^j(E^{(k)}) : k = 1, 2, \ldots, j = 0, 1, 2, \ldots\}. \quad (7.2.73)$$

Note that Lemma 7.1 and Proposition 7.2 easily apply to this set as well. Hence, it is clear that $\mathcal{E}_F$ is a compact subset of X that attracts solutions exponentially with the exponent $\ln \theta(T)$. It remains to verify that $\mathcal{E}_F$ has finite fractal dimension; as we have shown with the first construction, we consider

$$C_\infty = \operatorname{cl}_H\left(\bigcup_k E^{(k)}\right) \subseteq \left(\bigcup_{k=1}^M E^{(k)}\right) \bigcup S^{M+1} X \quad (7.2.74)$$

The set $E^M = \bigcup \{E^{(k)} : k = 1, 2, \ldots, M\}$ contains only finitely many points. The cardinality of E^M can be estimated using (7.2.56) and the fact that $\nu(T) > 1$ as

$$\operatorname{card}(E^M) \leq \sum_{k=1}^M \tilde{N}\nu(T)^{k-1} \leq \tilde{N} M \nu(T)^{M-1} \doteq \tilde{M}. \quad (7.2.75)$$

Consequently,

$$N_\epsilon(C_\infty) \leq \tilde{M} + N_\epsilon(S^{M+1} X), \quad (7.2.76)$$

choosing $N^* = N^*(\epsilon)$ such that

$$r\theta^{N^*} < \epsilon < r\theta^{N^*-1} \quad (7.2.77)$$

and $\bar{\rho} \in [1, 1/\theta]$ as

$$\theta^{N^*} \bar{\rho} = \epsilon/r; \quad (7.2.78)$$

then from (7.2.71)
$$N_\epsilon(S^{N_*+1}X) = N_{r\theta N^*\bar{\rho}}(S^{N_*+1}X)$$
$$\leq N_{r\theta N^*}(S^{N_*+1}X) \qquad (7.2.79)$$
$$\leq \beta(T)^{N^*} N_r(SX) = \beta(T)^{N^*}\tilde{N}.$$

Consequently,
$$d_F(C_\infty) = \limsup_{\epsilon \to 0^+} \frac{\ln(N_\epsilon(C_\infty))}{\ln(1/\epsilon)} \leq \limsup_{\epsilon \to 0^+} \frac{\ln(\tilde{M} + \beta(T)^{N^*}\tilde{N})}{\ln(1/\epsilon)}$$
$$\leq \limsup_{\epsilon \to 0} \frac{\ln\left(\frac{\tilde{M}+\beta(T)^{N^*}\tilde{N}}{\beta(T)^{N^*}\tilde{N}}\right) + N^* \ln \beta(T) + \ln \tilde{N}}{\ln(1/\epsilon)}. \qquad (7.2.80)$$

As $\epsilon \to 0$, it follows from the fact $\theta < 1$ that $N^* \to \infty$, hence for N^* large enough
$$\frac{\tilde{M} + \beta(T)^{N^*}\tilde{N}}{\beta(T)^{N^*}\tilde{N}} = \frac{\tilde{N}N^*\nu(T)^{N^*-1} + \beta(T)^{N^*}\tilde{N}}{\beta(T)^{N^*}\tilde{N}} \leq 1 + N^*\left[\frac{[\beta(T)]+1}{\beta(T)}\right]^{N^*}$$
$$\leq 2N^*\left(\frac{[\beta(T)]+1}{\beta(T)}\right)^{N^*}. \qquad (7.2.81)$$

Therefore,
$$d_F(C_\infty) \leq \limsup_{\epsilon \to 0} \left(\frac{N^* \ln \beta(T) + \ln(2N^*) + N^* \ln(([\beta(T)]+1)/\beta(T))}{\ln(\frac{1}{\epsilon})}\right)$$
$$\leq \limsup_{\epsilon \to 0} \left(\frac{N^* \ln([\beta(T)]+1) + \ln(2N^*)}{|\ln \theta|}\right) \qquad (7.2.82)$$

solving (7.2.78) for N^*,
$$N^* = \left(\ln\left(\frac{\epsilon}{\bar{\rho}r}\right)\right)/\ln\theta = \frac{\ln(\bar{\rho}r/\epsilon)}{|\ln\theta|} \qquad (7.2.83)$$

it follows from (7.2.82) that
$$d_F(C_\infty) \leq \frac{\ln([\beta(T)]+1)}{|\ln \theta(T)|} \qquad (7.2.84)$$

here $\theta(T) = 2\bar{m}_{K+1}(T)$ where T will be determined very soon. If $\beta(T)$ goes to infinity as $T \to \infty$ then $[\beta(T)] + 1$ can be replaced by $\beta(T)$ and we have
$$\liminf_{t\to\infty} \frac{\ln \beta(t)}{|\ln \theta(t)|} = \liminf_{t\to\infty} \frac{\ln C_K \max_{1\leq k_0 \leq K}(\pi_{k_0}(t)/\bar{m}_{K+1}(t)^{k_0})}{|\ln 2\bar{m}_{K+1}(t)|}$$
$$= \max_{1\leq k_0\leq K} \liminf_{t\to\infty} \frac{\ln C_K + \ln \pi_{k_0}(t) - k_0 \ln \bar{m}_{K+1}(t)}{|\ln \bar{m}_{K+1}(t)|}$$
$$\doteq \max_{1\leq k_0\leq K}\left\{\frac{\lim_{t\to\infty}\frac{1}{t}\ln\pi_{k_0}(t)}{\limsup_{t\to\infty}\frac{1}{t}|\ln\bar{m}_{K+1}(t)|} + k_0\right\} \qquad (7.2.85)$$
$$= \max_{1\leq k_0\leq K}\left\{k_0 + \frac{\mu_1^0 + \mu_2^0 + \cdots + \mu_{k_0}^0}{|\bar{\mu}_{K+1}^0|}\right\} = d_{0L}(\mathcal{A}).$$

On the other hand, if $\beta(T)$ remains bounded for large T, then since $\theta(T) \to 0$, $d_{0L}(\mathcal{A}) = 0$.

Finally, we can specify the order of choices: we start with K such that $\bar{\mu}_{K+1}^0$ is negative; in order to obtain optimal dimension we must choose smallest such K, see Remark at the end for further ramifications. Then given $\delta > 0$, by (7.2.66) there exists $T = T(\delta)$ such that

1) $$\left| \frac{\ln \beta(T)}{|\ln 2\bar{m}_{K+1}(T)|} - d_{0L}(\mathcal{A}) \right| < \delta, \tag{7.2.86}$$

2) $$\theta(T) = 2\bar{m}_{K+1}(T) < 1, \tag{7.2.87}$$

next the initial cover with "$\tilde{\theta}R$" must be modified, so we have to start with a cover such that $r = \tilde{\theta}R$ satisfies

3) $$\max\{r, r^\gamma\} \leq \frac{\bar{m}_{K+1}(T)}{2c(T)} \tag{7.2.88}$$

to satisfy (7.2.54) in return.

Finally, it follows from (7.273) that

$$\mathcal{E}_F = \bigcup_{j=0}^\infty S^j(C_\infty \cup \mathcal{A}) \tag{7.2.89}$$

where $C = C_\infty \cup \mathcal{A}$ is a compact subset of X with fractal dimension estimated by (7.2.84). Through (7.2.71) the stage is set for Corollary to Lemma 2.4, which gives

Theorem 7.3. *Let* $\{S(t) : t \geq 0\}$ *be a continuous semi-flow on a compact set X that leaves X invariant. Let*

$$\mathcal{A} = \bigcap_{t \geq 0} S(t)X \tag{7.2.90}$$

be the global attractor of $(S(t), X)$. Assume that there exists $K > 0$ such that

$$\bar{\mu}_{k+1}^0 = \limsup_{t \to \infty} \frac{1}{t} \ln \left[\sup_{u_0 \in X} m_{k+1}(t; u_0) \right] < 0. \tag{7.2.91}$$

a) *Given $\delta > 0$, if $T = T(\delta)$ is chosen such that (7.2.86), (7.2.87) and (7.2.88) are satisfied, then the set*

$$\mathcal{E}_F = \mathcal{A} \cup \cup \{S(jT)(E^{(k)}) : k = 1, 2, \ldots, j = 0, 1, \ldots\} \tag{7.2.92}$$

with $E^{(k)}$ as in (7.2.69) is an exponential attractor for the map $S = S(T)$ on X. Moreover,

$$d_F(\mathcal{E}_F) \leq d_{0L}(\mathcal{A}) + \delta \tag{7.2.93}$$

where

$$d_{0L}(\mathcal{A}) = \max_{1 \leq k_0 \leq K} \left\{ k_0 + \frac{\mu_1^0 + \cdots + \mu_{k_0}^0}{|\bar{\mu}_{k+1}^0|} \right\} \qquad (7.2.94)$$

and the rate of convergence is estimated by

$$\text{dist}_H(S(jT)u_0, \mathcal{E}_F) \leq c\theta(T)^j, \qquad (7.2.95)$$

where $\theta(T) = 2\bar{m}_{k+1}(T) < 1$, u_0 in X and the constant depends only on the diameter $2R$ of X and $\tilde{\theta}$ which is chosen so that $r = \tilde{\theta}R$ satisfy (7.2.88).

b) If, furthermore, the map $(t, u_0) \to S(t)u_0$ is Lipschitz continuous from $[0,T] \times X$ into X with Lipschitz constant L_*, then the set

$$\mathcal{E} = \bigcup_{0 \leq t \leq T} S(t)\mathcal{E}_F \qquad (7.2.96)$$

is an exponential attractor for $(S(t), X)$ that satisfy

$$d_F(\mathcal{E}) \leq d_{0L}(\mathcal{A}) + \delta + 1 \qquad (7.2.97)$$

and for any u_0 in X

$$\text{dist}_H(S(t)u_0, \mathcal{E}) \leq c_1 \exp\left\{ \frac{\ln \theta(T)}{T} t \right\} \qquad (7.2.98)$$

where c_1 depends only on c, T and the Lipschitz constant L_*.

Proof. Most of the argument is given before the statement of the Theorem. The estimate (7.2.93) follows from (7.2.84), (7.2.85) and (7.2.86) combined with the application of Corollary of Lemma 2.4. Whereas, the rate of convergence estimate (7.2.95) follows from (7.2.70) and the fact that $E^{(j)} \subset \mathcal{E}_F$. The second part can be proven as in the Proof of Theorem 3.1. □

Remark 7.4. In applications, the condition (7.2.91) is guaranteed through (7.2.20)

$$\bar{\mu}_{k+1}^0 \leq \frac{1}{K+1}\{\mu_1^0 + \mu_2^0 + \cdots + \mu_{k+1}^0\}$$

and the right hand side is estimated through the trace formula which depends on uniform estimates over the absorbing set. Consequently, the estimate of the fractal dimension of the global attractor $\mathcal{A}$ and of any exponential attractor that is constructed through Lyapunov exponents differ by one, up to a small perturbation. However, the rate of convergence can only be estimated through a lower estimate of $\theta(T)$ and the trace formula is of no avail, since

$$\bar{\mu}_{k+1}^0 \geq \mu_{k+1}^0 = (\mu_1^0 + \cdots + \mu_{k+1}^0) - 1(\mu_1^0 + \cdots + \mu_k^0)$$

requires a lower estimate of the sum $\mu_1^0 + \cdots + \mu_{k+1}^0$.

Chapter 8
Inertial Manifolds: A Brief Review and Comparison

The theory of inertial manifolds is too extensive to give a full treatment here. Instead, we will only outline the method of spectral barriers which is in the spirit of what we have been doing so far and give a simple application. For a more complete treatment of the method of spectral barriers we refer the reader to the original paper by Constantin et al. [CFNT3], and for other methods of constructing inertial manifolds to Foias et al. [FST1,2], [FNST1,2], Temam [T1], Constantin et al. [CFNT2], Foias et al. [FSTi], and also, for a nice exposition of some of these ideas, to Constantin [C].

We first recall the basic definitions and the main theorem for the existence of inertial manifolds. As we have done in Chapter 3, we consider an evolution equation of the form

$$\frac{d}{dt}u + Au + R(u) = 0, \tag{8.1}$$

on a separable Hilbert space H, where A is a positive, self-adjoint operator with $D(A) \subset H$ with a compact inverse. For convenience, we set

$$V = D(A^{1/2}), \tag{8.2}$$

and denote the $D(A^{1/2})$-norm by

$$\|u\| = |u|_{D(A^{1/2})}. \tag{8.3}$$

We further assume that the initial value problem (8.1) is well-posed and is solved by a nonlinear semigroup of operators $\{S(t)\}_{t \geq 0}$ such that

$$S(t) : H \to D(A), \quad \text{for} \quad t > 0. \tag{8.4}$$

As in Chapter 3, we assume the existence of an absorbing ball of the form

$$B = \{u \in H : |u|_H \leq \rho_0 \quad \text{and} \quad \|u\| \leq \rho_1\}. \tag{8.5}$$

In order to assure the existence of an inertial manifold, we need to restrict the flow to such an absorbing ball. This can be achieved by multiplying the nonlinearity by a cut-off function θ; without loss of generality, we can then assume that

(R1) $$R(u) = 0 \quad \text{for} \quad |u|_H \geq \rho_0. \tag{8.6}$$

Furthermore, we assume that the nonlinearity R is continuous from $D(A)$ into H and satisfies, see (3.10) and (3.11), for $u, v \in D(A)$,

(R2) $$|R(u) - R(v)|_H \leq c_0 |A^\beta(u-v)|_H \tag{8.7}$$

with some $\beta \in (0, 1/2]$ and $c_0 > 0$. Note that (R2) implies a weaker condition

(R2P) $$(R(u) - R(v), u-v)_H \geq -\mu_0^\alpha |u-v|_H^{2\alpha} |A^{1/2}(u-v)|_H^{2(1-\alpha)} \tag{8.8}$$

where $\alpha = 1 - \beta$ and $\mu_0 = c_1 c_0^{1/(1-\beta)}$, which is sufficient for the theory of spectral barriers [CFNT3]) (compare also with Remark 3.5).

Definition 8.1. A Lipschitz manifold $\mathcal{M}$ is an *inertial manifold* for the evolution equation (8.1) if

(i) $S(t)\mathcal{M} \subseteq \mathcal{M}$, for every $t \geq 0$,

(ii) $\mathcal{M}$ attracts all orbits of (8.1) exponentially.

Depending on the method of construction, one of the three conditions, including the Lipschitzianity of $\mathcal{M}$ mentioned above is automatically satisfied. In the case of the Lyapunov-Perron method of construction (see [FST1,2], [FNST1,2], [T1] and [FSTi]) one obtains a Lipschitz function

$$\Phi : PH \to (I-P)H \tag{8.9}$$

such that

$$\mathcal{M} = \{(p, \Phi(p)) : p \in PH\} \tag{8.10}$$

is an inertial manifold. The existence of the Lipschitz function Φ follows from a fixed point argument, but then to check the invariance condition (i) and the exponential convergence of solutions (ii) requires some more work. At this point, we have been ambiguous about the orthogonal projection P, which is of finite rank, but this is on purpose. In the more geometrical method of Hadamard that utilizes the idea of integral manifolds (see [CFNT1] and [CFNT2]), one starts with a suitably chosen finite dimensional surface and follows the evolution of this surface under the flow $\{S(t)\}_{t \geq 0}$. For the method of spectral barriers, this is the integral manifold that passes through

$$\Gamma = \{u \in PH : |u|_H = \rho_0\}. \tag{8.11}$$

Exponential Attractors for Dissipative Evolution Equations

Again, the orthogonal projection P is to be specified during the construction. Clearly, such an integral manifold is invariant under the flow. Moreover, it turns out that this construction results in an inertial manifold that satisfies, for all $t \geq 0$,

$$S(t)\mathcal{M} = \mathcal{M}. \tag{8.12}$$

In order to motivate the idea of the spectral barriers within the theory of exponential attractors, let us recall that the quotient norm $\lambda(t)$, see (3.33), played a crucial role. Namely, in Chapter 3, it was shown that if the quotient norm is large enough at $t = t_*$, then by controlling its past evolution, by (3.40), one can guarantee the existence of an exponential attractor. Here, under stronger restriction on the behavior of the quotient norm, following [CFNT3], the existence of an inertial manifold is shown. The key concept that allows this control is called a *spectral barrier*.

Definition 8.2. A positive real number μ is called a *spectral barrier* for the evolution equation (8.1) if for every u and v in $D(A)$ satisfying

$$\|u - v\|^2 = \mu |u - v|_H^2 \tag{8.13}$$

one also has

$$|(A - \mu)(u - v)|_H^2 + (R(u) - R(v), (A - \mu)(u - v))_H > 0. \tag{8.14}$$

Clearly, a spectral barrier cannot be an eigenvalue of A; moreover, as the name implies, μ blocks the growth of the quotient norm. This is the first part of the following proposition (from [CFNT3]):

Proposition 8.1. *Let μ be a spectral barrier for (8.1) and let $u(t) = S(t)u_0$, $v(t) = S(t)v_0$ be two solutions of (8.1). Setting*

$$\lambda(t) = \frac{\|u(t) - v(t)\|^2}{|u(t) - v(t)|_H^2} \tag{8.15}$$

one has

(i) *If $\lambda(0) \leq \mu$, then $\lambda(t) \leq \mu$ for all $t \geq 0$.*

(ii) *If, on the other hand, $\lambda(t) > \mu$ for some $t > 0$ and if $\mu > \mu_0$, with μ_0 as in (8.8), then*

$$|u(t) - v(t)|_H \leq |u(s) - v(s)|_H \exp\{-\mu^{1-\alpha}(\mu^\alpha - \mu_0^\alpha)(t - s)\} \tag{8.16}$$

for all s, such that $0 \leq s \leq t$.

Proof. Because of our preparations on the quotient norm in Chapter 3, the proof now is easy. Recall that the quotient norm satisfies the differential equation, see (3.43),

$$\frac{1}{2}\frac{d}{dt}\lambda(t) + |(A - \lambda(t))\xi(t)|_H^2 = \frac{1}{|w|_H}(R(v) - R(u), (A - \lambda(t))\xi(t))_H \tag{8.17}$$

where $w(t) = u(t) - v(t)$ and $\xi(t) = w(t)/|w(t)|_H$. Assume that $\lambda(0) \leq \mu$ and $\lambda(t_0) = \mu$ for some $t_0 \geq 0$, then $u(t_0)$ and $v(t_0)$ satisfy

$$\|u(t_0) - v(t_0)\|^2 = \mu |u(t_0) - v(t_0)|_H^2. \tag{8.18}$$

But then, by definition of the spectral barrier, one also has

$$|(A - \mu)(u(t_0) - v(t_0))|_H^2 + (R(u(t_0)) - R(v(t_0)), (A - \mu)(u(t_0) - v(t_0)))_H > 0, \tag{8.19}$$

which, in turn, automatically implies by (8.17) that

$$\frac{d}{dt}\lambda(t)|_{t=t_0} < 0. \tag{8.20}$$

Thus, if μ is a spectral barrier, then $\lambda(t) < \lambda(t_0) = \mu$, for all $t > t_0$.

If, on the other hand, $\lambda(t) > \mu$, then, using (8.8) in (8.17), it follows that

$$\frac{1}{2}\frac{d}{dt}|w(s)|_H^2 + \mu^{1-\alpha}(\mu^\alpha - \mu_0^\alpha)|w(s)|_H^2 \leq 0, \quad \text{for } s \in [0,t], \tag{8.21}$$

(8.15) now easily follows from Gronwall's inequality. □

Corollary 8.2. *If the evolution equation* (8.1) *has a spectral barrier μ such that $\mu > \mu_0$, then the dynamical system generated by the evolution equation* (8.1) *has an exponential attractor.*

Proof. Let $\mu > \mu_0$ be a spectral barrier, with the notation of Chapter 3, choose N_0 large enough so that $\lambda_{N_0+1} > 2\mu$, where λ_{N_0+1} is the (N_0+1)th eigenvalue of A. Then, if $P = P_{N_0} = $ the orthogonal projection to the first N_0-eigenvectors of A, then it follows that, for $S_* = S(t_*)$, $w = u - v$,

$$|(I - P)(S_* u - S_* v)|_H > |P(S_* u - S_* v)|_H \tag{8.22}$$

implies that

$$\lambda_* = \lambda(t_*) > \frac{1}{2}\lambda_{N_0+1} > \mu. \tag{8.23}$$

Hence, by Proposition 8.1(ii),

$$|u(t_*) - v(t_*)|_H \leq |u_0 - v_0|_H \exp\{-\mu^{1-\alpha}(\mu^\alpha - \mu_0^\alpha)t_*\}. \tag{8.24}$$

Clearly, one can choose t_* so that

$$|S_*(u_0) - S_*(v_0)|_H \leq \delta |u_0 - v_0|_H \tag{8.25}$$

with $\delta < 1/8$. Consequently, the squeezing property is satisfied and the evolution equation has an inertial set.

Remark 8.3. If one wants to obtain $t_* = 1/c_3$, as in Corollary 3.1, then one can start with this time t_*, choose the spectral barrier large enough so that

$$\mu^{1-\alpha}(\mu^\alpha - \mu_0^\alpha)t_* \geq -3\ln 2, \tag{8.26}$$

and, finally, choose N_0 so that $\lambda_{N_0+1} > 2\mu$. In this setup the existence of exponential attractors would be guaranteed, no matter how small t_* is, at the cost of very large spectral barriers.

The existence of spectral barriers implies more than the existence of exponential attractors. Now, we outline the construction of inertial manifolds based on the existence of large spectral barriers. Since A is a positive, self-adjoint operator with compact inverse, its spectrum is discrete and is a subset of $[0, \infty)$. Let us denote by P_μ the spectral projector of A corresponding to the interval $[0, \mu)$. From now on we assume that:

(B) There exists a spectral barrier $\mu > \mu_0$. (8.27)

We then set $P = P_\mu$ and $N = \dim PH$ with λ_N being the largest eigenvalue of A on PH. The object is to show that there exists a Lipschitz map

$$\Phi : PH \to D(A^{1/2}) = V \tag{8.28}$$

such that the N-dimensional manifold Σ defined by

$$\Sigma = \{p + \Phi(p) : p \in PH\} \tag{8.29}$$

is an inertial manifold for the flow. The Lipschitz map is obtained through a limiting process. For any fixed $t \geq 0$, one first considers the set Σ_t, defined by

$$\Sigma_t = S(t)PH, \tag{8.30}$$

and defines a map Φ_t on $P\Sigma_t$ by

$$\Phi_t(Pu) = (I - P)u, \text{ for } u \in \Sigma_t \tag{8.31}$$

for two distinct elements u and v in Σ_t, $Pu \neq Pv$. Hence, the map Φ_t is well-defined on $P\Sigma_t$. Moreover, it follows from degree theory that $P\Sigma_t = PH$ and, consequently, the map

$$\Phi_t : PH \to D(A) \cap (I - P)H \tag{8.32}$$

is continuous. On the other hand, in order to monitor the behavior of Φ_t outside the absorbing ball B, one considers the sets

$$D_t = PS(t)\{p \in PH : |p|_H \geq \rho_0\}, \tag{8.33}$$

and show that, for $t > t_0$, $D_{t_0} \subset D_t$. Moreover, Φ_{t_0} agree with Φ_t on D_{t_0}, where they are both well-defined. As for elements outside D_{t_0}, one obtains

$$|\Phi_t(p) - \Phi_{t_0}(p)|_H \leq 2\rho_0 \exp\{-\mu^{1-\alpha}(\mu^\alpha - \mu_0^\alpha)t_0\}. \tag{8.34}$$

These observations allow one to consider

$$\Phi(p) = \lim_{t \to \infty} \Phi_t(p) \quad \text{for } p \in PH. \tag{8.35}$$

Passing to the limit in (8.34),

$$|\Phi(p) - \Phi_{t_0}(p)| \leq 2\rho_0 \exp\{-\mu^{1-\alpha}(\mu^\alpha - \mu_0^\alpha)t_0\} \tag{8.36}$$

for $p \in PH$, and for any $t_0 \geq 0$. The N-dimensional manifold Σ obtained as the graph of Φ as PH can then be shown to be an inertial manifold ([CFNT1,2], Theorem 2.1 and Theorem 2.2). We refer the reader to the original paper for details.

In most of the applications, the spectral barrier μ will be of the form

$$\mu = \frac{\lambda_{N+1} + \lambda_N}{2} \tag{8.37}$$

that is the midpoint between two consecutive eigenvalues of A, with N chosen large enough. A simple sufficient condition that guarantees the existence of a spectral barrier is the following: (see [C])

Lemma 8.4. *If μ is a real number and k large enough such that*

$$\text{dist}(\mu, \sigma(A)) > k\mu^\alpha, \tag{8.38}$$

then μ is a spectral barrier for (8.1).

Proof. Let u and v be any two elements of $D(A)$ that satisfy

$$\|u - v\|^2 = \mu |u - v|_H^2, \tag{8.39}$$

then, clearly, it is sufficient to show that

$$|R(u) - R(v)|_H^2 < |(A - \mu)(u - v)|_H^2. \tag{8.40}$$

From the assumption on μ, it follows that

$$|(A - \mu)(u - v)|_H^2 \geq k\mu^\alpha |u - v|_H^2 = k\mu^{\alpha - 1} \|u - v\|^2. \tag{8.41}$$

On the other hand, by (R2), in (8.7)

$$|R(u) - R(v)|_H^2 \leq c_0 |A^\beta(u - v)|_H^2 \leq c_0 c_1 \|u - v\|^2. \tag{8.42}$$

Hence, if $c_0 c_1 \leq k\mu^{\alpha - 1}$, then μ is a spectral barrier. □

In the case where $\mu = \frac{\lambda_{N+1}+\lambda_N}{2}$, the sufficient condition for the existence of a spectral barrier reads as

$$\frac{1}{2}(\lambda_{N+1} - \lambda_N) > k \left(\frac{\lambda_{N+1} + \lambda_N}{2}\right)^\alpha. \tag{8.43}$$

Following the above procedure, it was shown in [CFNT3] that

1) The Kuramoto-Sivashinsky equation has an inertial manifold whose dimension is of the same order as L^3.

2) The Kolmogorov-Sivashinsky-Spiegel equation has an inertial manifold whose dimension is of the order:
$$N \sim c(L^5 + L^5 \delta^{-1/4} \alpha^{-1/2} + L^{7/2} \delta^{-3/8} \alpha^{-1/2}\}.$$

3) The Ginzburg-Landau equation has an inertial manifold, in one space dimension, of dimension

$cR^{3/2}$ when $|\mu| \leq \sqrt{3}$,

and

$c'R^2$ when $|\mu| > \sqrt{3}$.

Further improvements on GL have been made in Constantin ([C]) where it was shown that $N \sim R^{4/3}$ if $\mu/\nu > 0$.

Chapter 9
Finite Dimensional Dynamics on Exponential Attractors

In the first few chapters of this study we have shown a construction of exponential attractors based on the infamous discrete squeezing property. As the wealth of examples provided in the previous chapters suggests, the discrete squeezing property holds under quite general circumstances without recourse to any kind of spectral gap condition. Although the numerous applications might seem quite promising, one still needs to define some kind of dynamics on these exponential attractors that will unravel their finite dimensional nature. This brief chapter tries to achieve such a goal under favorable conditions. That is, we propose to show that if the underlying PDE already admits an inertial manifold, then one can construct an exponential attractor that lies in the inertial manifold, of possibly smaller fractal dimension, and the dynamics on the exponential attractor is the "lifted" dynamics from a dynamical system defined on an n-dimensional Euclidean space by a system of ODE's.

Although it is desirable to consider a slightly more general framework, in which the map Φ is only assumed to be Hölder continuous, we will stick to the standard framework already discussed in Chapter 8. Let us recall once again the definition of an inertial manifold.

Definition 9.1. Let $\Phi : P_N H \to (I - P_N)H$ be a Lipschitz continuous function with Lipschitz constant L. Set

$$\mathcal{M} = \{(p, \Phi(p)) : p \in P_N H\}. \tag{9.1}$$

Then $\mathcal{M}$ is called a *Lipschitz inertial manifold* for the flow $\{S(t) : t \geq 0\}$ if

(i) $S(t)\mathcal{M} \subseteq \mathcal{M}$

(ii) $\operatorname{dist}_H(S(t)u_0, \mathcal{M}) = O(\exp\{-c_1 t\})$ where c_1 is a constant that depends only on the size of u_0.

At the very end of this chapter, we will show the existence of an exponential attractor in an Inertial Manifold. But first, let us recall once again the p and q equations in the abstract setting of dissipative evolution equations of first order, i.e.,

$$\frac{du}{dt} + Au + R(u) = 0. \tag{9.2}$$

Setting $p = P_N u$ and $q = (I - P_N)u = Q_N u$, one obtains (see [FST]) that

$$\frac{dp}{dt} + Ap + P_N R(p+q) = 0, \tag{9.3}$$

$$\frac{dq}{dt} + Aq + Q_N R(p+q) = 0. \tag{9.4}$$

In the special case when there is an inertial manifold $q = \Phi(p)$, the equations (9.3) and (9.4) are strictly equivalent to the following inertial form, for trajectories on $\mathcal{M}$:

$$\frac{dp}{dt} + Ap + P_N R(p + \Phi(p)) = 0. \tag{9.5}$$

We have already shown, at least when the inertial manifolds are constructed via spectral barriers in Corollary 8.2, that the known conditions that guarantee the existence of an inertial manifold is sufficient also to assure the existence of an exponential attractor. On the other hand, we have already observed that the intersection of the absorbing set B with $\mathcal{M}$ gives an exponential attractor. Moreover, given Φ, the equation (9.5) is a system of ODE's on $P_N H$, hence can be considered so in $\mathbf{R}^N$. Finally, the full dynamics of the inertial manifold $\mathcal{M}$ is achieved by lifting the dynamics of p from (9.5) by the map Φ. In this sense, the dynamics on the inertial manifold $\mathcal{M}$ are the "lifted" dynamics from a system of ODE's.

It is desirable to obtain a similar result for the exponential attractor. The remark at the end of this chapter allows us to verify DSP for the inertial form and construct a exponential attractor. Let us denote the exponential attractor for the inertial form (9.5) in $P_N H$ by $\sum_0$, i.e., $\sum_0 \subseteq P_N H$, and consider the lifting of $\sum_0$ by Φ,

$$\sum = \{(p, \Phi(p)) : p \in \sum_0\}. \tag{9.6}$$

Then, since $\sum_0$ has finite fractal dimension and Φ is Lipschitz continuous, $\sum$ also has finite fractal dimension. Moreover, since the graph of Φ is invariant under the original flow and the projected exponential attractor $\sum_0$ remains invariant under the flow induced by (9.5), $\sum$ is also invariant under the original flow. Finally, we utilize the exponential tracking property of the inertial manifolds, also called asymptotic completeness (see [CFNT], [CFNT2] or [FSTi]) which reads as follows:

Let $u(t)$ be any solution of the dynamical system given in (9.2). Then there exists a time $\tau \geq 0$ and a solution $v(t)$ on the inertial manifold such that

$$\|u(\tau + t) - v(t)\| \leq K e^{-\alpha t} \quad \forall t \geq 0 \tag{9.7}$$

where α, K are positive constants and α is independent of u and v.

So that every solution $u(t)$ is tracked by a trajectory on $\mathcal{M}$ after a finite delay τ. On the other hand, since $\sum_0$ is an exponential attractor for (9.5)

$$\text{dist}_{P_N H}(p(t), \sum\nolimits_0) \leq K_1 \exp(-c_2 t) \tag{9.8}$$

where $p(t) = P_N v(t)$. Consequently, from $v(t) = p(t) + \Phi(p(t))$, it follows that

$$\text{dist}_H(u(t+\tau), \sum) \leq \|u(t+\tau) - v(t)\|_H + \text{dist}_H(v(t), \sum). \tag{9.9}$$

Now let $\hat{p}_0(t) \in \sum_0$ such that

$$\min_{p_0 \in \sum_0} \|p(t) - p_0\|_H \equiv \|p(t) - \hat{p}_0(t)\|_H;$$

now

$$\text{dist}_H(v(t), \sum) = \min_{p_0 \in \sum_0} \|p(t) + \Phi(p(t)) - p_0 - \Phi(p_0)\|_H$$
$$\leq \|p(t) + \Phi(p(t)) - \hat{p}_0(t) - \Phi(\hat{p}_0(t))\|_H$$
$$\leq \|p(t) - \hat{p}_0(t)\| + L\|p(t) - \hat{p}_0(t)\|$$
$$\leq (1+L) \min_{p_0 \in \sum_0} \|p(t) - p_0\|_H;$$

and

$$\text{dist}_H(u(t+\tau), \sum)$$
$$\leq \|u(t+\tau) - v(t)\|_H + (1+L)\text{dist}_H(p(t), \sum\nolimits_0);$$

where we have used the fact that $\|\Phi(p) - \Phi(p')\|_H \leq L\|p - p'\|_H$. Therefore,

$$\text{dist}_H(u(t+\tau), \sum) \leq K e^{-\alpha t} + (1+L)K_1 e^{-c_2 t}$$
$$\leq K_2 e^{-c_3 t} \tag{9.10}$$

where $K_2 = \max\{K, (1+L)K\}$ and $c_3 = \min\{\alpha, c_2\}$. That is to say, $\sum$ exponentially attracts all solutions and, therefore, is the desired exponential attractor in $\mathcal{M}$.

Let us remark that although at this point all the known inertial manifolds are at least Lipschitz manifolds (see [FST1,2], [CFNT2], [CFNT3]), the framework of Hölder continuity seems more natural. In order to justify this looser framework we will indulge ourselves into interpreting some numerical results of 2D Navier Stokes equations (Kolmogorov flows) where it is observed that (see [NS1–3]) the small scale Fourier modes remain quite excited, that is, $|q|_H$ remain of the same order; whereas at the same time the large scale Fourier modes have little contribution, that is, $|p|_H$ is small relative to the total energy. If there were an inertial manifold for the 2D Navier-Stokes equations, then through the map Φ, q-modes will be controlled by p-modes. In the case of Lipschitz Φ, this control is linear and the q-modes are said to be *enslaved* by the p-modes. In contrast, when Φ is only assumed to be Hölder, hence $\|q\|_H = O(\|p\|_H^\theta)$, so that for θ very small the effect of p-modes in the q-modes can be quite unobservable. It is natural, therefore, to hope for the existence of a Hölder manifold that will not contradict these numerical results. We also refer to the discussion from the perspective of turbulence in [EFNS].

The situation suddenly becomes more dramatic in the absence of an inertial manifold that embeds a given exponential attractor. In such a case, one is forced to start from scratch and "construct" finite rank projections P such that for suitably large N

$$P : \sum \to \mathbf{R}^N \text{ is injective,} \quad (9.11)$$

and, moreover, P *carries faithfully the dynamics* into $\mathbf{R}^N$. The latter part is rigorously established with the help of a map Φ, in the special case described above. However, assuming the existence of an inertial manifold limits the applicability of the theory considerably. Therefore, it is desirable to obtain a map Φ with similar properties using only the properties of the finite dimensional exponential attractor rather than the underlying evolution equation.

We would like to remark that obtaining an invertible projection P on a set of finite fractal dimensions is plausible, up to a small perturbation, due to the celebrated theorem of Mañé [Ma3] that assures a rich set of projections that are invertible. More specifically, if X is a compact set of finite Hausdorff dimension less than or equal to d and P is a projection into $\mathbf{R}^N$ with $N \geq 2d+1$, then for any $\delta > 0$ there exists P_0 a projection from H into $\mathbf{R}^N$ such that $\|P - P_0\| < \delta$ and $P_0|_X$ is injective. (For a more accurate description of this theorem and a constructive proof of it, see Appendix A). However, an injective projection P by itself is not sufficient to carry back and forth the dynamics from $\sum$ to $P\sum$. Therefore, one is required to search for projections P who have nicely behaving inverses, e.g., Hölder continuous. What we are considering at this point is quite independent of the dynamics on $\sum$, i.e., we are only considering $\sum$ as a compact fractal set and looking at finite rank injective projections on $\sum$. The program initiated in the next chapter deals with such projections. In the finite dimensional case, we can guarantee the existence of a projection that has Hölder continuous inverse; this is the Hölder version of the Mañé's theorem that we prove in Appendix A. Again in the favorable case when there is such a projection, in infinite dimensions this time, the dynamics on $\sum$ can be realized as a lifted dynamics from a finite dimensional projected dynamics on $\mathbf{R}^N$. The remainder of this monograph deals with questions related with this program.

Remark 9.1. As promised before, we now show how to construct an exponential attractor inside the inertial manifold via the discrete squeezing property using the inertial form (9.5). The key idea is that by enlarging the base space P_1H the Lipschitz constant λ of the function Φ can be decreased. Let $\mathcal{M} = \text{Graph } \Phi$ be the inertial manifold

$$\Phi : P_1 H \to (I - P_1)H \text{ with Lip } (\Phi) = \lambda. \tag{9.12}$$

We claim that if the original flow $(\{S(t)\}_{t\geq 0}, B)$ has the Discrete Squeezing Property at $t = t_0$ with P_0 and δ_0 such that $P_0 \leq P_1$, then the flow induced by the evolution equation

$$\frac{dy}{dt} + Ay + P_1 R(y + \Phi(y)) = 0,$$

$$y(0) = y_0, \tag{9.13}$$

also enjoy the D.S.P. Let us call this flow on $B_1 = P_1 B$ by $\{T(t)\}_{t\geq 0}$ we will show that $T(t_0)$ has D.S.P. with P_0 and δ_0' where

$$\delta_0' = \delta_0 (1 + \lambda^2)^{1/2}. \tag{9.14}$$

Let $S = S(t_0)$ and $T = T(t_0)$, then from the definition of the T-flow, we have

$$S(y + \Phi(y)) = Ty + \Phi(Ty) \tag{9.15}$$

so that for $x_1 = y_1 + \Phi(y_1)$ and $x_2 = y_2 + \Phi(y_2)$, with y_1 and y_2 in the absorbing set B_1, we deduce that

$$|(I - P_0)(S(x_1) - S(x_2))|_H^2$$
$$= |(I - P_0)(Ty_1 - Ty_2)|_H^2 + |(I - P_0)(\Phi(Ty_1) - \Phi(Ty_2))|_H^2$$
$$\geq |(I - P_0)(Ty_1 - Ty_2)|_H^2 = |(P_1 - P_0)(Ty_1 - Ty_2)|_H^2$$

where we have used the facts that $P_0 = P_1 P_0 = P_0 P_1$ and $P_1(Ty) = Ty$. Consequently,

$$|(I - P_0)(Ty_1 - Ty_2)|_{P_1H}^2 \geq |P_0(Ty_1 - Ty_2)|_{P_1H}^2 \tag{9.16}$$

implies that

$$|(I - P_0)(S(x_1) - S(x_2))|_H^2 \geq |(I - P_0)(Ty - Ty_2)|_{P_1H}^2 \geq |P_0(Ty_1 - Ty_2)|_{P_1H}^2$$
$$\geq |P_0(S(x_1) - S(x_2))|_H^2$$

since $P_0(Ty_1) = P_0(S(x_1))$. From the DSP of S, it follows that

$$|S(x_1) - S(x_2)|_H^2 \leq \delta_0^2 |x_1 - x_2|_H^2, \tag{9.17}$$

hence

$$|T(y_1) - T(y_2)|_{P_1H}^2 \leq |S(x_1) - S(x_2)|_H^2 \leq \delta_0^2(|y_1 - y_2|_{P_1H}^2 + |\Phi(y_1) - \Phi(y_2)|_H^2)$$
$$\leq \delta_0^2(1 + \lambda^2)|y_1 - y_2|_{P_1H}^2 = (\delta_0')^2 |y_1 - y_2|_{P_1H}^2,$$

that is to say, T satisfies the squeezing property with P_0 and δ_0'. Note that δ_0' can be made arbitrarily small in two ways. One is to choose P_1 large enough so that $\text{Lip}(\Phi) = \lambda$ will be as small as desired. The other way passes through monitoring P_0 so that if P_0 is large enough and $P_0 \leq P_1$, then δ_0 will be arbitrarily small, hence δ_0' will be as small as desired.

Chapter 10
Mañé's Projections and Inertially Equivalent Dynamical Systems

The existence of a compact set of finite fractal dimension, towards which all solutions of a dissipative evolution equation converge, brings with it the natural question about the dynamics on this set. The question we would like to address is the following:

Is there a natural way of reconstructing the dynamics on the exponential attractor as a finite dimensional dynamic without direct recourse to the underlying evolution equation?

An affirmative answer to this question is supplied in the previous chapter via inertial manifolds. There we have argued that the whole dynamics of the evolution equation coincide with the lifted dynamics from a system of ODE's (9.5). However, due to the stringent theoretical conditions, e.g., the spectral gap condition, that is associated with the inertial manifolds, we would like to carry out an alternative program. The essential ingredient in our analysis is the existence of Mañé projections [Ma3] from sets of finite Hausdorff dimension X into $\mathbf{R}^N$. Once their existence is established we proceed by projecting the full evolution equation into $\mathbf{R}^N$. As long as we are in the invariant set of finite Hausdorff dimension the Mañé projection P_M is injective. However, we need to define the projected evolution equation differently outside $P_M X$. In order to carry out the first steps of this program, we recall the basic theorem on Mañé projections and the improved version, i.e., Hölder-Mañé theorem for the case $H = \mathbf{R}^N$. The complete proofs for both of these theorems are given in Appendix A, Corollary 1 and Proposition 1, respectively.

Mañé's Theorem. *Let H be a separable Hilbert space and X be a compact subset of H such that $d_H(X) \leq k$ and $d_H(X \times X) \leq k'$. Also let P_0 be an orthogonal projection in H of rank equal to $k' + 1$. Then for every $\delta \in (0,1)$,* there exists an orthogonal projection $P = P(\delta)$ in H such that

$$\|P - P_0\| < \delta \quad \text{and} \quad P|_X \text{ is injective.} \tag{10.1}$$

Hölder-Mañé's Theorem. *Let X be a compact subset of $\mathbf{R}^N$ such that $d_F(X) < d$ with $D = 2d < N - 1$. Let P_0 be an orthogonal projection on $\mathbf{R}^N$ of rank $\tilde{N} = [[D+1]]$. Then for every $\delta > 0$ and for every θ such that*

$$0 < \theta < 1 - D/N,$$

there exists an orthogonal projection $P = P(\theta, \delta)$ of the same rank as P_0 and a positive constant C such that

$$\|P - P_0\| < \delta \quad \text{and} \quad |y_1 - y_2|_H \leq C|Py_1 - Py_2|_H^{\theta} \tag{10.2}$$

for every y_1 and y_2 in X.

Clearly, Hölder-Mañé's theorem is stronger since it concludes not only that P^{-1} exists but also that it is Hölder continuous. This strengthening of the Mañé theorem follows from the stronger assumption on X. Namely, instead of controlling the Hausdorff dimension of X and $X \times X$, one assumes that the fractal dimension of X is controlled. Keeping in mind that $d_H(X) \leq d_F(X)$, where the inequality can be strict, in some extreme cases $d_H(X) = 0$ and $d_F(X) = \infty$, see Appendix A. Before applying these results to the evolution equation, we still need a preliminary lemma.

Lemma 10.1. *Let Y be a compact subset of $\mathbf{R}^{\tilde{N}}$. Define a map ν from $\mathbf{R}^{\tilde{N}}$ onto Y by*

$$\nu(x) = \begin{cases} x & \text{if } x \in Y \\ y & \text{if } x \notin Y \text{ and } \text{dist}_{\mathbf{R}^{\tilde{N}}}(x, Y) = |x - y|_{\mathbf{R}^{\tilde{N}}} \end{cases} \tag{10.3}$$

where in the above definition y is chosen randomly for each x and is fixed thereafter. The map ν satisfies the following properties:

(i) *the continuity points of ν form a G_δ subset of $\mathbf{R}^{\tilde{N}}$ that consists of points whose distance to Y is achieved by a unique y in $\mathbf{R}^{\tilde{N}}$,*

(ii) *ν is the pointwise limit of a sequence of continuous functions,*

(iii) *ν is a Borel function.*

Proof. Setting

$$G = \{x \in \mathbf{R}^{\tilde{N}} : \text{dist}_{\mathbf{R}^{\tilde{N}}}(x, Y) = |x - y|_{\mathbf{R}^{\tilde{N}}} \text{ is achieved by a unique } y \text{ in } \mathbf{R}^{\tilde{N}}\}$$

we proceed to show that G is a G_δ dense subset on $\mathbf{R}^{\tilde{N}}$ and that G is the set of continuity points of ν. To this end, we consider the following subset of $\mathbf{R}^{\tilde{N}} \setminus Y$.

$$F_n = \{x \in \mathbf{R}^{\tilde{N}} : \text{there exist } y_1 \text{ and } y_2 \text{ in } Y \text{ with } |y_1 - y_2| \geq \frac{1}{n}$$
$$\text{and such that } \text{dist}_{\mathbf{R}^{\tilde{N}}}(x, Y) = |x - y_i|_{\mathbf{R}^{\tilde{N}}}, i = 1, 2\}.$$

From the compactness of Y and the continuity of the distance function $x \to \text{dist}_{\mathbf{R}^{\tilde{N}}}(x, Y)$, it follows that F_n is a closed subset of $\mathbf{R}^{\tilde{N}} \backslash Y$. Furthermore, we claim that F_n is nowhere dense. If not, there exists x_0 in $F_n = \overline{F}_n$ such that $B(x_0; r) \subseteq F_n$. Without loss of generality, we can assume that $r < \text{dist}_{\mathbf{R}^{\tilde{N}}}(x_0, Y)$. Since x_0 in F_n, there exist y_1 and y_2 in Y such that $|y_1 - y_2|_{\mathbf{R}^{\tilde{N}}} \geq 1/n$ and $|x_0 - y_i|_{\mathbf{R}^{\tilde{N}}} = \text{dist}_{\mathbf{R}^{\tilde{N}}}(x_0, Y)$ for $i = 1, 2$. We will show that a complete sphere around x_0 cannot be included in F_n. Let z be the point on the surface of the sphere $B(x_0; r)$ such that

$$|x_0 - z| + |z - y_2| = |x_0 - y_2|,$$

i.e., we assume that z is on the line connecting x_0 to y_2. Then, $|z - y_2| = \text{dist}(z, Y)$ since otherwise,

$$|x_0 - w| \leq |x_0 - z| + |z - w| < |x_0 - z| + |z - y_2| = |x_0 - y_2| = \text{dist}_{\mathbf{R}^{\tilde{N}}}(x_0, Y)$$

for some w in Y, which is a contradiction. Secondly, if y is a point in Y for which the distance to z is achieved, then

$$|x_0 - y| \leq |x_0 - z| + |z - y| = |x_0 - z| + |z - y_2| = |x_0 - y_2| \leq \text{dist}(x_0, Y) \leq |x_0 - y|,$$

hence

$$|x_0 - y| = |x_0 - z| + |z - y|.$$

But this can only happen if x_0, z and y are collinear, which in turn implies that $y = y_2$. Therefore, $z \notin F_n$ and F_n is nowhere dense.

Next we observe that

$$G = \bigcap_{n=1}^{\infty} (\mathbf{R}^{\tilde{N}} \backslash F_n);$$

hence, G is a G_δ-dense subset of $\mathbf{R}^{\tilde{N}}$ by Baire's first category theorem. It remains to show that ν is continuous on G. Let $\{x_\delta : \delta \in \Delta\}$ be a net in G that converges to x_0 in G. By definition of G, for each δ, there exists a unique y_δ in Y such that $|x_\delta - y_\delta| = \text{dist}(x_\delta, Y)$. Using the compactness of Y, we can choose a subnet of $\{y_\delta : \delta \in \Delta\}$ that converges to y_0 in Y. Without loss of generality, we therefore assume that $y_\delta \to y_1$ in Y. Consequently, we have $|x_\delta - y_\delta| \to |x_0 - y_1|$ and $\text{dist}(x_\delta, Y) \to \text{dist}(x_0, Y)$. Since x_0 is in G it follows that y_1 is the unique element y_0 of Y for which $\text{dist}(x_0, Y) = |x_0 - y_0|$. Therefore,

$$y_\delta = \nu(x_\delta) \to y_0 = \nu(x_0).$$

Parts (ii) and (iii) follow from (i) by a direct application of Baire's second category theorem (see [Ku]). □

Remark 10.1. Although for $x \notin G$, $\nu(x)$ is not uniquely defined we will fix a choice for the map ν and keep it throughout this chapter.

10.1. Generalized Dynamical Systems and the Induced Dynamics under Mañè's Projection

Let H be a Hilbert space on which the following evolution problem is posed:
$$\frac{du}{dt} = F(u), \qquad u(0) = u_0, \qquad (10.1.1)$$
where, placing ourselves in the context of Chapter 3, F has the form
$$F(u) \doteq -Au - R(u); \qquad (10.1.2)$$
and the following strengthening of the conditions (3.6)–(3.10): we assume that $R(0)$ is in $D(A^{1/2})$ and that R is a Lipschitz map from $D(A^{3/2})$ into $D(A^{1/2})$. Then, one can show the existence of an absorbing set B bounded in $D(A^{3/2})$. Consequently, the exponential attractor construction outlined in Chapter 4 gives a bounded subset X of $D(A^{3/2})$. Next, we note that since by conditions (3.6)–(3.10)
$$F : D(A) \to H \qquad (10.1.3)$$
is Lipschitz, by a simple $(H, D(A^{3/2}))$ interpolation of $D(A)$:
$$\|F(u) - F(v)\|_H \leq L\|u-v\|_{D(A)} \leq L'\|u-v\|_H^{1/3}\|A^{3/2}(u-v)\|_H^{2/3}. \qquad (10.1.4)$$

Furthermore, since u and v belong to the bounded subset X of $D(A^{3/2})$, the map $F : X \to H$ is Hölder continuous from H into H with Hölder exponent $\theta = 1/3$. A standard result on fractal dimensions, (Appendix C) implies that
$$d_F(F(X)) \leq 3d_F(X). \qquad (10.1.5)$$

Consequently, the subset Z of H defined by
$$Z = X \cup Y \quad \text{with} \quad Y \doteq \{u + F(u) : u \in X\} \qquad (10.1.6)$$

still has finite fractal dimension. By the Hölder continuity of the map $u \to u + F(u)$, with Hölder exponent $1/3$, we have as before
$$d_F(Z) \leq \max\{d_F(X), d_F(Y)\}$$
$$\leq \max\{d_F(X), 3d_F(X)\} = 3d_F(X). \qquad (10.1.7)$$

Now we will invoke Mañè's theorem with X being replaced by Z and choose a projection $P_M : H \to P_M H$ such that
$$P_M|_Z \quad \text{is injective.} \qquad (10.1.8)$$

This elaborate construction allows us to project the evolution equation (10.1.1) without introducing new steady solutions.

Exponential Attractors for Dissipative Evolution Equations

In order to study the induced dynamics on $P_M X$, we first replace the nonlinear operator $F(u)$ by another nonlinear operator $\overline{T}$, defined on $P_M H$ in the following manner. First, define a nonlinear operator T on $P_M X$ by

$$T(P_M u) = P_M F(u) \tag{10.1.9}$$

then extend T to all $P_M H$ as follows

$$\overline{T}(x) = \begin{cases} T(x) & \text{if } x \in P_M X, \\ \alpha(\nu(x) - x) + T(\nu(x)) & \text{if } x \notin P_M X. \end{cases} \tag{10.1.10}$$

In the definition of $\overline{T}$, we have used the map ν, from $P_M H$ onto $P_M X$, introduced in Lemma 10.1, and a fixed positive number $\alpha > 0$. Let us remark that, if $T(x_0) = 0$ for $x_0 \in P_M X$ then $P_M F(u_0) = 0$ with $x_0 = P_M u_0$. On the other hand, P_M is chosen to be injective on Z, hence

$$P_M(F(u_0) + u_0) - P_M(u_0) = 0 \quad \text{implies that} \quad F(u_0) + u_0 = u_0, \tag{10.1.11}$$

that is, $F(u_0) = 0$. In other words, the projected evolution equation does not introduce new steady solutions on $P_M X$ other than those already given by $F(u) = 0$. Identifying $\mathbf{R}^{\tilde{N}}$ with $P_M H$, we intend to study the differential equation

$$\frac{dx}{dt} = \overline{T}(x(t)) \quad \text{with} \quad x(0) = x_0 \in \mathbf{R}^{\tilde{N}}. \tag{10.1.12}$$

Note, however, that the map $\overline{T}$ need not even be continuous, hence (10.1.12) does not give us a dynamical system in the classical sense. However, the existence of unique solutions on $P_M X$ is guaranteed by the original evolution equation (10.1.1); furthermore, (10.1.12) can be solved by recasting (10.1.12) as an equivalent integral equation. Before doing that, let us remark that as a simple corollary to Lemma 10.1, we have

Lemma 10.2. $\overline{T}$ *as defined in* (10.13) *is a locally bounded vector valued function with the following properties:*

(i) *The continuity points of $\overline{T}$ form a dense G_δ-subset of $\mathbf{R}^{\tilde{N}}$ that consists of points whose distance to $P_M X$ is uniquely achieved.*

(ii) *There exists a sequence of continuous, locally bounded, vector valued functions T_n from $\mathbf{R}^{\tilde{N}}$ into $\mathbf{R}^{\tilde{N}}$ such that $\{T_n(x)\}$ converges to $\overline{T}(x)$ for every x in $\mathbf{R}^{\tilde{N}}$.*

(iii) $\overline{T}$ *is a Borel function.*

For $x(\cdot) \in C([0,\infty); \mathbf{R}^{\tilde{N}})$, the function $\overline{T}(x(t))$ is thus defined as the pointwise limit of the sequence $\{T_n(x(t))\}$, where each $T_n(x(\cdot))$ is a continuous function, uniformly bounded on any time interval $[0,\tau]$. Consequently, $\overline{T}(x(t))$ is integrable on any finite time interval $[0,\tau]$. Then for any positive time t, the operator ψ defined by

$$\psi(x)(t) = x_0 + \int_0^t \overline{T}(x(s))\, ds \tag{10.1.13}$$

maps $\mathcal{C}([0,\infty);\mathbf{R}^{\tilde{N}})$ into itself. Note also that any solution of (10.1.12) is a fixed point of Ψ. We will show that, as a partial converse, the fixed points of (10.1.12) give rise to generalized solutions of (10.1.12). In order to guarantee the existence of fixed points, we first show that the map Ψ when restricted to a suitable space $\mathcal{C}([0,t_0];\mathbf{R}^{\tilde{N}})$ is compact. Setting

$$C = \max\{|T(x)|_{\mathbf{R}^{\tilde{N}}} : x \in P_M X\} \text{ and } r = \max\{|x|_{\mathbf{R}^{\tilde{N}}} : x \in P_M X\} \tag{10.1.14}$$

and also

$$t_0 = (C + \alpha(r + |x_0| + 1))^{-1} \tag{10.1.15}$$

we have:

Lemma 10.3. *The map Ψ defined by (10.1.13) is a compact map from*

$$\mathcal{F} = \{x(\cdot) \in \mathcal{C}([0,t_0];\mathbf{R}^{\tilde{N}}) : |x(t)| \leq |x_0| + 1 \text{ for } t \in [0,t_0] \text{ and } x(0) = x_0\} \tag{10.1.16}$$

into itself.

Proof. For all t in $[0,t_0]$, it follows from the definition of $\overline{T}$ given in (10.1.10) that

$$|\Psi(x)(t)| \leq |x_0| + \int_0^t |\alpha(\nu(x(s)) - x(s)) + T(\nu(x(s)))| \, ds$$

$$\leq |x_0| + \int_0^t (\alpha r + \alpha|x(s)| + C) \, ds \tag{10.1.17}$$

$$\leq |x_0| + \int_0^t (\alpha(r + |x_0| + 1) + C) \, ds$$

$$\leq |x_0| + 1,$$

where we have repeatedly utilized the fact that $x \in \mathcal{F}$ and (10.1.14), (10.1.15). Clearly, $\Psi(x)$ is still in $\mathcal{F}$. It remains to show that Ψ is compact by satisfying the conditions of the Arzela-Ascoli theorem. Note that, as before, for t_1, t_2 in $[0,t_0]$,

$$|\psi(x)(t_1) - \psi(x)(t_2)| \leq |t_1 - t_2|\max\{|\overline{T}(x(t))| : t_1 \leq t \leq t_2\}$$
$$\leq |t_1 - t_2|\max\{C + \alpha(r + |x(t)|) : t_1 \leq t \leq t_2\}$$
$$\leq |t_1 - t_2|(C + \alpha(r + |x_0| + 1)), \tag{10.1.18}$$

which proves that the family $\{\psi(x) : x \in \mathcal{F}\}$ is equicontinuous. Invoking Arzela-Ascoli theorem, it follows that the map Ψ is compact. $\square$

Corollary 10.3. *There exists a fixed point x of Ψ in $\mathcal{F}$, that is, for all t in $[0,t_0]$,*

$$x(t) = x_0 + \int_0^t \overline{T}(x(s)) \, ds. \tag{10.1.19}$$

Because of the particular way $\overline{T}$ is defined we can deduce further information about the fixed point $x(t)$.

Lemma 10.45. *The fixed point of (8.16), guaranteed to exist by Corollary 10.3, satisfies*

$$\operatorname{dist}_{\mathbf{R}\tilde{N}}(x(t), P_M X) \leq \operatorname{dist}_{\mathbf{R}\tilde{N}}(x_0, P_M X) - \alpha \int_0^t \operatorname{dist}_{\mathbf{R}\tilde{N}}(x(s), P_M X) \, ds \qquad (10.1.20)$$

for $t \in [0, t_0]$.

Proof. First, let us observe that $x(t)$ is not only continuous but also Lipschitz, since for $t_1, t_2 \in [0, t_0]$ we have

$$|x(t_2) - x(t_1)| \leq |t_1 - t_2|(C + \alpha(r + |x_0| + 1)). \qquad (10.1.21)$$

Combined with the fact that the distance function is Lipschitz, we can easily deduce that the map $t \to \operatorname{dist}(x(t), P_M X)$ is also Lipschitz. On the other hand, by the Lebesque Differentiation theorem for a.e. t in $[0, t_0]$ we have

$$\frac{dx(t)}{dt} = \overline{T}(x(t)). \qquad (10.1.22)$$

From now on, we will denote the lifting from $P_M Z$ onto Z by Φ, i.e.,

$$\Phi(y) = P_M^{-1}(y) \qquad \forall y \in P_M Z. \qquad (10.1.23)$$

For a t that satisfies (10.1.22), we set

$$y(t + \epsilon) = P_M S(\epsilon, \Phi(\nu(x(t)))), \qquad (10.1.24)$$

where $S(t, u_0)$ is the nonlinear semiflow generated by (10.1.1) on X. It follows from the differentiability properties of $S(t, u_0)$ that

$$|y(t + \epsilon) - [\nu(x(t)) + \epsilon T(\nu(x(t)))]| = o(\epsilon) \quad \text{as} \quad \epsilon \to 0. \qquad (10.1.25)$$

On the other hand, from the differential equation (10.1.22) where we have chosen t a Lebesgue point, we also obtain that

$$|x(t + \epsilon) - [x(t) + \epsilon \overline{T}(x(t))]| = o(\epsilon) \quad \text{as} \quad \epsilon \to 0. \qquad (10.1.26)$$

Combining the estimates in (10.1.25) and (10.1.26), we deduce that

$$\begin{aligned}
\operatorname{dist}(x(t + \epsilon), P_M X) &\leq |x(t + \epsilon) - y(t + \epsilon)| \\
&\leq |x(t) + \epsilon \overline{T}(x(t)) + o(\epsilon) - (\nu(x(t)) - \epsilon T(\nu(x(t))) + o(\epsilon)| \\
&\leq |x(t) - \nu(x(t))| + \epsilon(\overline{T}(x(t)) - T(\nu(x(t)))| + o(\epsilon) \\
&\leq |x(t) - \nu(x(t))| + \epsilon\alpha(\nu(x(t)) - x(t))| + o(\epsilon) \\
&\leq (1 - \alpha\epsilon)|x(t) - \nu(x(t))| + o(\epsilon) \\
&\leq (1 - \alpha\epsilon)\operatorname{dist}(x(t), P_M X) + o(\epsilon) \qquad (10.1.27)
\end{aligned}$$

where we have utilized the definition of ν. Consequently, in the limit

$$\overline{D}_+\text{dist}(x(t), P_M X) \doteq \overline{\lim}_{\epsilon \to 0+} \frac{\text{dist}(x(t+\epsilon), P_M X) - \text{dist}(x(t), P_M X)}{\epsilon}$$

$$\leq -\alpha \text{dist}(x(t), P_M X). \tag{10.1.28}$$

Using the fact that $t \to \text{dist}(x(t), P_M X)$ is Lipschitz and hence differentiable for a.e. t, we deduce that

$$\text{dist}(x(t), P_M X) = \text{dist}(x_0, P_M X) + \int_0^t \frac{d}{ds}\text{dist}(x(s), P_M X)\,ds$$

$$= \text{dist}(x_0, P_M X) + \int_0^t \overline{D}_+\text{dist}(x(s), P_M X)\,ds$$

$$\leq \text{dist}(x_0, P_M X) - \alpha \int_0^t \text{dist}(x(s), P_M X)\,ds.$$

$\square$

Once the existence of a solution for a small time interval is established we next proceed to show that each solution can be extended to all times.

Theorem 10.1. *For every initial value x_0 in $\mathbf{R}^{\tilde{N}}$, there exists a solution $x(t)$ in $C([0, \infty); \mathbf{R}^{\tilde{N}})$ such that*

$$x(t) = x_0 + \int_0^t \overline{T}(x(s))\,ds \quad \text{for all} \quad t \geq 0. \tag{10.1.29}$$

Moreover, the solution satisfies

$$\text{dist}(x(t), P_M X) \leq e^{-\alpha t}\text{dist}(x_0, P_M X) \quad \text{forall} \quad t \geq 0. \tag{10.1.30}$$

Proof. Let us start by remarking that one can apply Corollary 10.3 to $x(t_0)$ as the initial value instead of x_0 and obtain another function $x_1(t)$ in $C([0, t_1]; \mathbf{R}^{\tilde{N}})$. We can then define a new function by connecting these two solutions by

$$x(t) = \begin{cases} x(t) & \text{if } 0 \leq t \leq t_0, \\ x_1(t - t_0) & \text{if } t_0 \leq t \leq t_0 + t_1. \end{cases} \tag{10.1.31}$$

Then the new function is in $C([0, t_0 + t_1]; \mathbf{R}^{\tilde{N}})$ and satisfies

$$x(t) = x_0 + \int_0^t \overline{T}(x(s))\,ds \quad \text{for all} \quad t \text{ in } [0, t_0 + t_1]. \tag{10.1.32}$$

Moreover, (10.1.20) still applies to this solution; hence, for $t \in [0, t_0 + t_1]$

$$\text{dist}(x(t), P_M X) \leq \text{dist}(x_0, P_M X) - \alpha \int_0^t \text{dist}(x(s), P_M X)\,ds. \tag{10.1.33}$$

Consequently, the solution can be extended to an interval $[0, t_\infty)$ such that $|x(t)| \to \infty$ as $t \to t_\infty$. If t_∞ is finite, then by (10.1.33) and (10.1.34)

$$|x(t)| - r \leq \text{dist}(x(t), P_M X) \leq e^{-\alpha t}\text{dist}(x_0, P_M X) \leq e^{-\alpha t}(|x_0| + r) \tag{10.1.34}$$

where we have used Gronwall's inequality in conjunction with (10.1.33). Hence, $|x(t)|$ remains bounded on $[0, t_\infty)$, which implies that $t_\infty = \infty$. $\square$

It is worthwhile summarizing the results obtained so far and to point to the weak link in this approach. First, we start out with a dissipative PDE written in the evolution form as in (10.1.1) and projected the evolution equation on X via Mañé's projection P_M, onto a system of ODE's on an Euclidean space, i.e., (10.1.12). The solutions of this system of ODE's are obtained by solving an integral equation (10.1.19); they are only Lipschitz continuous and satisfy the ODE's almost everywhere in time. So, the information we have on the differential equation in $\mathbf{R}^{\tilde{N}}$ in itself, does not guarantee the existence and uniqueness of differentiable solutions. But as a result of Theorem 10.1, the solutions exist globally in time and are attracted exponentially to $P_M X$.

The lack of uniqueness for the initial value problem given in (10.1.12) suggests a more relaxed definition for a dynamical system. We will say that the map taking x_0 into $\{x(t) : t \geq 0\}$ is a generalized dynamical system from X into $\mathcal{C}([0,\infty); X)$ if $x(0) = x_0$ and if $x_1(t)$ is a solution of (10.1.12) such that $x_1(t_0) = x_0$ then the trajectory $y(t)$ defined by

$$y(t) = \begin{cases} x_1(t) & \text{for } 0 \leq t \leq t_0 \\ x(t - t_0) & \text{for } t > t_0 \end{cases}$$

is also a solution of the initial value problem (10.1.12). In addition to this superposition principle, we also require the following continuity property with respect to initial values: if x_{0j} converges to x_0 and $x_j(t)$ is a solution of (10.1.12) such that $x_j(0) = x_{0j}$, then there exists a subsequence $x_{j_k}(t)$ that converges to $x(t)$ uniformly on compact time intervals, where $x(0) = x_0$.

Corollary 10.4. *The $\tilde{N}$ dimensional ODE system, (10.1.22), where $\tilde{N} = [[2d + 1]]$ gives rise to a generalized finite dimensional dynamical system on $\mathbf{R}^{\tilde{N}}$, which reduces on $P_M X$ to*

$$\frac{dx}{dt}(t) = P_M F(\Phi(x(t))), \qquad x(0) = P_M x_0, \qquad (10.1.35)$$

and the dynamical system (10.1.12) admits $P_M X$ as an exponential attractor. The exponential attractor $P_M X$ is topologically homeomorphic to X and the exponential rate of convergence, i.e., α, can be made arbitrarily large.

10.2. Lifting the Generalized Dynamical System

Unfortunately, without further knowledge on the lifting $\Phi = (P_M|_Z)^{-1}$ and on $\bar{T}$, we cannot lift the generalized dynamical system that is defined on $\mathbf{R}^{\tilde{N}}$ to H, which in turn would admit X as an exponential attractor. From this point on, we will make a further restriction on Mañé's projection, namely,

(H$_0$) The Mañé's projection P_M from H to $\mathbf{R}^{\tilde{N}}$ further satisfies

$$|x_1 - x_2|_H \leq C|P_M(x_1 - x_2)|_{\mathbf{R}^{\tilde{N}}}^\theta \quad \text{forevery } x_1 \text{ and } x_2 \text{ in } X, \qquad (10.2.1)$$

where $\theta \leq 1$ and $C > 0$ are fixed constants independent of x_1 and x_2.

The assumption (H$_0$) is fully justified when the underlying PDE has an inertial manifold. In such a case, the Hölder-Mañé theorem, stated in the beginning, guarantees that $P_M|_X$ has a Hölder continuous inverse. Once a projection satisfying (10.2.1) is found, we proceed to lift the dynamics on $\mathbf{R}^{\tilde{N}}$ to H by Φ.

Consider the identity function on H and define on $P_M H$ the function f from $P_M H$ into H by

$$f(w) = w + (I - P_M)\Phi(\nu(w)) \qquad (10.2.2)$$

where

$$\Phi = (P_M|_X)^{-1} \text{ on } P_M X \qquad (10.2.3)$$

and ν is as defined in Lemma 10.1. It follows from Lemma 8.1 and the continuity of Φ that f is a Borel function. However, we can conclude a little more.

Lemma 10.5. *The function f defined on $\mathbf{R}^{\tilde{N}}$ by (10.2.2) is a locally bounded, vector valued Borel function which satisfies*

$$f(P_M z) = z \text{ for } z \text{ in } X \text{ and } \operatorname{dist}_H(f(w), X)$$
$$= \operatorname{dist}_H(w, P_M X) \text{ for } w \in P_M H. \qquad (10.2.4)$$

Proof. The facts that f is a Borel function and $f(P_M z) = z$ follow easily from Lemma 10.1 and the definition of f. Let us remind the reader that Φ is only assumed to be continuous in this argument. As for the distance function, we have, for w in $P_M H$ and z in X,

$$|f(w) - z|_H^2 = |(I - P_M)[\Phi(\nu(w)) - z]|_H^2 + |w - P_M z|_H^2. \qquad (10.2.5)$$

Taking infimum in both sides of (10.2.5) and noting that $|\nu(w) - w| = \operatorname{dist}(w, P_M X)$ we obtain

$$\operatorname{dist}(f(w), X) = \operatorname{dist}(w, P_M X).$$

$\square$

Next, we are going to show that under the hypothesis (H_0) the dynamics on $P_M H$ can be lifted to a different dynamics on H, such that the lifted trajectories of (10.1.12) also converge exponentially to X in H. Consequently, a new dynamical system is obtained on H which has the same exponential attractor as the original PDE and the dynamics on the exponential attractor coincide.

Definition 10.1. Two dynamical systems are *inertially equivalent* if:
  i) they have a common exponential attractor;
  ii) the dynamics on that exponential attractor coincide.

Analogously, we will call two dynamical systems on the same set *asymptotically equivalent* if they have the same attractor $\mathcal{A}$ and the dynamics on

Exponential Attractors for Dissipative Evolution Equations

the attractor coincide. The upshot of the above argument is that under assumption (H_0), the dynamical system that arises from the evolution equation (10.1.1) is inertially equivalent to the lifted dynamics of a generalized finite dimensional dynamical system. The role of the exponential attractor can also be played by the global attractor $\mathcal{A}$ and we can also deduce that the lifted dynamics is asymptotically equivalent to the original dynamics on H. Moreover, the lifted dynamics admit $\mathcal{A}$ as an exponential attractor.

Now, we proceed to carry out the details.

Lemma 10.6. *Let P_M be a Hölder-Mañé projection. Then for every w and w_0 in $P_M H$,*

$$|w - w_0| \leq \mathrm{dist}(w_0, P_M X)$$
$$\text{implies that } |f(w) - f(w_0)|_H \leq \mathrm{dist}(w_0, P_M X)$$
$$+ 4^\theta C \,\mathrm{dist}\,(w_0, P_M X)^\theta \qquad (10.2.6)$$

Proof. From the definition of f given in (10.2.2), it follows that

$$|f(w) - f(w_0)|_H \leq |w - w_0|_H + |(I - P_M)[\Phi(\nu(w)) - \Phi(\nu(w_0))]|_H. \quad (10.2.7)$$

Hence, by the assumption on $|w - w_0|_H$,

$$\begin{aligned}|f(w) - f(w_0)|_H &\leq \mathrm{dist}(w_0, P_M X) + |\Phi(\nu(w)) - \Phi(\nu(w_0))|_H \\ &\leq \mathrm{dist}(w_0, P_M X) + C|\nu(w) - \nu(w_0)|^\theta \\ &\leq \mathrm{dist}(w_0, P_M X) + C(\mathrm{dist}(w, P_M X) \\ &\quad + |w - w_0| + \mathrm{dist}(w_0, P_M X))^\theta \\ &\leq \mathrm{dist}(w_0, P_M X) + C(\mathrm{dist}(w, P_M X) \\ &\quad + 2\mathrm{dist}(w_0, P_M X))^\theta. \end{aligned} \qquad (10.2.8)$$

It follows from

$$|\mathrm{dist}(w, P_M X) - \mathrm{dist}(w_0, P_M X)| \leq |w - w_0|_H \leq \mathrm{dist}(w_0, P_M X) \quad (10.2.9)$$

that

$$|f(w) - f(w_0)|_H \leq \mathrm{dist}(w_0, P_M X) + C 4^\theta \mathrm{dist}(w_0, P_M X)^\theta.$$

$\square$

In order to define a continuous dynamic everywhere we extend the map f outside of $P_M X$ continuously in the following manner. To simplify the notation, we set for $w \in P_M H$

$$B_w \doteq B(w, \mathrm{dist}_H(w, P_M X)) \qquad (10.2.10)$$

and define

$$\bar{f}(y) \doteq \begin{cases} f(y) & \text{if } y \in P_M X, \\ \frac{1}{\mathrm{vol}(B_y)} \int_{B_y} f(y')\, dy' & \text{if } y \notin P_M X. \end{cases} \qquad (10.2.11)$$

Lemma 10.7. $\bar{f}$ as defined in (10.2.11) is Hölder continuous from $P_M H$ into H and locally Lipschitz continuous from $P_M H \backslash P_M X$ into $H \backslash X$.

Proof. We will consider three cases. If w and w_0 both belong to $P_M H \backslash P_M X$, then

$$|\bar{f}(w) - \bar{f}(w_0)| = \left| \frac{1}{\text{vol}(B_w)} \int_{B_w} \bar{f}(y)\, dy - \frac{1}{\text{vol}(B_{w_0})} \int_{B_{w_0}} \bar{f}(y)\, dy \right|$$

$$\leq \left| \left(\frac{1}{\text{vol}(B_w)} - \frac{1}{\text{vol}(B_{w_0})} \right) \right| \int_{B_w} |\bar{f}(y)|\, dy$$

$$+ \frac{1}{\text{vol}(B_{w_0})} \left(\int_{B_w \Delta B_{w_0}} |\bar{f}(y)|\, dy \right)$$

$$\leq \frac{C}{\text{vol}(B_w)} |d_0^{\tilde{N}} - d^{\tilde{N}}|$$

$$+ \frac{C_1}{\text{vol}(B_{w_0})} \text{vol}(B_w \Delta B_{w_0}), \tag{10.2.12}$$

where we have set

$$d_0 = \text{dist}(w_0, P_M X) \quad \text{and} \quad d = \text{dist}(w, P_M X), \tag{10.2.13}$$

Δ is the symmetric set difference and C and C_1 are constants that depend on $\bar{f}$, which are locally bounded. Let $d_1 = \min\{d_0, d\}$, then there exist constants c and c_1 that might be unbounded as $d_1 \to 0$ and that depend on d_0, d and $\tilde{N}$ such that

$$|\bar{f}(w) - \bar{f}(w_0)|_H \leq c|d_0 - d| + c_1|w - w_0|_H \leq k|w - w_0|_H. \tag{10.2.14}$$

In the final inequality, we have used the fact that the distance function is Lipschitz. (Note that $k = c + c_1$ does blow up as $d_1 \to 0$. This is the reason why we have only the local Lipschitz property for $\bar{f}$ on $P_M H \backslash P_M X$. However, the Hölder exponent θ_0 is universally 1 in this case.)

Next, we consider the case where $w \notin P_M X$ and $w' \in B_w$. Then by the definition of f, $f(w) - f(\nu(w)) = w - \nu(w)$, hence

$$|w' - w|_H \leq \text{dist}(w, P_M X) \doteq d \tag{10.2.15}$$

implies, through (10.2.6), that

$$|f(w') - f(w)|_H \leq d + C4^\theta d^\theta. \tag{10.2.16}$$

On the other hand, from the definition of f and (10.2.16),

$$|f(w') - f(\nu(w))|_H \leq |f(w') - f(w)|_H + |f(w) - f(\nu(w))|_H$$
$$\leq d + C4^\theta d^\theta + |w - \nu(w)|_H$$
$$= 2d + C4^\theta d^\theta. \tag{10.2.17}$$

Hence,
$$|\bar{f}(w) - f(\nu(w))|_H \leq \frac{1}{\text{vol}(B_w)} \int_{B_w} |f(w') - f(\nu(w))|_H \, dw'$$
$$\leq 2d + C4^\theta d^\theta \leq C_1 d^\theta. \qquad (10.2.18)$$

Consequently, for $w \notin P_M X$ and $P_M x \in P_M X$,
$$|\bar{f}(w) - f(Px)|_H \leq |\bar{f}(w) - f(\nu(w))|_H + |f(\nu(w)) - f(P_M x)|_H$$
$$\leq C_1 d^\theta + C|\nu(w) - P_M x|_H^\theta$$
$$\leq C_1 |\nu(w) - P_M x|_H^\theta + C(|\nu(w) - w| + |w - P_M x|)^\theta$$
$$\leq (C_1 + 2^\theta C)|\nu(w) - P_M x|_H^\theta =$$
$$C_2 |\nu(w) - P_M x|_H^\theta. \qquad (10.2.19)$$

Let us remark that, although we have proven that $\bar{f}$ is Lipschitz on $P_M H \setminus P_M X$, the Lipschitz constant of $\bar{f}$ may increase without bound as we approach to the boundary of $P_M X$. Therefore, we still need to prove the Hölder continuity of $\bar{f}$ when w and w_0 are in $P_M H \setminus P_M X$. It will suffice to consider the case where
$$0 < d_0 = \text{dist}(w_0, P_M X) \leq d = \text{dist}(w, P_M X) \leq 1 \qquad (10.2.20)$$
i.e., close enough to $P_M X$. We will separate this into two subcases:

If $|w - w_0|_H \geq \frac{1}{4} d^\alpha$, for $\alpha = \tilde{N} + 1$, then it follows from (10.2.19) that
$$|\bar{f}(w) - \bar{f}(w_0)|_H \leq |\bar{f}(w) - f(\nu(w))|_H + |f(\nu(w)) - w_0|_H$$
$$\leq C_2 |w - \nu(w)|_H^\theta + C_2 |\nu(w) - w_0|_H^\theta$$
$$\leq C_2 d^\theta + C_2(|\nu(w) - w|_H + |w - w_0|_H)^\theta$$
$$\leq C_2 d^\theta + C_2(d + |w - w_0|_H)^\theta$$
$$\leq C_2 4^{\theta/\alpha} |w - w_0|_H^{\theta/\alpha} + C_2(4^{1/\alpha}|w - w_0|_H^{1/\alpha} + |w - w_0|_H)^\theta$$
$$\leq C_3 |w - w_0|_H^{\theta/\alpha}. \qquad (10.2.21)$$

Finally, for the subcase $|w - w_0|_H \leq \min\{\frac{1}{4} d^\alpha, \frac{1}{4} d_0^\alpha\}$, with $\alpha = \tilde{N} + 1$, we note that
$$|\bar{f}(w) - \bar{f}(w_0)|_H \leq \left| \frac{1}{\text{vol}(B_w)} - \frac{1}{\text{vol}(B_{w_0})} \right| C_4 \text{vol}(B_{w_0}) + \frac{C_4}{\text{vol}(B_w)} \text{vol}(B_{w_0} \Delta B_w)$$
$$\leq \frac{2C_4}{\text{vol}(B_w)} \text{vol}(B_{w_0} \Delta B_w) = \frac{C_5}{d^{\tilde{N}}} \text{vol}(B_{w_0} \Delta B_w)$$
$$\leq C_6 \frac{(d^{\tilde{N}-1} + d_0^{\tilde{N}-1})}{d^{\tilde{N}}} |w - w_0|_H = \frac{C_7}{d^{\tilde{N}}} |w - w_0|_H$$
$$\leq \frac{2C_7}{4^{\tilde{N}/\tilde{N}+1}} |w - w_0|_H^{1/\tilde{N}+1}, \qquad (10.2.22)$$

where we have utilized the assumption on $|w - w_0|_H$. In all the cases, the worst Hölder exponent is $\theta/\alpha = \theta/\tilde{N} + 1$. □

We now derive an estimate on the distance of $\bar{f}(w)$ to X in H.

Corollary 10.5. *For w in $P_M H$,*

$$\operatorname{dist}_H(\bar{f}(w), X) \leq 2\operatorname{dist}_H(w, P_M X) + 4^\theta C \operatorname{dist}_H(w, P_M X)^\theta, \qquad (10.2.23)$$

with the constants C and θ as defined in (10.2.1).

Proof. The fact that the function $w \to \operatorname{dist}_H(w, X)$ is Lipschitz implies that

$$\operatorname{dist}_H(\bar{f}(w), X) \leq \operatorname{dist}_H(f(w), X) + |f(w) - \bar{f}(w)|_H. \qquad (10.2.24)$$

Also, we deduce from Lemma 10.5 that $\operatorname{dist}_H(f(w), X) = \operatorname{dist}_{P_M H}(w, P_M X)$. Therefore, $|w - w'| \leq \operatorname{dist}(w, P_M X)$ with

$$|f(w) - \bar{f}(w)| \leq \frac{1}{\operatorname{vol}(B_w)} \int_{B_w} |f(w) - f(w')|_H \, dw' \qquad (10.2.25)$$

implies, via Lemma 10.6, that

$$|f(w) - \bar{f}(w)| \leq \operatorname{dist}(w, P_M X) + C 4^\theta \operatorname{dist}(w, P_M X)^\theta \qquad (10.2.26)$$

and (10.2.23) follows. $\square$

Consider now the generalized dynamical system that arises from the system of ODE's considered in (10.1.12). With the help of the assumption (H_0) that guarantees a Hölder continuous inverse Φ to P_M and the continuous lifting $\bar{f}$ from $P_M H$ into H defined by (10.2.11), we can continuously lift any trajectory $x(t)$ into a trajectory $\bar{f}(x(t))$. Then, it follows from the previous corollary that:

Corollary 10.6. *Let $y(t)$ be a trajectory satisfying (10.1.19). Then $t \to \bar{f}(y(t))$ is continuous from $\mathbf{R}^+$ to H and satisfies*

$$\operatorname{dist}_H(\bar{f}(y(t)), X) \leq 2|P_M y_0|_H e^{-\alpha t} + C 4^\theta [|P_M y_0|_H e^{-\alpha t}]^\theta. \qquad (10.2.27)$$

In conclusion, from the lifting $\bar{f}$, we obtain a finite dimensional generalized dynamical system in H, which is *inertially equivalent to the original dynamical system* that arises from (10.1.1). Both systems are, of course, identical inside X. The key assumption is the hypothesis (H_0). In Appendix A, Proposition 1, we prove the Hölder-Mañé theorem for compact subsets of $\mathbf{R}^N$. Our results on inertially equivalent dynamical systems then hold for arbitrarily large Galerkin approximations (see Chapter 4) as well as for those evolution equations that admit an inertial manifold, see Chapter 9. The dimension of the inertially equivalent dynamical system is that of the Mañé's projection P_M, hence of much lower than the dimension N of $\mathbf{R}^N$. Otherwise, the problem of finding a finite dimensional generalized dynamical system inertially equivalent to (10.1.1) in H remains open. For large systems of ODE's we do have a definitive result:

Theorem 10.2. *Let X be an exponential attractor for a system in some arbitrarily large $\mathbf{R}^N$, let $d_F(X) < D < (N-1)/2$. Then there exists an inertially equivalent generalized dynamical system of dimension $\tilde{N} = [2D+1]$.*

Note also that if P_M is an arbitrarily Mañé projection then our discussion leads immediately to:

Theorem 10.3. *Let X be the finite dimensional global attractor of an evolution equation of the form (10.1.1) such that $d_H(X) < D$. Then there exists a generalized dynamical system of dimension $[[2D+1]] = \tilde{N}$ that is asymptotically equivalent to the original one and has X as its global attractor.*

Appendix A
A Constructive Proof of Mañé's Theorem for Hilbert Spaces

In a paper on compact attractors for non-linear maps, Mañé made the following interesting observation:

If X is a compact subset of a Banach space E such that the Hausdorff dimension of X is finite, say $d = d_H(X)$, then the set of projections $P : E \to F$, where $+\infty > \dim_E F > 2d + 1$, admits a G_δ dense subset consisting of projections that are injective on X (see [Ma3], Lemma 1.1).

As stated, the theorem is not true due to an unusual characteristic of Hausdorff dimension. Namely, the Hausdorff dimension of a Cartesian product of two sets is not necessarily less than or equal to the sum of Hausdorff dimensions of the respective sets (see Falconer [Fa2], pg. 97, Example 7.8). Therefore, it is not sufficient to assume that X has finite Hausdorff dimension but rather $X \times X$ does. So that Mañé's theorem should read as:

Modified Mañé's Theorem. *Let $X \subseteq E$ be a compact set such that $d' = d_H(X \times X) < +\infty$, then the set of projections $P : E \to F$, where F is finite dimensional and $\dim_E F > d' + 1$, admits a G_δ dense subset consisting of projections that are injective on X.*

An example of a set with zero Hausdorff dimension such that there exists no proper injective projection on it is supplied by Kan in [SYC] for finite dimensional setting. At the end of the proof, we follow Ben-Artzi et al. [BEFN] and furnish a similar example in the Hilbert space setting. Clearly, the Hausdorff dimension of the Cartesian product of this set with itself cannot be finite.

Mañé's proof relied on Baire's Category theorem, hence was nonconstructive in nature. However, for the special case when $E = H$ is a separable Hilbert space, it is possible to furnish a direct proof of his result (see Corollary A. 1 and the proof thereafter). We start with the definitions of Hausdorff and Fractal dimension for a compact subset of H.

Definition A.1. *If A is a compact subset of H, a separable Hilbert space,* then we set

$$\mu_{d,\epsilon}(A) \doteq \inf\left\{\sum_{i=1}^{k} r_i^d : r_i \leq \epsilon \text{ and } A \subseteq \bigcup_{i=1}^{k} B_{r_i}\right\}, \qquad (A.1)$$

where B_{r_i} denotes a ball of radius r_i in H.

Clearly, $\mu_{d,\epsilon}(A)$ increases as ϵ decreases, since the set of admissible covers will shrink as ϵ decreases.

Definition A.2. Let

$$\mu_d(A) = \sup_{\epsilon>0} \mu_{d,\epsilon}(A) = \lim_{\epsilon\to 0+} \mu_{d,\epsilon}(A). \qquad (A.2)$$

It follows from the definitions that, if $\mu_d(A)$ is finite then $\mu_c(A) = 0$, for $c < d$. On the other hand, if $\mu_d(A) = +\infty$ then $\mu_e(A) = +\infty$, for $e > d$. Consequently, the following definition is justified.

Definition A.3. The *Hausdorff dimension* of a compact set A is defined by

$$d_H(A) = \inf\{d > 0 : \mu_d(A) = 0\}. \qquad (A.3)$$

A stronger measure of dimension is furnished by the concept of Fractal dimension.

Definition A.4. Let A be a compact subset of H, let

$$N_\epsilon(A) = \text{the minimum number of balls of} \\ \text{radii } \leq r \text{ that is necessary to cover } A. \qquad (A.4)$$

Then the *Fractal dimension* of A, $d_F(A)$, is defined by

$$d_F(A) = \limsup_{\epsilon\to 0} \frac{\log N_\epsilon(A)}{\log(1/\epsilon)}. \qquad (A.5)$$

Notation. We will use $\overline{\lim}_{\epsilon\to 0}$ instead of $\limsup_{\epsilon\to 0}$.

The following Lemma gives a useful equivalent formulation for Fractal dimension.

Lemma A.1. Let

$$\mu_{d,F}(A) = \overline{\lim}_{\epsilon\to 0} \epsilon^d N_\epsilon(A) \qquad (A.6)$$

then

$$d_F(A) = \inf\{d > 0 : \mu_{d,F}(A) = 0\}. \qquad (A.7)$$

Proof. Let $D = \inf\{d > 0 : \mu_{d,F}(A) = 0\}$. Assume that $e > d > d_F(A)$, then by the definition of Fractal dimension, there exists r_0 such that for $r < r_0$

$$\log N_r(A) < d\log(1/r). \qquad (A.8)$$

Hence, for $r < r_0$,

Exponential Attractors for Dissipative Evolution Equations

$$N_r(A) < 1/r^d. \tag{A.9}$$

By (A.6)

$$\mu_{e,F}(A) \leq \overline{\lim}_{r \to 0} r^e r^{-d} = 0. \tag{A.10}$$

So that, $D < e$. Since $e > d_F(A)$ was arbitrary $d_F(A) \geq D$. Conversely, let $c < d < d_F(A)$. Then there exist infinitely many r_i's such that

$$\log N_{r_i}(A) > d \log(1/r_i). \tag{A.11}$$

In other words,

$$r_i^d N_{r_i}(A) > 1. \tag{A.12}$$

Consequently,

$$\mu_{c,F}(A) \geq \overline{\lim}_{i \to \infty} r_i^c N_{r_i}(A) \tag{A.13}$$
$$\geq \overline{\lim}_{i \to \infty} r_i^c r_i^{-d} > 1.$$

hat is, for every $d < d_F(A)$, $\mu_{d,F}(A) > 1$, therefore $d_F(A) \leq D$. □

Clearly, $\mu_{d,F}(A) \leq \mu_d(A)$ as given in (A.2) and (A.6). It follows from Lemma 1, that

$$d_H(A) \leq d_F(A). \tag{A.14}$$

Furthermore, the Hausdorff dimension of a countable set is always 0, whereas the Fractal dimension of such a set need not even be finite. We start with an infinite dimensional example:

Example A.1. Let H be an infinite dimensional separable Hilbert space. Let $\{e_n\}_{n=1}^\infty$ be an orthonormal basis for H. Consider

$$A = \left\{\frac{1}{\log n} e_n : n = 2, 3, \ldots \right\} \cup \{0\}. \tag{A.15}$$

Let

$$r_m = 1/\sqrt{2} \log m, \tag{A.16}$$

then, since $|e_n/\log n - e_k/\log k|_H^2 = \frac{1}{(\log n)^2} + \frac{1}{(\log k)^2} \geq \frac{2}{(\log n)^2}$ for $n > k$, the first $m - 1$ elements from A must belong to distinct r_m-balls. Hence,

$$N_{r_m}(A) \geq m - 1. \tag{A.17}$$

So that, $d_F(A) \geq \overline{\lim}_{m \to \infty} \frac{\log(N_{r_m}(A))}{\log(1/r_m)} \geq \overline{\lim}_{m \to \infty} \frac{\log(m-1)}{\log(\sqrt{2} \log m)} = +\infty$. Hence, $d_F(A) = +\infty$ but $d_H(A) = 0$.

The second example of a set with zero Hausdorff dimension and nonzero fractal dimension is furnished in Chapter 7.

Example A.2. Let $\mathcal{E}_0$ be the subset of $\mathbf{R}$ that is defined by

$$\mathcal{E}_0 = \left\{\frac{k}{2^m} : m = 0, 1, 2, \ldots \text{ and } k \text{ is a natural number s.t.} k \leq \frac{2^m}{m}\right\}.$$

Clearly, $\mathcal{E}_0$ is countable and then has zero Hausdorff dimension. On the other hand, $\mathcal{E}_0 \subseteq \mathbf{R}$, therefore $d_F(\mathcal{E}_0) \leq 1$. We claim that $d_F(\mathcal{E}_0) = 1$. Given $\epsilon > 0$, choose $m_0 = m_0(\epsilon)$ such that

$$\frac{1}{2^{m_0+1}} < 2\epsilon < \frac{1}{2^{m_0}}.$$

Since 0 is the only limit point of $\mathcal{E}_0$, any finite covering of $\mathcal{E}_0$ will contain a set U_0 that contains all but finitely many points of $\mathcal{E}_0$. Consider an ϵ-covering of $\mathcal{E}_0$, let B_0 be the ball that contains 0. Then 2^{-m_0} is not in B_0 by the choice of ϵ; furthermore, all the other ϵ-balls B_i can only include at most one of the points $k2^{-m_0}$, where $km_0 \leq 2^{m_0}$. Therefore, the number of ϵ-balls is at least $N+1$, where

$$N \geq \operatorname{card}\{k : k \leq 2^{m_0}/m_0\}.$$

Consequently,

$$\frac{\ln N_\epsilon(\mathcal{E}_0)}{\ln(1/\epsilon)} \geq \frac{\ln(2^{m_0}/m_0)}{(m_0+2)(\ln 2)} = \frac{m_0(\ln 2) - \ln m_0}{(m_0+2)(\ln 2)}$$

as $\epsilon \to 0$, $m_0 \to \infty$, hence

$$d_F(\mathcal{E}_0) \geq \lim_{m_0 \to \infty} \frac{m_0(\ln 2) - \ln m_0}{(m_0+2)(\ln 2)} = 1.$$

The third example is inspired by a similar example in K. Falconer ([Fa2], page 97, Example 7.8) and the example of I. Kan (quoted in [SYC]). Here the perils of taking Cartesian products of sets of zero Hausdorff dimension is amply revealed. The fourth example is due to Kan in $\mathbf{R}^m$; we extend this example to the Hilbert space setting as well.

Example A.3. One can construct two sets E and F in $[0,1]$ such that

$$d_H(E) = d_H(F) = 0$$

but

$$d_H(E \times F) \geq 1.$$

For this construction see [Fa2], page 97; also the example of J. Kan, as quoted in Sauer et al. [SYC].

The examples discussed above already suggest that if $d_F(A) = d < +\infty$ instead of $d_H(A) = d$ then one should be able to obtain a stronger conclusion. First, we give the proof of the Modified Mañé's theorem for Hausdorff dimension based on the following.

Theorem A.1. *Let H be a separable Hilbert space, let Y be a compact subset of H such that $\mu_m(Y) = 0$. If P_0 is an orthogonal projection with rank equal to $m+1$, then for every $\delta \in (0,1)$ there exists an orthogonal projection $P = P(\delta)$ such that*

$$\|P - P_0\| \leq \delta, \tag{A.18}$$

and
$$\text{Ker } P \cap Y = \{0\}. \tag{A.19}$$

A simple application of this theorem gives the following weak version of Modified Mañé's theorem for Hilbert Spaces:

Corollary A.1. *Let X be a compact subset of H such that $\mu_{k'}(X \times X) = 0$. Also let P_0 be an orthogonal projection in H of rank equal to $k' + 1$. Then for every $\delta \in (0,1)$ there exists $P = P(\delta)$ an orthogonal projection in H such that*
$$\|P - P_0\| \leq \delta, \tag{A.20}$$
and
$$P|_X \text{ is injective.} \tag{A.21}$$

Proof (of Corollary A.1). Assuming for the moment Theorem A.1, we set
$$Y \doteq X - X = \{x_1 - x_2 : x_1, x_2 \in X\}. \tag{A.22}$$
By assumption, $\mu_{k'}(X \times X) = 0$. The map $F : X \times X \to Y$ defined by
$$F(x_1, x_2) = x_2 - x_1 \tag{A.23}$$
is Lipschitz, hence $\mu_{k'}(Y) = \mu_{k'}(F(X \times X)) \leq \mu_{k'}(X \times X) = 0$, and Y is compact. Applying Theorem 1 with $m = k'$, we obtain $P = P(\delta)$ such that
$$\|P - P_0\| \leq \delta \quad \text{and} \quad \text{Ker } P \cap Y = \{0\}. \tag{A.24}$$
By definition of Y, if x_1, x_2 is in X then $x_2 - x_1 \in Y$, hence
$$P(x_2 - x_1) = 0 \text{ implies that } x_2 = x_1. \tag{A.25}$$
$\square$

Proof of the Modified Mañé's Theorem. The density of the orthogonal projections which are injective on X easily implies the stronger statement that those projections constitute a G_δ-set. To prove this statement, we set
$$F_n = \{P = \text{orthogonal projection of rank } k' + 1 : \text{there exist } x_1, x_2 \in X$$
$$\text{such that } |x_1 - x_2| \geq \tfrac{1}{n} \text{ and } Px_1 = Px_2\}$$
then the compactness of X implies that F_n is closed with respect to operator norm topology. Furthermore, for $P_0 \in F_n$, the δ-ball, with $\delta \in (0,1)$,
$$\mathcal{B}(p_0, \Delta) = \{Q : Q \text{ is an orthogonal projection and } \|Q - P_0\| < \delta\}$$
must necessarily contain a projection P that is not in F_n, since, by the density of projections that are injective on X, there exists an orthogonal projection Q such that $\|Q - P_0\| < \delta$ and $Qx_1 \neq Qx_2$ whenever $x_1 \neq x_2$ in X. Consequently, F_n's are closed and nowhere dense. Therefore, the complement of
$$\mathcal{F} = \bigcup_{n=1}^{\infty} F_n$$
in the set of orthogonal projections that have rank $k' + 1$ is a G_δ-set. Note, however that if a rank-$(k' + 1)$ projection $P \notin \mathcal{F}$ then for every $x_1, x_2 \in \delta$ such that $x_1 - x_2 \neq 0, Px_1 \neq Px_2$, i.e. P is injective on X. $\square$

Returning back to the proof of the Theorem 1, we will construct $P = P(\delta)$ inductively; we proceed with a sequence of lemmas from which the theorem will follow.

Lemma A.2. *Let Z be a compact subset of $\mathbf{R}^N$ satisfying*

$$R \cdot Z = Z \quad \text{and} \quad \mu_{m+1}(Z) = 0 \tag{A.26}$$

for some $m < N - 1$. If P_0 is an orthogonal projection of $\mathbf{R}^N$ of rank $m+1$, then for every $\eta \in (0,1)$ and for every non-zero vector b in $\mathbf{R}^N$, there exists a, not in Z, such that

$$|a - b| < \eta \quad \text{and} \quad |a| = |b|. \tag{A.27}$$

Lemma A.3. *Let Y be a compact subset of $\mathbf{R}^N$ such that $\mu_m(Y) = 0$. If P_0 is a rank-$m+1$ orthogonal projection in $\mathbf{R}^N$ then for every $\delta \in (0,1)$, there exists an orthogonal projection $P = P(\delta)$ in $\mathbf{R}^N$ such that*

$$\|P - P_0\| \leq \delta \quad \text{and} \quad \text{Ker } P \cap Y = \{0\}. \tag{A.28}$$

Lemma A.4. *Let H be a real separable Hilbert space and let Y be a compact subset of H such that $\mu_m(Y) = 0$. Given any orthogonal projection P_0 in H of rank $m+1$, and an orthonormal basis $\{e_j\}_{j=1}^\infty$ of $(I - P_0)H$, let P_n be the orthogonal projection defined by*

$$P_n \doteq P_0 + e_1^* \otimes e_1 + \cdots + e_n^* \otimes e_n, \tag{A.29}$$

then for any δ in $(0,1)$, there exist $P = P(\delta)$ such that

$$\|P - P_0\| \leq \delta \quad , \quad P \leq P_n; \tag{A.30}$$

and

$$\text{Ker } P \cap Y \subseteq \text{Ker } P_n. \tag{A.31}$$

Notation. In the above lemma, for x and y in H, $x^* \otimes y = P$, stands for the rank one projection that maps z into $(x, z)_H y$.

We start proving the lemmas in their stated order.

Proof (of Lemma A.2). Let b be a non-zero vector in $\mathbf{R}^N$. Since $\mu_{m+1}(P_0 Z) \leq \mu_{m+1}(Z) = 0$, the set $Z_0 = P_0 H \backslash P_0 Z$ has to be everywhere dense in $P_0 \mathbf{R}^N$. By slightly perturbing b, if necessary, one can also assume that $P_0 b \neq 0$, without changing its norm. Hence, there exists a_0 in Z_0 such that

$$|a_0 - P_0 b| \leq \frac{\eta}{2} \frac{|P_0 b|}{|P_0 b| + 1}. \tag{A.32}$$

Since $\eta < 1$, $a_0 \neq 0$. Define
$$a = ta_0 + (I - P_0)b, \tag{A.33}$$
with $t = |P_0 b|/|a_0|$. Then, using $\mathbf{R}Z = Z$,
$$P_0 a = tP_0 a_0 = ta_0 \notin tP_0 Z = P_0 Z \tag{A.34}$$
thus $a \notin Z$. Moreover,
$$\begin{aligned}|a - b| &= |ta_0 - P_0 b| \leq |a_0 - P_0 b| + |1 - t||a_0| \\ &\leq \frac{\eta}{2} + \left|1 - \frac{|P_0 b|}{|a_0|}\right||a_0| \\ &\leq \frac{\eta}{2} + ||a_0| - |P_0 b|| \\ &< \eta,\end{aligned} \tag{A.35}$$
and
$$\begin{aligned}|a|^2 &= t^2|P_0 a_0|^2 + |(I - P_0)b|^2 = t^2|a|^2 + |(I - P_0)b|^2 \\ &= |P_0 b|^2 + |(I - P_0 b)|^2 = |b|^2.\end{aligned} \tag{A.36}$$
$\square$

Proof (of Lemma A.3). Let $Z = \mathbf{R} \cdot Y$, then $\mu_m(Y) = 0$ implies that $\mu_{m+1}(Z) = 0$. By virtue of Lemma A.2, for any unit vector e orthogonal to $P_0 H$, there exists a unit vector a, outside of Z such that
$$|a - e| \leq \epsilon < \frac{\delta/4}{N - m - 1}. \tag{A.37}$$
Let
$$Q_1 = I - a^* \otimes a, \tag{A.38}$$
then, $y \in \operatorname{Ker} Q_1 \cap Y$ implies that $(y, a)a = y$. Since $a \notin Z = \mathbf{R} \cdot Y$, y has to be zero. That is,
$$\operatorname{Ker} Q_1 \cap Y = \{0\}. \tag{A.39}$$
In this case, since $|a| = 1$ and $P_0 e = 0$
$$\|P_0 Q_1 - P_0\| = |P_0 a| = |P_0(a - e)| \leq |a - e| \leq \epsilon. \tag{A.40}$$
We now proceed by induction, assume that there exists an orthogonal projection Q_k of rank $N - k$, which is greater than $m + 1$, such that
$$\|P_0 Q_k - P_0\| \leq k\epsilon \text{ and } \operatorname{Ker} Q_k \cap Y = \{0\}. \tag{A.41}$$
Let e be a unit vector in $Q_k \mathbf{R}^N$ orthogonal to $P_0 \mathbf{R}^N$. Again by Lemma A.2, there exists a unit vector a outside $Q_k Z$ such that
$$|a - e| \leq \epsilon. \tag{A.42}$$

Setting,
$$Q_{k+1} = Q_k - a^* \otimes a, \tag{A.43}$$

we see that
$$\|P_0 Q_{k+1} - P_0\| \le \|P_0 Q_k - P_0\| + |P_0 a|$$
$$\le k\epsilon + |P_0(a-e)| \le (k+1)\epsilon. \tag{A.44}$$

Thus, by induction we have shown that:
There exists an orthogonal projection $P = Q_{N-m-1}$ such that
$$\text{rank } P = m+1, \tag{A.45}$$
$$\|P_0 P - P_0\| \le (N-m-1)\epsilon = \eta < \delta/4, \tag{A.46}$$

and
$$\text{Ker } P \cap Y = \{0\}. \tag{A.47}$$

From (A.46) it follows that
$$\|P P_0 - P_0\| = \|P_0 P - P_0\| < \delta/4 < 1/4. \tag{A.48}$$

Therefore, Ker $P \cap P_0 \mathbf{R}^N = \{0\}$, and thus dim $P P_0 \mathbf{R}^N = $ dim $P_0 \mathbf{R}^N = $ dim $P \mathbf{R}^N$. It follows that $P P_0 \mathbf{R}^N = P \mathbf{R}^N$. Hence for any z in $\mathbf{R}^N$ there exists x such that
$$x = P_0 x \quad \text{and} \quad Pz = Px. \tag{A.49}$$

Now, we start with z in Ker P_0 and choose x as in (A.49), then by (A.48)
$$|P_0 P(z-x) - P_0(z-x)| \le \delta/4 |z-x|, \tag{A.50}$$

thus, by (A.49) and $P_0 z = 0$,
$$x = P_0 x = P_0(x-z) = P_0(x-z) + P_0 P(z-x) - P_0 P(z-x)$$
$$= P_0(x-z) + P_0 P(z-x) - P_0(Pz - Px) \tag{A.51}$$
$$= P_0(x-z) + P_0 P(z-x).$$

Hence, it follows from (A.51) and (A.50) that
$$|x|^2 \le |P_0 P(z-x) - P_0(z-x)|^2 \le (\delta/4)^2 |z-x|^2$$
$$\le (\delta/4)^2 (|z|^2 + |x|^2). \tag{A.52}$$

after simplification and using $\delta < 1$, we obtain
$$|x| \le \frac{(\delta/4)}{\sqrt{1-(\delta/4)^2}} |z| \le \frac{\delta}{\sqrt{15}} |z| \le \frac{\delta}{3} |z| \tag{A.53}$$

Finally, from (A.49) and (A.53),

$$|Pz| = |Px| \leq |x| \leq \frac{\delta}{4}|z|. \qquad (A.54)$$

Consequently, by (A.48) and (A.54)

$$\|P - P_0\| \leq \|PP_0 - P_0\| + \|P(I - P_0)\| \qquad (A.55)$$
$$\leq \delta/4 + \delta/3 \leq \delta.$$

Proof (of Lemma A.4). Given Y a compact subset of H, with $\mu_m(Y) = 0$, and P_0 an orthogonal projection of rank $m+1$, we set as in (A.29)

$$P_n \doteq P_0 + e_1^* \otimes e_1 + e_2^* \otimes e_2 + \cdots + e_n^* \otimes e_n, \qquad (A.56)$$

and also
$$Y_n = P_n Y. \qquad (A.57)$$

Then Y_n is a compact subset of $P_n H$ with $\mu_m(Y_n) = 0$. Applying Lemma A.3 to $Y = Y_n$, $P_0 = P_0 P_n$ we get, for any $\delta \in (0,1)$, there exists P an orthogonal projection on $P_n H$ such that

$$\|P - P_0 P_n\| \leq \delta, \qquad (A.58)$$

and
$$\text{Ker } P \cap P_n Y = \{0\}. \qquad (A.59)$$

It follows from (A.59) that in H

$$\text{Ker } P' \cap Y \subseteq \text{Ker } P_n. \qquad (A.60)$$

where P' is the orthogonal projection in H with $P'H = P(P_n H)$. Clearly, from the definition of P', $P' \leq P_n$. Finally, $P' \leq P_n$, (A.58) and $P_0 P_n = P_0$ implies that

$$\|P' - P_0\| \leq \|P' P_n - P_0 P_n\| \leq \delta. \qquad (A.61)$$

□

Proof (of Theorem A.1). Let Y be a compact subset of H such that $\mu_m(Y) = 0$, let P_0 be a rank-$(m+1)$ projection. Since multiplying Y by a small constant will change neither $\mu_m(Y) = 0$, nor Ker $P \cap Y = \{0\}$, we can assume that

$$Y \subset \overline{B}_1^H(0). \qquad (A.62)$$

Let $\epsilon > 0$, let $\{e_j\}_{j=1}^\infty$ be an orthonormal basis for $(I - P_0)H$ and set for $n = 1, 2, \ldots$

$$P_n = P_0 + e_1^* \otimes e_1 + e_2^* \otimes e_2 + \cdots + e_n^* \otimes e_n \qquad (A.63)$$

By applying Lemma A.4 to P_0, P_1 and with $\delta = \eta_1 = \epsilon/4$ we obtain an orthogonal projection Q_1 such that

$$\|Q_1 - P_0\| \leq \eta_1, \qquad Q_1 \leq P_1; \tag{A.64}$$

and

$$\text{Ker } Q_1 \cap Y \subseteq \text{Ker } P_1. \tag{A.65}$$

Next, we consider:

$$Y_1 \doteq \left\{ y \in P_1 Y : |y| \geq \frac{1}{2} \right\} \tag{A.66}$$

Setting

$$F_1(y) = |Q_1 y|^{-1} \tag{A.67}$$

it is easy to see that F_1 is everywhere defined and continuous on Y_1 hence must achieve its maximum on Y_1

$$\theta_1^{-1} \doteq \max\{F_1(y) : y \in Y_1\}. \tag{A.68}$$

Applying Lemma A.4 now to Q_1, P_2 with

$$\delta = \eta_2 \doteq \min\left\{ \epsilon/4^2, \theta_1/4 \right\}, \tag{A.69}$$

we obtain Q_2 such that

$$\|Q_2 - Q_1\| \leq \eta_2 \quad \text{and} \quad Q_2 \leq P_2, \tag{A.70}$$

and

$$\text{Ker } Q_2 \cap Y \subseteq \text{Ker } P_2.$$

Continuing in this manner, we set

$$Y_2 = \{y \in P_2 Y : |y| \geq 1/2^2\}. \tag{A.71}$$

Then

$$\theta_2^{-1} \doteq \max\{F_2(y) : y \in Y_2\} \tag{A.72}$$

where

$$F_2(y) \doteq |Q_2 y|^{-1} \tag{A.73}$$

is well-defined and continuous on Y_2. Hence, applying Lemma A.4 to Q_2, P_3 with

$$\delta = \eta_3 = \min\{\epsilon/4^3, \theta_1/4^2, \theta_2/4^2\} \tag{A.74}$$

we thus obtain by iteration orthogonal projections $Q_0 = P_0, Q_1, Q_2, \ldots$ satisfying

$$\|Q_{j+1} - Q_j\| \leq \eta_{j+1} = \min\{\epsilon/4^{j+1}, \theta_1/4^2, \theta_2/4^3, \ldots, \theta_j/4^j\}, \tag{A.75}$$

$$Q_{j+1} \leq P_{j+1} \quad \text{and} \quad \text{Ker } Q_{j+1} \cap Y \subseteq \text{Ker } P_{j+1}, \tag{A.76}$$

where θ_j's are recursively defined by $\theta_j^{-1} = \max\{|Q_j y|^{-1} : y \in Y_j\}$ where $Y_j = \{y \in P_j Y : |y| \geq 1/2^j\}$.

The sequence $\{Q_j\}$ is clearly a Cauchy sequence in norm topology, thus the limit of Q_j's as $j \to \infty$ exists, we denote it by P, i.e.

$$\|Q_j - P\| \to 0 \text{ as } j \to \infty \tag{A.77}$$

On the other hand,

$$\|P - P_0\| = \lim_{j \to \infty} \|Q_j - Q_0\| \leq \sum_{j=1}^{\infty} \frac{\epsilon}{4^j} = \frac{\epsilon}{3} < \epsilon. \tag{A.78}$$

Now let y be a non-zero element in Y, since by (A.63), $P_n y \to y$, as $n \to \infty$

$$\lim_{n \to \infty} |P_n y| = |y| > 0 \tag{A.79}$$

hence, there exists $j \geq 1$ such that

$$P_j y \in Y_j. \tag{A.80}$$

Moreover, $Q_j \leq P_j$ implies that $|Q_j y| \geq \theta_j$ and

$$|(P - Q_j)y| \leq \sum_{n=j}^{\infty} |Q_{n+1} y - Q_n y| \leq |y| \sum_{n=j}^{\infty} \eta_{n+1}$$

$$\leq |y| \sum_{n=j}^{\infty} \frac{\theta_n}{4^n} = \frac{\theta_j}{4^j} \frac{3}{4} < \frac{\theta_j}{4}. \tag{A.81}$$

Hence,

$$|Q_j y| - |Py| < \theta_j/4, \tag{A.82}$$

therefore

$$|Py| \geq \theta_j - \theta_j/4 = \frac{3}{4}\theta_j > 0. \tag{A.83}$$

□

A further strengthening of Mañé's theorem can be achieved when the underlying space is finite dimensional and the set X has finite fractal dimension. In this special case, it is possible to show that not only the projection is invertible on X, but also its inverse is Hölder continuous.

Proposition A.1. *Let Y be a compact subset of $\mathbf{R}^N$, with $d_F(Y) < D < N - 1$. Let P be an orthogonal projection on $\mathbf{R}^N$ of rank $[D+1]$. Then for every $\delta > 0$ and for every θ such that*

$$\theta < \prod_{i=1}^{N-[D+1]} \left(1 - \frac{D}{N-i}\right), \tag{A.84}$$

there exists an orthogonal projection $P_0 = P_0(\delta, \theta)$ of rank $[D+1]$ such that $\|P - P_0\| < \delta$ and for every y in Y,

$$|y| \leq C|P_0 y|^\theta, \tag{A.85}$$

where C is a constant that depends on D, N, θ and δ.

Proof. Without loss of generality, we can assume that $Y \subseteq B_1(0)$, since multiplication by a real constant will neither change the fractal dimension of Y, nor will effect the value of θ. Here as well as below we denote $B_r(a) = \{x \in \mathbb{R}^N : |x - a| \leq r\}$.

Let $r_n = 1/2^n$, and let us consider the sets

$$Y_n = \{y \in Y : r_n < |y| \leq 2r_n\}. \tag{A.86}$$

Since, $d_F(Y) < D$ there exists a cover of Y_n consisting of m_n-balls centered at a_j^n in Y_n of radius equal to ρ_n, with

$$m_n \leq c_Y (1/\rho_n)^D. \tag{A.87}$$

where

$$\rho_n \doteq (Kr_n)^{1/\theta} \quad \text{and} \quad K \doteq \min\left\{1, \frac{c_0}{2c_Y^{1/(N-1)}}\right\}, \tag{A.88}$$

and c_0 will be fixed later. For this cover,

$$\{B_{\rho_n}(a_j^n) : a_j^n \in Y_n, \quad j = 1, 2, \ldots, m_n\} \tag{A.89}$$

if we have

$$(I - P)\mathbb{R}^N \cap B_{2\rho_n}(a_j^n) = \emptyset \text{ for every } n \text{ and for } j = 1, 2, \ldots, m_n \tag{A.90}$$

then we claim that

$$|Py|^\theta \geq K|y| \quad \text{for every } y \quad \text{in } Y. \tag{A.91}$$

In order to see this, let y be in Y; so y is in Y_n for some n, hence $y \in B_{\rho_n}(a_j^n)$ for some j. Then

$$|Py| \geq |(I - P)y - a_j^n| - |a_j^n - y| \geq 2\rho_n - \rho_n = \rho_n \tag{A.92}$$

therefore

$$|Py|^\theta \geq \rho_n^\theta = Kr_n \geq \frac{K}{2}|y|. \tag{A.93}$$

Clearly, we would like to perturb P in a way to satisfy (A.90) and this would give us the desired result. Our basic step is the case when

$$Q = I - P = y \otimes y, \tag{A.94}$$

and where a projection P_0 is being searched such that
$$Q_0 = I - P_0 = y_0 \otimes y_0, \tag{A.95}$$
and satisfies (A.90), in other words
$$\mathbf{R}y_0 \cap B_{2\rho_n}(a_j^n) = \emptyset \text{ for every } n \text{ and for } j = 1, \ldots, m_n. \tag{A.96}$$
Geometrically, one can imagine the N-dimensional unit ball as a big bubble and all the small $2\rho_n$-balls as a collection of steel balls. Then, in order to satisfy (A.96) one needs a ray emanating from the origin in both directions, and missing all the steel balls. If we imagine a point light source centered at the origin then this will cast shadows of the steel balls onto the surface of the unit ball, i.e., the bubble. If we can show that these shadows do not cover all the surface then it would be possible to find a beam of light that extends in both directions outside of the bubble. This would be guaranteed if we can show that the shadowed area is less than half of the unit sphere's surface; then there would be two diametrically opposite beams piercing through the bubble's surface. So we isolate a $2\rho_m (= \rho)$-ball centered at $a_j^n = a$ and denote its shadow by $A_s(a, \rho)$ on the sphere centered at 0 and of radius s.

By proportionality, if μ_{N-1} denotes the $(N-1)$-surface measure then we have,
$$\frac{\mu_{N-1}(A_1(a,\rho))}{\mu_{N-1}(A_{|a|}(a,\rho))} = \frac{1}{|a|^{N-1}} \leq \frac{1}{r^{N-1}} \text{ with } r = rn \tag{A.97}$$
hence
$$\mu_{N-1}(A_1(a,\rho)) \leq \frac{1}{r^{N-1}} \mu_{N-1}(A_{|a|}(a,\rho))$$
$$\leq \frac{1}{r^{N-1}} \omega_{N-1} \rho^{N-1}. \tag{A.98}$$
In the last inequality, we have used the fact that the spherical sector (centered at 0) passing through a and contained in $B_\rho(a)$ has $(N-1)$-volume less than the whole surface of $B_\rho(a)$, the ρ-ball centered at a. If we now let μ denote the surface volume of all the shadows $\sum$, then

$$\mu = \mu_{N-1}\left(\bigcup_{n=1}^{\infty} \bigcup_{j=1}^{m_n} A_1(a_j^n, 2\rho_n)\right)$$
$$\leq \sum_{n=1}^{\infty} m_n \omega_{N-1} \left(\frac{2\rho_n}{r_n}\right)^{N-1} \leq \sum_{n=1}^{\infty} c_Y \left(\frac{1}{\rho_n}\right)^D \omega_{N-1} \left(\frac{2\rho_n}{r_n}\right)^{N-1}$$
$$\leq c_Y 2^{N-1} \omega_{N-1} \sum_{n=1}^{\infty} \rho_n^{N-D-1} r_n^{1-N} \tag{A.99}$$
$$= c_Y 2^{N-1} \omega_{N-1} \sum_{n=1}^{\infty} (Kr_n)^{\frac{N-D-1}{\theta}} r_n^{1-N}$$
$$\leq c_Y 2^{N-1} \omega_{N-1} K^{\frac{N-D-1}{\theta}} \sum_{n=1}^{\infty} r_n^{(N-1)(\frac{1}{\theta}-1)-\frac{D}{\theta}}.$$

Since $\theta < 1 - \frac{D}{N-1}$, $(N-1)(1-\theta) > D$ which implies that

$$\lambda \doteq (N-1)\left(\frac{1}{\theta} - 1\right) - \frac{D}{\theta} > 0 \qquad (A.100)$$

and the sum that appears in (A.99) gives by $r_n = 1/2^n$

$$\sum_{n=1}^{\infty} r_n^\lambda = \sum_{n=1}^{\infty} \left(\frac{1}{2^\lambda}\right)^n = \frac{1}{2^\lambda - 1}. \qquad (A.101)$$

Hence, (A.99) implies that

$$\begin{aligned}\mu &\le c_Y 2^{N-1} \omega_{N-1} K^{\frac{N-D-1}{\theta}} (2^\lambda - 1)^{-1} \\ &\le c_Y 2^{N-1} K^{N-1} (2^\lambda - 1)^{-1} \omega_{N-1} \end{aligned} \qquad (A.102)$$

where we have used $\theta < 1 - \frac{D}{N-1} = \frac{N-1-D}{N-1}$ and the fact that $K \le 1$. In order to obtain $\mu < \frac{1}{2}\omega_{N-1}$, we use the value of K from (A.88), with

$$c_0 = c_0(D, N, \theta) = \left(\frac{2^\lambda - 1}{2}\right)^{\frac{1}{N-1}} \qquad (A.103)$$

then

$$\mu < \frac{1}{2}\omega_{N-1}. \qquad (A.104)$$

Consequently, the existence of y_0 on the surface of the unit ball is assured, i.e., (A.96) holds. After this basic step, we let $Y_0 = P_0 Y$ and follow the same construction on $P_0 \mathbf{R}^N$ to obtain y_1 on the surface of the unit ball of $P_0 \mathbf{R}^N$. Setting

$$P_1 = I - y_1 \otimes y_1 \qquad (A.105)$$

and noting that (A.96) implies (A.93), that is

$$|y| \le C_1 |P_1 y|^{\theta_1} \quad \text{for} \quad y \in P_0 Y = Y_0. \qquad (A.106)$$

We can continue this way up to

$$N_D = [D + 1] + 1. \qquad (A.107)$$

In each case, we will require

$$\theta_i < 1 - \frac{D}{N-i} \qquad (A.108)$$

and choose C_i accordingly, to obtain in the end

$$P_\ell = I - (y_l \otimes y_l) \qquad (A.109)$$

and
$$|y| \leq C_1 C_2^{\theta_1} C_3^{\theta_1 \theta_2} \cdots C_\ell^{\theta_1 \cdots \theta_{\ell-1}} |P_\ell y|^{\theta_1 \cdot \theta_2 \cdots \theta_\ell}. \tag{A.110}$$

By the choice of θ_i's,

$$\theta = \theta_1 \cdot \theta_2 \ldots \theta_\ell < \prod_{i=1}^{\ell}\left(1 - \frac{D}{N-i}\right) = \theta_0 \tag{A.111}$$

where $\ell = N - N_D$. The rank of the operator P_ℓ is $[D+1]$, and it is the required projection P_0.

Untill now, we have only proved the existence of one orthogonal projection that has a Hölder continuous inverse. To prove the density of such projections a little more care is required. First, note that by refining the choice for c_0 in (A.103) the coefficient of ω_{N-1} in (A.102) can be made as small as we please. Hence the ball $B(y_0, \delta/2)$ intersects $\sum' \equiv S(0,1) \setminus \sum$, i.e. there exists y in $\sum'$ such that $|y - y_0| < \delta/2$. We then proceed as in (A.105) - (A.111) making sure that at each stage the closeness of the approximating orthogonal projection is preserved.

Now, we assume that the theorem is true if the codimension of P_0 is less than or equal to N_0, whenever $1 \leq N_0 < N - D$. In the case $N_0 + 1 \geq N - D$, the theorem is already proven. Otherwise, consider that the projection P_0 has rank $M = N - N_0 - 1$ and $M > D$. Choose a unit vector h_0 such that

$$P_0 h_0 = 0 \tag{A.112}$$

and set
$$P'_0 = P_0 + (h_0 \otimes h_0) \tag{A.113}$$

By the induction assumption, for any fixed θ' satisfying $0 < \theta' < \theta_0$, where θ_0 is defined by

$$\theta_0 = \prod_{k=N-N_0}^{N-1}\left(1 - \frac{D}{k}\right) \tag{A.114}$$

and for any $\delta' > 0$, there exists an orthogonal projection P', of rank $M+1$, such that

$$\|P' - P'_0\| < \delta' \text{ and for some fixed } \eta' > 0, \ \eta'|y| \leq |P'y|^{\theta'} \tag{A.115}$$

for all y in Y. We set $Y' = P'Y$ and apply the previous argument to Y' in $P'\mathbb{R}^N \simeq \mathbb{R}^{M+1}$ and to the orthogonal projection P''_0 from $P'\mathbb{R}^N$ onto $P'P_0\mathbb{R}^N$. Note that in such a case, we have

$$P''_0 \mathbb{R}^N = P'P_0\mathbb{R}^N \text{ and } P''_0 P' P_0 = P' P_0. \tag{A.116}$$

Also note that if δ' is small enough, the rank of P''_0 (i.e. the dimension of $P'P_0\mathbb{R}^N$ equals M). For δ replaced by δ', we obtain an orthogonal projection P'' satisfying, for some fixed $\eta'' > 0$, the inequalities

$$\|P'' - P''_0\| < \delta' \text{ and } \eta''|P'y| \leq |P''P'y|^{\theta''}| \text{ for all } y \in Y. \tag{A.117}$$

Next, we set
$$P = P''P' \tag{A.118}$$
and claim that P is the desired orthogonal projection. Obviously, P is an orthogonal projection in $\mathbb{R}^N$ of rank M such that
$$(\eta'')^{\theta'} \eta' |y| \le |Py|^{\theta'\theta''} \quad \text{for all } y \text{ in } Y \tag{A.119}$$

At the same time,

$$\begin{aligned}
\|P - P_0\| &= \|P''P' - P_0\| & \text{by the definition of } P, \\
&\le \|P''P' - P'P_0\| + \|P'P_0 - P'_0P_0\| + \|P'_0P_0 - P_0\| \\
&\le \|P''P' - P'P_0\| + \|P' - P'_0\| & \text{since } P'_0P_0 = P_0, \\
&\le \|P''P' - P'P_0\| + \delta' & \text{by the choice of } P', \\
&\le \|P''P' - P''_0P_0\| + \|P''_0P_0 - P'P_0\| + \delta' \\
&\le 2\delta' + \|P''_0P_0 - P'P_0\| & \text{by the choice of } P'', \\
&\le 2\delta' + \|P''_0 P(I - P_0)\| & \text{from (A.116)} \\
&\le 2\delta' + \|P''_0 P'_0(I - P_0)\| + \|P''_0(P' - P'_0)(I - P_0)\| \\
&\le 3\delta' + \|P''_0 P'_0(I - P_0)\| & \text{by the choice of } P' \\
&\le 3\delta' + \|P''_0(h_0 \otimes h_0)\| \\
&\le 3\delta' + |P''_0 h_0|.
\end{aligned} \tag{A.120}$$

Hence it remains to estimate $|P''_0 h_0|$. We can write h_0 as
$$h_0 = h''_0 + h_0^\perp, \quad \text{where } h''_0 = P''_0 h_0, \ P_0 P' h_0^\perp = 0; \tag{A.121}$$
then
$$P_0 P' h_0 = P_0 P' h''_0 = P_0 h''_0. \tag{A.122}$$
On the other hand, it follows from (A.112) that
$$\begin{aligned}
|P_0 h''_0| = |P_0 P' h_0| &= |P_0 P'(I - P_0) h_0| \le |P_0 P'_0 (I - P_0) h_0| \\
&\quad + |P_0 (P' - P'_0)(I - P_0) h_0| \\
&\le |P_0(I - P_0) h_0| + \|P' - P'_0\| = 0 + \delta' = \delta'.
\end{aligned} \tag{A.123}$$

To estimate $|P''_0 h_0|$, we will use $|P_0 h''_0| < \delta'$ and a general estimate on $k = P'h$ with $P_0 h = h$. By the definition of k,
$$P_0 k = P_0 P' h = P_0(P' - P'_0)h + P_0 P'_0 h = P_0(P' - P'_0)h + h \tag{A.124}$$
and
$$k = P'h = (P' - P_0)h + P_0 h = (P' - P'_0)h + h, \tag{A.125}$$
where we used $P'_0 P_0 = P_0$. Taking the difference
$$k - P_0 k = (I - P_0)(P' - P'_0)h \tag{A.126}$$

so
$$|k| \leq |P_0 k| + |(I - P_0)(P' - P_0')h| \leq |P_0 k| + \delta'|h|. \tag{A.127}$$
On the other hand,
$$|h| = |P_0(P' - P_0')h - P_0 k| \leq \delta'|h| + |P_0 k| \tag{A.128}$$
hence
$$|h| \leq \frac{1}{1 - \delta'}|P_0 k|. \tag{A.129}$$
Then
$$|k| < |P_0 k| + \delta'|h| \leq |P_0 k|\left(1 + \frac{\delta'}{1 - \delta'}\right) = \frac{1}{1 - \delta'}|P_0 k|. \tag{A.130}$$

By (A.121) and the definition of P_0'', we can take $k = h_0''$. Then using (A.130) and (A.123) we obtain

$$|P_0'' h_0| \leq |h_0''| = |P_0 h_0''|\left(\frac{1}{1 - \delta'}\right) \leq \frac{\delta'}{1 - \delta'} \text{ by (A.123)}. \tag{A.131}$$

Consequently,
$$\|P - P_0\| \leq 3\delta' + |P_0'' h_0| \leq 3\delta' + \frac{\delta'}{1 - \delta'} = \delta'\left(\frac{2 - \delta'}{1 - \delta'}\right) = \delta''. \tag{A.132}$$

But δ' can be chosen so that $\delta'' < \delta$, which completes the induction step as in (A.109 - A.111); moreover $\|P - P_0\| < \delta$ is guaranteed by the choice of δ'.

Remark A.1. An alternative proof using an idea from integral geometry is given in [BEFN]. We only remark that using the finite dimensional Hölder-Mañé theorem one can obtain a short proof for the Modified Mañé's theorem when $d_F(x) \leq d < +\infty$.

A partial converse of Proposition A.1 is also valid.

Proposition A.2. *Let H be a separable Hilbert space and P be a finite rank orthogonal projection. Let X be the set $\{n^{-\alpha} e_n : n = 1, 2, \ldots\} \cup \{0\}$. If the projection P satisfies condition (A.85) for $Y = X$ the exponent θ must satisfy*

$$\theta < \frac{2}{2 + d_F(X)}. \tag{A.133}$$

Conversely, every such exponent θ can be achieved by a rank-one projection.

Proof. First, let us show that for $\alpha \in (0, 1)$ the compact set

$$X = \{n^{-\alpha} e_n : n = 1, 2, \ldots\} \cup \{0\} \tag{A.134}$$

has fractal dimension equal to $\frac{1}{\alpha}$. Let $x_n = n^{-\alpha} e_n$, then

$$|x_n - x_m|^2 = |x_n|^2 + |x_m|^2 = \frac{1}{n^{2\alpha}} + \frac{1}{m^{2\alpha}} \quad \text{for } m \neq n. \tag{A.135}$$

Hence, given $\rho \in (0,1)$ and taking n_ρ such that

$$n_\rho^{-\alpha} < \rho \leq (n_\rho - 1)^{-\alpha}, \tag{A.136}$$

then by (A.135),

$$X \subseteq B_\rho(0) \cup \left(\bigcup_{j=1}^{n_\rho - 1} B_\rho(x_j) \right). \tag{A.137}$$

Therefore,

$$N_\rho(X) \leq n_\rho \tag{A.138}$$

which implies that

$$\log N_\rho(X) \leq \log n_\rho \leq \frac{1}{\alpha} \log \frac{n_\rho^\alpha}{(n_\rho - 1)^\alpha} + \frac{1}{\alpha} \log(n_\rho - 1)^\alpha \tag{A.139}$$

$$\leq \log \frac{n_\rho}{n_\rho - 1} + \frac{1}{\alpha} \log \frac{1}{\rho}$$

hence

$$d_F(X) = \overline{\lim_{\rho \to 0}} \frac{\log N_\rho(X)}{\log(1/\rho)} \leq \frac{1}{\alpha}. \tag{A.140}$$

On the other hand, for every $\rho \in (0,1)$ there exists m_ρ such that

$$\frac{1}{\sqrt{2}(m_\rho + 1)^\alpha} \leq \rho < \frac{1}{\sqrt{2} m_\rho^\alpha}. \tag{A.141}$$

Hence, for $i \neq j$, $1 \leq i, j \leq m_\rho$ we have

$$|x_i - x_j|^2 \geq \frac{2}{m_\rho^{2\alpha}} > 4\rho^2. \tag{A.142}$$

Thus $x_i, x_j \in B_\rho(a)$ with $1 \leq i, j \leq m_\rho$ would imply that $i = j$, therefore

$$N_\rho(X) \geq m_\rho \tag{A.143}$$

.which in turn implies that

$$\log N_\rho(X) \geq \frac{1}{\alpha} \log(m_\rho + 1)^\alpha \sqrt{2} + \log \frac{m_\rho}{m_\rho + 1} - \log \sqrt{2} \tag{A.144}$$

so that
$$\liminf_{\rho \to 0} \frac{\log N_\rho(X)}{\log(1/\rho)} \geq \alpha^{-1}. \tag{A.145}$$

Consequently, $d_F(X) = \alpha^{-1}$. Now, if $P = P^* = P^2$ is an orthogonal projection of finite rank such that
$$C|Px|^\theta \geq |x| \text{ for every } x \text{ in } X, \tag{A.146}$$
for some $\theta \in (0,1)$ and $C < +\infty$, then we have
$$C|Pe_n|^\theta \frac{1}{n^{\alpha\theta}} \geq \frac{1}{n^\alpha} \quad \text{for } n = 1, 2, \ldots \tag{A.147}$$
therefore
$$C|Pe_n| \geq n^{\alpha(1-\frac{1}{\theta})}. \tag{A.148}$$
But then
$$C \text{ rank } P = C \text{ Trace } P = C\sum_{n=1}^\infty (Pe_n, e_n) = C\sum_{n=1}^\infty |Pe_n|^2 \geq \sum_{n=1}^\infty n^{2\alpha(1-\frac{1}{\theta})}. \tag{A.149}$$

Since the rank of P is finite, θ must satisfy
$$2\alpha\left(\frac{1}{\theta} - 1\right) > 1, \tag{A.150}$$
that is
$$\theta < \frac{1}{1 + 1/2\alpha} = \frac{2}{2 + d_F(X)} \tag{A.151}$$
which proves the first part of the Proposition. To prove the second part, we consider the projection defined by
$$P \doteq \frac{1}{|x_0|^2} x_0 \otimes x_0, \tag{A.152}$$
where
$$x_0 \doteq \sum_{n=1}^\infty n^{-\gamma} e_n \quad \text{with} \quad \gamma > 1/2. \tag{A.153}$$
Then
$$|Px_n| = \frac{1}{|x_0|} n^{-(\gamma+\alpha)} = \frac{1}{|x_0|} |x_n|^{-\frac{\gamma+\alpha}{\alpha}}, \tag{A.154}$$
and
$$|x_n| \leq |x_0|^{\frac{\alpha}{\alpha+\gamma}} |Px_n|^{\frac{\alpha}{\alpha+\gamma}} \quad \text{for} \quad n = 1, 2, \ldots . \tag{A.155}$$
Hence, setting
$$\theta = \alpha/(\gamma + \alpha) \quad \text{with} \quad \gamma > 1/2, \tag{A.156}$$
we see that for θ as in (A.151), one can find a rank-one orthogonal projection satisfying (A.146), by suitably choosing γ. □

Appendix B
A Simple Estimate of the Topological Entropy

All of the examples treated in this book have at least two features in common; the first is that the exponential attractor $\mathcal{M}$ has finite fractal dimension and the flow $S(t)$ restricted to $\mathcal{M}$ is Lipschitz with its Lipschitz constant estimated explicitly in terms of the constants that arise from the linear term A and from the non-linear term R. Here we will quote a simple result estimating the topological entropy of $S(t)$ restricted to $\mathcal{M}$ and give the explicit estimates using the results of Chapters 3 and 5.

First, we recall the definition of topological entropy. Let X be a compact set in a normed vector space $(B, \|\cdot\|)$, also let $\{S(t)\}_{t\geq 0}$ be a continuous flow that maps X into X. Consider the set

$$\hat{X}_t = \{\hat{u} \in \mathcal{C}([0,t]; X) : \hat{u}(s) = S(s)u, \quad s \in [0,t] \text{ and } u \in X\} \quad \text{(B.1)}$$

furnished with the uniform distance d_t, that is

$$d_t(\hat{u}, \hat{v}) = \sup\{\|S(s)u - S(s)v\| : s \in [0,t]\}. \quad \text{(B.2)}$$

Then the topological entropy of $\{S(t)\}_{t\geq 0}$ on X is defined by, see [Y] and [W],

$$h(S) = h(\{S(t)\}_{t\geq 0}) \doteq \lim_{\epsilon \to 0} \overline{\lim_{t \to \infty}} t^{-1} \log n_\epsilon(\hat{X}_t) \quad \text{(B.3)}$$

where

$$n_\epsilon(\hat{X}_t) = \text{the minimum number of } \epsilon\text{-balls in} \quad \text{(B.4)}$$
$$d_t\text{-metric necessary to cover } \hat{X}_t.$$

Furthermore, we assume that for any $t > 0$, there exists a smallest number $k(t)$ such that for every u and v in X,

$$\|S(t)u - S(t)v\| \leq k(t)\|u - v\|. \quad \text{(B.5)}$$

In such a case, for any t_1 and t_2 positive, we have

$$k(t_1 + t_2) \leq k(t_1) \cdot k(t_2), \quad \text{(B.6)}$$

hence,
$$\lambda \doteq \lim_{t\to\infty} t^{-1} \log k(t) \tag{B.7}$$

is well defined if $k(t) \leq M$ for $t \in [0,1]$. Under these conditions, we have, see [EFT],

Proposition B.1.
$$h(S) \leq \lambda d_F(X). \tag{B.8}$$

Proof. Let $\gamma > \lambda$ and $d > d_F(X)$, then for t large enough and ϵ small enough

$$k(t) \leq e^{\gamma t} \quad \text{and} \quad n_\epsilon(X) \leq \epsilon^{-d}. \tag{B.9}$$

On the other hand, $\|u - v\| < \epsilon e^{-\gamma t}$ implies that

$$\|S(s)u - S(s)v\| \leq \epsilon \quad \text{for all} \quad s \in [0,t]. \tag{B.10}$$

Therefore, it follows from (9) that for t large enough

$$n_\epsilon(\hat{X}_t) \leq n_{\epsilon e^{-\gamma t}}(X) \leq (\epsilon e^{-\gamma t})^d, \tag{B.11}$$

hence
$$t^{-1} \log n_\epsilon(\hat{X}_t) \leq d\gamma - t^{-1} d \log \epsilon. \tag{12}$$

Consequently, passing to the limit in (12) we obtain that

$$h(S) \leq \gamma d. \tag{B.13}$$

Since $\gamma > \lambda$ and $d > d_F(X)$ was arbitrary, we get the desired result. □

As the prime application of this proposition, we consider as in Chapter 3 the general set-up of the dissipative evolution equations and estimate the topological entropy of the flow restricted to the exponential attractor $\mathcal{M}$, whose existence is guaranteed by Theorem 3.1.

Proposition B.2. *Let $\mathcal{M}$ denote the exponential attractor corresponding to the dissipative evolution equation*

$$u_t + Au + R(u) = 0, \tag{B.14}$$
$$u(0) = u_0, \tag{B.15}$$

where A is a positive self-adjoint operator with compact inverse, and assume that there exists a compact subset X of the absorbing set

$$B = \{u \in H : |u|_H \leq \rho_0 \quad \text{and} \quad |A^{1/2}u|_H \leq \rho_1\}$$

such that there exists a real number $\beta \in (0, 1/2]$ and $c_0 > 0$ such that

$$|R(u) - R(v)|_H \leq c_0 |A^\beta(u-v)|_H \tag{B.16}$$

Exponential Attractors for Dissipative Evolution Equations

for all u and v in X. Then the flow restricted to the exponential attractor has finite topological entropy and it can be estimated by

$$h(\{S(t)\}_{t\geq 0}) \leq K(\beta, c_0, N_0, \lambda_{N_0+1}). \tag{B.17}$$

Proof. In order to get the explicit estimate (B.17), we must carefully figure out the constants $c_1, c_2, c_3 \ldots$, etc., that appear during the proof of Proposition 3.1. First let us note that from (3.29)

$$c_1 = 2(1-\beta)c_0^{\frac{1}{1-\beta}}, \tag{B.18}$$

and hence the Lipschitz constant for $S(t)$ on $\mathcal{M}$ can be estimated by the Lipschitz constant on X and by (3.31)

$$L = \mathrm{Lip}_{\mathcal{M}}(S(t)) \leq \mathrm{Lip}_X(S(t)) \leq e^{c_1 t}. \tag{B.19}$$

On the other hand, the constants c_2 and c_3 that arise from (3.45) are given by

$$c_2 = \begin{cases} 0 & \text{if } \beta = 1/2 \\ (1-2\beta)c_0^{2/1-2\beta} & \text{if } \beta < 1/2 \end{cases} \tag{B.20}$$

and

$$c_3 = \begin{cases} c_0^2 & \text{if } \beta = 1/2, \\ 2\beta & \text{if } \beta < 1/2. \end{cases} \tag{B.21}$$

For simplicity, we will only consider the case $\beta = 1/2$ from now on. By (3.51) we can choose N_0 large enough so that

$$\lambda_{N_0+1} > 6(\ln 2)c_3 + 2\left(\frac{c_2}{c_3} + c_1\right) \geq (6(\ln 2) + 2)c_0^2 \tag{B.22}$$

Moreover, substituting (B.18) and (B.21) into (3.54) we obtain that

$$L_* \leq \exp(c_1/c_3) = e \tag{B.23}$$

Consequently, by (3.60) and (3.62)

$$d_F(\mathcal{M}) \leq d_F(\mathcal{M}^*) + 1 \leq N_0 \max\{1, c_5\}, \tag{B.24}$$

where
$$c_5 = \ln\left(\frac{2L_*}{\delta_*} + 1\right)/\ln(1/4\delta_*), \qquad (B.25)$$

hence combined with (3.50) implies that
$$\delta_* = \exp\left\{-\frac{1}{4c_3}\lambda_{N_0+1}\right\} = \exp\left\{-\frac{1}{4c_0^2}\lambda_{N_0+1}\right\} \qquad (B.26)$$

we obtain from (B.24) that
$$d_F(\mathcal{M}) \leq N_0 \cdot \max\left\{1, \ln(2e^{(\frac{1}{4c_0^2}\lambda_{N_0+1}+1)} + 1)/\ln\left(\frac{1}{4}e^{\frac{1}{4c_0^2}\lambda_{N_0+1}+1}\right)\right\}. \qquad (B.27)$$

In conjunction with (B.7), (B.19) implies that
$$\lambda = \lim_{t\to\infty} t^{-1}\log k(t) \leq \lim_{t\to\infty} t^{-1}\log e^{c_1 t} = c_1 \qquad (B.28)$$
$$\leq 2(1-\beta)c_0^{\frac{1}{1-\beta}}.$$

Finally, combining (B.27) with (B.28) and applying Proposition 1,
$$h(S) \leq \lambda d_F(\mathcal{M}) \leq c_0^2 N_0 \left\{1, \ln(2e^{(\frac{1}{4c_0^2}\lambda_{N_0+1}+1)} + 1)/\ln\left(\frac{1}{4}e^{\frac{1}{4c_0^2}\lambda_{N_0+1}} + 1\right)\right\}$$
(B.29)
□

Remark B.1. For the particular examples discussed in Chapter 5 it is possible to get explicit estimates using Proposition 1 and the estimates on λ and $d_F(\mathcal{M})$.

Appendix C
Mathematical Background
of Fractal Sets

For the reader's convenience, we give a brief synopsis of the definitions and basic properties of fractal sets referred to throughout this monograph. We closely follow [Fa2].

C.1. Hausdorff measure and dimension.

Hausdorff dimension has the advantage of being defined for any set in $\mathbf{R}^n$; however, in many cases it is hard to calculate or estimate by computational methods. It is based on the concept of Hausdorff measure. Recall that if Ω is any non-empty subset of n-dimensional Euclidean space, $\mathbf{R}^n$, the *diameter* of Ω is defined as $|\Omega| = \sup\{|x - y| : x, y \in \Omega\}$, i.e., the greatest distance apart of any pair of points in Ω. If $\{\Omega_i\}$ is a countable (or finite) collection of sets of diameter at most δ that cover F, i.e., $F \subset \cup_{i=1}^{\infty} \Omega_i$ with $0 < |\Omega_i| \leq \delta$ for each I, we say that $\{\Omega_i\}$ is a δ-*cover* of F.

Suppose that F is a subset of $\mathbf{R}^n$ and s is a nonnegative number. For any $\delta > 0$ we define

$$\mathcal{H}_\delta^s(F) = \inf\left\{\sum_{i=1}^{\infty} |\Omega_i|^s : \{\Omega_i\} \text{ is a } \delta\text{-cover of } F\right\}. \tag{C.1}$$

Thus we look at all covers of F by sets of diameter at most δ and seek to minimize the sum of the sth powers of the diameters. As δ decreases, the class of permissible covers of F in (C.1) is reduced. Therefore, the infimum $\mathcal{H}_\delta^s(F)$ increases, and so approaches a limit as $\delta \to 0$. We write

$$\mathcal{H}^s(F) = \lim_{\delta \to 0} \mathcal{H}_\delta^s(F). \tag{C.2}$$

This limit exists for any subset F of $\mathbf{R}^n$, though the limiting value can be (and usually is) 0 or ∞. We call $\mathcal{H}^s(F)$ the *s-dimensional Hausdorff measure* of F.

$\mathcal{H}^s$ may be shown to be a measure. In particular, $\mathcal{H}^s(\emptyset) = 0$; if E is contained in F, then $\mathcal{H}^s(E) \leq \mathcal{H}^s(F)$, and if $\{F_i\}$ is any countable collection of disjoint Borel sets, then

$$\mathcal{H}^s\left(\bigcup_{i=1}^{\infty} F_i\right) = \sum_{i=1}^{\infty} \mathcal{H}^s(F_i). \tag{C.3}$$

Returning to equation (C.1) it is clear that for any given set F and $\delta < 1$, $\mathcal{H}^s_\delta(F)$ is nonincreasing with s, so by (C.2) $\mathcal{H}^s(F)$ is also nonincreasing. In fact, rather more is true: if $t > s$ and $\{\Omega_i\}$ is a δ-cover of F, we have

$$\sum_i |\Omega_i|^t \leq \delta^{t-s} \sum_i |\Omega_i|^s \tag{C.4}$$

so, taking infima, $\mathcal{H}^t_\delta(F) \leq \delta^{t-s} \mathcal{H}^s_\delta(F)$. Letting $\delta \to 0$, we see that if $\mathcal{H}^s(F) < \infty$ then $\mathcal{H}^t(F) = 0$ for $t > s$. Thus a graph of $\mathcal{H}^s(F)$ against s shows that there is a critical value of s at which $\mathcal{H}^s(F)$ 'jumps' from ∞ to 0. This critical value is called the *Hausdorff dimension* of F and is written $\dim_H F$. Formally

$$\dim_H F = \inf\{s : \mathcal{H}^s(F) = 0\} = \sup\{s : \mathcal{H}^s(F) = \infty\} \tag{C.5}$$

so that

$$\mathcal{H}^s(F) = \begin{cases} \infty & \text{if } s < \dim_H F \\ 0 & \text{if } s > \dim_H F. \end{cases} \tag{C.6}$$

If $s = \dim_H F$, then $\mathcal{H}^s(F)$ may be zero or infinite, or may satisfy

$$0 < \mathcal{H}^s(F) < \infty.$$

A Borel set satisfying this last condition is called an *s-set*. Hausdorff dimension satisfies the following properties (which might well be expected to hold for any reasonable definition of dimension).

The definition of Hausdorff dimension given by (C.5) is equivalent to the one furnished in (A.3).

Open sets. If $F \subset \mathbf{R}^n$ is open, then $\dim_H F = n$, since F contains a ball of positive n-dimensional volume.

Smooth sets. If F is a smooth (i.e., continuously differentiable) m-dimensional submanifold (i.e., m-dimensional surface) of $\mathbf{R}^n$, then $\dim_H F = m$. In particular, smooth curves have dimension 1 and smooth surfaces have dimension 2. Essentially, this may be deduced from the relationship between Hausdorff and Lebesgue measures.

Monotonicity. If $E \subset F$, then $\dim_H E \leq \dim_H F$. This is immediate from the measure property that $\mathcal{H}^s(E) \leq \mathcal{H}^s(F)$ for each s.

Countable stability. If $F_1, F_2, \ldots$ is a (countable) sequence of sets, then $\dim_H \cup_{i=1}^{\infty} F_i = \sup_{1 \leq i < \infty} \{\dim_H F_i\}$. Certainly, $\dim_H \cup_{i=1}^{\infty} F_i \geq \dim_H F_j$ for each j from the monotonicity property. On the other hand, if $s > \dim_H F_i$ for all i, then $\mathcal{H}^s(F_i) = 0$, so that $\mathcal{H}^s(\cup_{i=1}^{\infty} F_i) = 0$, giving the opposite inequality.

Exponential Attractors for Dissipative Evolution Equations

Countable sets. If F is countable, then $\dim_H F = 0$. For if F_i is a single point, $\mathcal{H}^0(F_i) = 1$ and $\dim_H F_i = 0$, so by countable stability $\dim_H \cup_{i=1}^{\infty} F_i = 0$.

The transformation properties of Hausdorff dimension under maps follow from:

Proposition C.1. *Let $F \subset \mathbf{R}^n$ and suppose that $f : F \to \mathbf{R}^m$ satisfies a Hölder condition*

$$|f(x) - f(y)| \leq c|x - y|^\alpha \qquad (x, y \in F). \tag{C.7}$$

Then $\dim_H f(F) \leq (1/\alpha)\dim_H F$. Setting $\alpha = 1$ in Proposition C.1, we have:

Corollary C.1. (a) *If $f : F \to \mathbf{R}^m$ is a Lipschitz transformation, then $\dim_H f(F) \leq \dim_H F$.*

(b) *If $f : F \to \mathbf{R}^m$ is a bi-Lipschitz transformation, i.e.,*

$$c_1|x - y| \leq |f(x) - f(y)| \leq c_2|x - y| \qquad (x, y \in F) \tag{C.8}$$

where $0 < c_1 \leq c_2 < \infty$, then $\dim_H f(F) = \dim_H F$.

This corollary reveals a fundamental property of Hausdorff dimension: *Hausdorff dimension is invariant under bi-Lipschitz transformations.* Thus, if two sets have different dimensions there cannot be a bi-Lipschitz mapping from one onto the other.

Remark C.1. The above definitions and properties hold for any *compact* set Ω in an infinite-dimensional separable Hilbert space H. Clearly, the infimum in (C.1) always exists and $|\cdot|$ is replaced by the Hilbert space norm $\|\cdot\|$.

C.2. Fractal or Box-Counting Dimensions.

Box-counting dimension is one of the most widely used dimensions. Its popularity is largely due to its relative ease of mathematical calculation and empirical estimation. However, in the context of attractors and/or exponential attractors for dynamical systems, its real significance lies in its usefulness to unravel properties of Lyapunov exponents and Lyapunov dimension (see Chapter 7, Section 2).

Let F be any non-empty bounded subset of $\mathbf{R}^n$, or any *compact* set of some separable Hilbert space H.

Definition C.1. Let $N_\delta(F)$ be the smallest number of sets of diameter at most δ which can cover F. The *lower* and *upper box-counting dimensions* of F respectively are defined as

$$\underline{\dim}_B F = \underline{\lim}_{\delta \to 0} \frac{\log N_\delta(F)}{-\log \delta} \tag{C.9}$$

$$\overline{\dim}_B F = \overline{\lim}_{\delta \to 0} \frac{\log N_\delta(F)}{-\log \delta}. \tag{C.10}$$

If these are equal we refer to the common value as the *box-counting dimension* or *box dimension* of F

$$\dim_B F = \lim_{\delta \to 0} \frac{\log N_\delta(F)}{-\log \delta}. \tag{C.11}$$

In this monograph, we follow the usage of:

Definition C.2. The fractal dimension of a compact set $\Omega \subset H$ is its upper box-counting dimension.

The following properties of box dimension mirror those of Hausdorff dimension:

(i) a smooth m-dimensional submanifold of $\mathbf{R}^n$ has $\dim_B F = m$.

(ii) $\underline{\dim}_B$ and $\overline{\dim}_B$ are monotonic.

(iii) $\overline{\dim}_B$ is *finitely* stable, i.e.,

$$\overline{\dim}_B(E \cup F) = \max\{\overline{\dim}_B E, \overline{\dim}_B F\}$$

though $\underline{\dim}_B$ is not.

(iv) $\underline{\dim}_B$ and $\overline{\dim}_B$ are Lipschitz invariant. This is so because, if $|f(x)-f(y)| \leq c|x-y|$ and F can be covered by $N_\delta(F)$ sets of diameter at most δ, then the $N_\delta(F)$ images of these sets under f form a cover by sets of diameter at most $c\delta$, thus $\dim_B f(F) \leq \dim_B F$. Similarly, box dimensions behave just like Hausdorff dimensions under bi-Lipschitz and Hölder transformations.

However, box dimensions are not stable under infinite union.

Example C.1. $F = \{0, 1, 1/2, 1/3, \ldots, \}$ is a compact set in $\mathbf{R}$ with $\dim_B F = 1/2$. (Proof in [Fa2], Chapter 3, Example 3.5).

Remark C.2. $\dim_H F \leq \overline{\dim}_B(F)$.

C.3. Product of Fractals.

Hausdorff dimension behaves quite differently from fractal (upper box-counting) dimension under Cartesian product:

Proposition C.2. *For any sets $E \subset \mathbf{R}^n$, $F \subset \mathbf{R}^m$, we have*

$$\dim_H(E \times F) \geq \dim_H E + \dim_H F. \tag{C.12}$$

In general, inequality (C.12) cannot be reversed. Example (7.8) in Falconer [F2] shows that there exist sets $E, F \subset \mathbf{R}$ with $\dim_H E = \dim_H F = 0$ and $\dim_H(E \times F) \geq 1$. However:

Proposition C.3. *For any sets $E \subset \mathbf{R}^n$ and $F \subset \mathbf{R}^m$,*

$$\dim_H(E \times F) \leq \dim_H E + \overline{\dim}_B F; \tag{C.13}$$

if, moreover, $\dim_H F = \overline{\dim}_B F$, then:

$$\dim_H(E \times F) = \dim_H E + \dim_H F. \tag{C.14}$$

Fractal dimension is better behaved under Cartesian product:

Proposition C.4. *For any sets $E \subset \mathbf{R}^n$ and $F \subset \mathbf{R}^m$*

$$\overline{\dim}_B(E \times F) \leq \overline{\dim}_B E + \overline{\dim}_B F. \tag{C.15}$$

Remark C. 3. The proof of (C.15) easily extends to E and F compact sets in a separable Hilbert space H.

Some Open Problems

1. Construction of exponential attractors of ordinary differential equations (ODE's). The results presented in this book apply to ODE's but a more specific and more systematic study of the ODE's case would be useful.

2. Exponential tracking (see p. 120 and [CFNT1,2], [FSTi]) is a property enjoyed by inertial manifolds. It would be interesting to construct exponential attractors with the exponential tracking property.

3. Is there an exponential form of a dynamical system?

   Here as in 2. the question is to compare inertial manifolds and exponential attractors. The inertial form of a system is a finite dimensional dynamical system which possesses the same dynamics as the initial system.

   When an inertial manifold exists, an inertial system is obtained by simply restricting the dynamics to the inertial manifold.

   It would be interesting to produce a finite dimensional **smooth** dynamical system associated with an exponential attractor and reproducing the same dynamics (exponential form). Note that in this work we have constructed a weak version of an inertial form (see Chapter 9). Indeed our candidate for an inertial form is an ordinary differential system which may not engender a classical dynamical system and the exponential attraction property was established only if the original equation was already living a finite dimensional space. This last restriction would be lifted if one could give a positive answer to the next open problem.

4. Prove or disprove the existence of a Hölder-Mañé projector in the case of infinite dimensional Hilbert spaces (see Chapter 10).

Index

For frequently quoted words we indicate the first appearance and some of the most significant appearances.

Absorbing set 1, 40, 47, 54, 70, 75

Approximations 5

Bergers equations 65

Chaffee-Infante equation 5, 74

Damped nonlinear equations of second order:
    See Damped wave equations

Damped Wave equations 6, 34, 81

Dichotomy principle
    See Squeezing property

Dissipative evolution equations 1, 39, 160

Entropy (topological entropy) 159, 161

Exponential attractor 3, 9, 43, 52, 60, 65, 73, 80, 94, 96, 108, 114, 120, 139, 161

Exponential tracking 120

First order evolution equations 1, 39
    See also the name of the equation

Fractal dimension 2, 9, 14, 15, 32, 43, 52, 60, 65, 73, 80, 94, 109, 142, 165

Galerkin approximation 5, 36

Ginzburg-Landau equation 1, 117

Global attractor 2, 9, 98, 108

Grashoff number 60, 61

Guzburg-Landan equation 1, 117

Hausdorff dimension 2, 142, 163

Hölder-Mañé's Projection Theorem 6, 122, 125, 126, 128, 135, 141, 145, 155

Inertially equivalent systems 135

Inertial manifolds 2, 111, 119

Inertial sets 4

Kuramoto-Sivashinsky equations 1, 39, 117

Klein Gordon equations 90

Kolmogorov-Sivashinsky-Spiegel equation 5, 44, 117

Lyapunov exponents 2, 109

Mãné's Projection or Theorem
　　See Hölder's-Mãné's Projection or Theorem

Navier-Stokes equations 1, 53, 61

Optimal
　　– Hausdorff dimension 94
　　– Lyapunov dimension 97

Perturbations 5, 35

Reaction–Diffusion equation 1, 74

Second order evolution equations 6, 81
　　See also damped wave equations and the name of the equation

Sine-Gordon equation 1, 81,91

Spectral barrier 113, 116

Spectral gap condition 3

Squeezing property 4, 10, 27, 41, 50, 57, 63, 70, 78, 81

Uniform Gronwall's lemma 48

Universal attractor: see global attractor

References

[BV1] Babin, A. V., and Vishik, M. I. Attractors of partial differential equations and estimates of their dimension, *Uspekhi Mat. Nauk*, **38** (1983), 133–187 (in Russian). *Russian Math. Surveys*, **38** (1983), 151–213 (in English).

[BV2] Babin, A. V., and Vishik, M. I. Regular attractors of semigroups and evolution equations, *J. Math. Pures Appl.*, **62** (1983), 441–491.

[BV3] Babin, A. V., and Vishik, M. I. Maximal attractors of semigroups corresponding to evolution differential equations, *Mat. Sbornik*, **126** (168), 1985 (in Russian). *Math. USSR-Sbornik*, **54** (1986), 387–408 (in English).

[BV4] Babin, A. V., and Vishik, M. I. *Attractors of Evolution Equations*, Nauka, Moscow, 1989 (in Russian). North-Holland, Amsterdam, 1992 (in English).

[BEFN] Ben-Artzi, A., Eden, A., Foias, C., and Nicolaenko, B. Hölder continuity for the inverse of Mañé's projection, *J. Math. Anal. and Appl.*, **178**, (1993), 22-29.

[Bi] Biler, P. On the Stationary Solutions of Burgers' Equation, Colloquium Mathematicum, **52**, fas. 2, 1987.

[BGT] Bréfort, B., Ghidaglia, J. M., and Temam, R. Attractors for the penalized Navier-Stokes equations, *SIAM J. Math. Anal.*, **19** (1988), 1–21.

[Bu1] Burgers, J. M. Mathematical examples illustrating relations occurring in the theory of turbulent fluid motion, Verhandel-Kon. Nedert. Akad. Wetenschappen Amsterdam, *Afdeel. Natuurkunde* (1st Section), **17** no. 2, (1939), 1–53.

[Bu2] Burgers, J. M. A mathematical model illustrating the theory of turbulence, in *Advances in Applied Mechanics*, **1**, (1948), 171–199.

[CI] Chaffee, N., and Infante, E. F. A bifurcation problem for a nonlinear partial differential equation of parabolic type, *Applicable Anal.*, **4** (1974) 17–37.

[CL] Chow, S. N., and Lu, K. Invariant manifolds for flows in Banach spaces, *J. Differential Equations*, **74**, no. 2, (1988).

[C]	Constantin, P., A Construction of inertial manifolds, in The Connection between Infinite Dimensional and Finite Dimensional Dynamical Systems, *Contemporary Mathematics*, **99**, 27–62.
[CF1]	Constantin, P., and Foias, C. Global Lyapunov exponents, Kaplan-Yorke formulas and the dimension of the attractors for two-dimensional Navier-Stokes equations, *Comm. Pure Appl. Math.*, **38** (1985), 1–27.
[CF2]	Constantin, P., and Foias, C. *The Navier-Stokes Equations*, Univ. of Chicago Press, Chicago, 1988.
[CFNT1]	Constantin, P., Foias, C., Nicolaenko, B., and Temam, R. Nouveaux résultats sur les variétés inertielles pour les équations différentielles dissipatives, *C. R. Acad. Sci. Paris, Sér. I*, **302** (1986), 375–378.
[CFNT2]	Constantin, P., Foias, C., Nicolaenko, B., and Temam, R. *Integral and Inertial Manifolds for Dissipative Partial Differential Equations*, Springer-Verlag, Applied Math. Sciences, **70**, New York, 1989.
[CFNT3]	Constantin, P., Foias, C., Nicolaenko, B., and Temam, R. Spectral barriers and inertial manifolds for dissipative partial differential equations, *J. Dynamics and Differential Equations*, **1** (1989), 45–73.
[CFT1]	Constantin, P., Foias, C., and Temam, R. *Attractors Representing Turbulent Flows*, Memoirs of AMS, **53**, no. 314, 1985.
[CFT2]	Constantin, P., Foias, C., and Temam, R. On the dimension of the attractors in two-dimensional turbulence, *Physica D* **30** (1988), 284–296.
[DT]	Debussche, A., and Temam, R., Inertial manifolds and their dimension, in *Dynamical Systems, Theory and Applications*, S.I. Andersson, A.E. Andersson and O. Ottoson Eds., World Scientific Publishing Co., (1993).
[D1]	Dłotko, T. The one-dimensional Burgers' equation: existence, uniqueness and stability, *Zeszyty Naukave Uniwerstetu Jagiellońskiego, Prace Matematzczne*, **23**, 157–172, 1982.
[D2]	Dłotko, T. The classical solution of the one-dimensional Burgers' equation ibidem **23**, 173–182, 1982.
[DGHN1]	Doering, Ch., Gibbon, J.D., Holm, D., and Nicolaenko, B. Low-dimensional behavior in the complex Ginzburg-Landau equations, *Nonlinearity* **1**, 279–309 (1988).
[DGHN2]	Doering, Ch., Gibbon, J.D., Holm, D., and Nicolaenko, B. Exact Lyapunov dimension of the universal attractor for the complex Ginzburg-Landau equation, *Phys. Letters* (1988).

[E] Eden, A. On Burger's Original Mathematical Model of Turbulence, *Nonlinearity*, 1990.

[EFN] Eden, A., Foias, C., and Nicolaenko, B. Exponential Attractors of Optimal Lyapunov Dimension for Navier Stokes Equations, *C.R. Acad. Sci. Paris*, Serie I, **316** (1993), 1211–1215.

[EFNS] Eden, A., Foias, C., Nicolaenko, B., and She, Z. S. Exponential Attractors and Their Relevance to Fluid Mechanics Systems, *Physica D* **63** (1993), 350–360.

[EFNT1] Eden, A., Foias, C., Nicolaenko, B., and Temam, R. Ensembles inertiels pour des équations d'évolution dissipatives, *C. R. Acad. Sci. Paris*, **310**, Série I, (1990), 559–562.

[EFNT2] Eden, A., Foias, C., Nicolaenko, B., and Temam, R. Inertial Sets for Dissipative Evolution Equations, *IMA preprint #912* (1991), University of Minnesota, Minneapolis (1991).

[EFT] Eden, A., Foias, C., and Temam, R. Local and Global Lyapunov Exponents, *Journal of Dynamics and Differential Equations* **3**, No. 1 (1991), 133–177.

[EL] Eden, A., and Libin, A. Explicit Dimension Estimates of Attractors for the MHD Equations in Three-Dimensional Space, *Physica D* **40** (1989), 338–352.

[EMN1] Eden, A., Milani, A. J., and Nicolaenko, B. Finite Dimensional Exponential Attractors for Semilinear Wave Equations with Damping, *JMAA* **169** (1992), 408–419.

[EMN2] Eden, A., Milani, A. J., and Nicolaenko, B. Exponential Attractors for models of phase change for compressible gas dynamics, *Nonlinearity*, **6** (1993), 93–117.

[EMR1] Eden, A., Michaux, B., and Rakotoson, J. M. Doubly Nonlinear Parabolic Equations as Dynamical Systems, *Journal of Dynamics and Differential Equations*, **3**, No. 1 (1991), 87–132.

[EMR2] Eden, A., Michaux, B., and Rakotoson, J. M. Some Results on Doubly Nonlinear Parabolic Equations as Dynamical Systems, *Appl. Math. Lett.*, **3**, No. 1, (1990), 5–8.

[EMR3] Eden, A., Michaux, B., and Rakotoson, J. M. Semi-Discretized Nonlinear Evolution Equations as Discrete Dynamical Systems and Error Analysis, *Indiana University Mathematics Journal*, **39**, No. 3 (1990), 737–783.

[EMR4] Eden, A., Michaux, B., and Rakotoson, J. M. Error Analysis of Non-linear Evolution Equations and Associated Dynamical Systems, *Appl. Math. Lett.*, **3**, No. 3 (1990), 31–34.

[ER] Eden, A., and Rakotoson, J. M. Exponential Attractors for Some Doubly Nonlinear Parabolic Equations, *J. Math. Anal. and Appl.*, to appear.

[Fa1] Falconer, K. J. *The Geometry of Fractal Sets*, Cambridge University Press, Cambridge, 1985.

[Fa2] Falconer, K. J. *Fractal Geometry: Mathematical Foundations and Applications*, John Wiley & Sons, 1990.

[FaOY] Farmer, J. D., Ott, E., and Yorke, J. A. The dimension of chaotic attractors, *Physica* **7D** (1983), 153–180.

[FMT1] Foias, C., Manley, O. and Temam, R. Attractors for the Bénard Problem, Existence and Physical Bounds for their fractal dimension, *Nonlinear Analysis, TMA*, **11** (1987), 939–967.

[FMT2] Foias, C., Manley and Temam, R. Sur l'interaction des petits et grands tourbillons dans les ecoulements turbulents, *C.R. Acad. Sc. Paris, Série I*, **305**, (1987), 497–500.

[FMT3] Foias, C., Manley, O., and Temam, R., On the interaction of small and large eddies in two–dimensional turbulent flows, *Math. Mod. and Num. Anal.* (M2AN) **22** (1988), 93–114.

[FNST1] Foias, C., Nicolaenko, B., Sell, G. R., and Temam, R. Variétés inertielles pour l'equation de Kuramoto-Sivashinski, *C. R. Acad. Sci. Paris, Sér. I*, **301** (1985), 285–288.

[FNST2] Foias, C., Nicolaenko, B., Sell, G. R., and Temam, R. Inertial manifolds for the Kuramoto-Sivashinsky equation and an estimate of their lowest dimension, 1986, *J. Math. Pures Appl.*, **67** (1988), 197–226.

[FNT] Foias, C., Nicolaenko, B., and Temam, R. Asymptotic study of an equation of G. I. Sivashinsky for two-dimensional turbulences of the Kolmogorov flow, *Acad. Sci. Paris*, **303**, 717–720.

[FST1] Foias, C., Sell, G., and Temam, R., Varieétés inertielles deséquations différentielles dissipatives, *C.R. Acad. Sci. Paris, Serie I*, **304** (1985), 139–142

[FST2] Foias, C., Sell, G., and Temam, R. Inertial Manifolds for Nonlinear Evolution Equations, *J. Diff. Equ.* **73** (1988), 309–353.

[FSTi] Foias, C., Sell, G., and Titi, E. S. Exponential Tracking and Approximation of Inertial Manifolds for Dissipative Nonlinear Equations, *J. of Dynamics and Diff. Equations*, **1**, no. 2, 1989.

[FT1] Foias, C., and Temam, R. Some analytic and geometric properties of the solutions of the Navier-Stokes equations, *J. Math. Pures Appl.*, **58** (1979), 339–368.

[FT2] Foias, C., and Temam, R. Determination of the solutions of the Navier-Stokes equations by a set of nodal values, *Math. Comput.*, **43**, no. 167 (1984), 117–133.

[GH] Ghidaglia, J. M., and Héron, B. Dimension of the attractor associated to the Ginzburg-Landau equation, *Physica* **28D** (1987), 282–304.

[GT1] Ghidaglia, J. M., and Temam, R. Attractors for damped nonlinear hyperbolic equations, *J. Math. Pures Appl.*, **66** (1987), 273–319.

[GT2] Ghidaglia, J. M., and Temam, R. Dimension of the universal attractor describing the periodically driven sine-Gordon equations, *Transport Theory Statist. Phys.*, **16**, 2 and 3 (1987), 253–265.

[GT3] Ghidaglia, J. M., and Temam, R. Periodic dynamical systems with application to sine-Gordon equations: estimates on the fractal dimension of the universal attractor, *Contemporary Mathematics*, AMS, **99** (1989), 1–26.

[GT4] Ghidaglia, J. M., and Temam, R. Regularity of the solutions of second-order evolution equations and their attractors, *Annali della Scuola Normale Superiore di Pisa*, Serie IV, **14**, 1987, 485–511.

[GT5] Ghidaglia, J. M., and Temam, R. Long-time behavior for partly dissipative equations: the slightly compressible two-dimensional Navier-Stokes equations. Attractors and their dimension, *Asymptotic Analysis*, **1** (1988), 23–49.

[H] Hale, J. *Asymptotic Behavior of Dissipative Systems*. Mathematical Surveys and Monographs, **25**, AMS, Providence, 1988.

[HR] Hale, J. K., and Raugel, G. Upper semicontinuity of the attractor for a singularly perturbed hyperbolic equation, Lefschetz Center for Dynamical Systems, *Jour. of Diff. Eqns.* **73**, no. 2 (1988), 197–214.

[HLR] Hale, J. K., Lin, X.-B., and Raugel, G. Upper semicontinuity of attractors for approximations of semigroups and partial differential equations, *Mathematics of Computation* **50**, no. 181 (1988), 89–123.

[Ha] Haraux, A. Two remarks on dissipative hyperbolic problems, in *Nonlinear Partial Differential Equations and Their Applications*, Collège de France Seminar, Vol. VII, H. Brézis, J. L. Lions (Eds.), Pitman, London, 1985.

[He] Henry, D. *Geometric Theory of Semilinear Parabolic Equations*, Lecture Notes in Mathematics, **840**, Springer-Verlag, New York, 1981.

[Ho] Horgan, C. C. and Olmstead, W. E. Stability and uniqueness for a turbulence model of Burgers, Quarterly of Applied Mathematics, **36**, n.2, 121–128, 1978.

[HN] Hyman, J., Nicolaenko, B. The Kuramoto-Sivashinsky Equation: a bridge between PDE's and Dynamical Systems, Physica D**18**, 113–126 (1986).

[HNZ] Hyman, J., Nicolaenko, B., and Zaleski, S. Order and Complexity in the Kuramoto-Sivashinsky model of weakly turbulent interfaces, Physica D**23** (1986), 265–292.

[KNS] Kevrekidis, I., Nicolaenko, B., and Scovel, C. Back in the saddle: a computer assisted study of the first bifurcations of the Kuramoto-Sivashinsky equation, *SIAM J. Appl. Math.* **50**, #3, (1990), 760–790.

[Ko] Kolmogorov, A. N. Inertial Range in Turbulence, *Proc. Acad. Sc. USSR*, Vol. **30**, p. 301 (1941); Vol. **31**, p. 538 (1941); Vol. **32**, p. 1417–1423 (1941).

[Kr] Kraichnan, R. H. Inertial Ranges in Two-dimensional turbulence, *Phys. Fluids*, Vol. **10** (1967), 1417–1423.

[Kur] Kuramoto, Y. Diffusion induced chaos in reaction systems, *Progr. Theoret. Phys. Suppl.*, **64** (1978), 346–367.

[Ku] Kuratowski, *Topology*, 2 Vol., Academic Press, New York (1966–68).

[Kw1] Kwak, M. Finite dimensional description of convective reaction-diffusion equation, *Journal of Dynamics and Differential Equations*, **3**, (1992), 515-543.

[Kw2] Kwak, M. Finite dimensional inertial forms for the 2D Navier-Stokes equations, *Indiana J. of Math.*, **41**, (1992), 927-982.

[La1] Ladyzhenskaya, O. A. On the finiteness of the dimension of bounded invariant sets for the Navier-Stokes equations and other related dissipative systems, in *The Boundary Value Problems of Mathematical Physics and Related Questions in Functional Analysis*, Seminar of the Steklov Institute, **14**, Leningrad, 1982; see also *J. Soviet. Math.*, **28**, no. 5 (1985), 714–725.

[La2] Ladyzhenskaya, O. A. On the attractors of nonlinear evolution problems, in *The Boundary Value Problems of Mathematical Physics and Related Questions in Functional Analysis*, Seminar of the Steklov Institute, **18**, Leningrad, 1987.

[La3] Ladyzhenskaya, O.A. On the determination of minimal global B-attractors for semigroups generated by boundary value problems for nonlinear dissipative partial differential equations, Steklov Institute, Leningrad, 1987, Preprint.

[La4]   Ladyzhenskaya, O.A. *Attractors for Semigroups and Evolution Equations*, Accademia Nazionale dei Lincer series, Cambridge University press, Cambridge, 1991.

[Le]   Ledrappier, F. Some relations between dimension and Lyapunov exponents, *Comm. Math. Phys.*, 81 (1981), 229–238.

[MP]   Mallet-Paret, J. Negatively invariant sets of compact maps and an extension of a theorem of Cartwright, *J. Differential Equations*, 22 (1976), 331.

[MS]   Mallet-Paret, J., and Sell, G. Inertial manifolds for reaction-diffusion equations in higher space dimensions, *J. Amer. Math. Soc.*, 1 (1988), 805–866.

[Man1]   Mandelbrot, B. *Fractals: Form, Chance and Dimension*, Freeman, San Francisco, 1977.

[Man2]   Mandelbrot, B. *The Fractal Geometry of Nature*, Freeman, San Francisco, 1982.

[Ma1]   Mañé, B. *Ergodic Theory and Differentiable Dynamics*, Springer Verlag, Berlin (1987).

[Ma2]   Mañé, B. Reduction of semilinear parabolic equations to finite dimensional C^1 flows, in *Geometry and Topology, Lecture Notes in Mathematics*, 597, pp. 361–378, Springer-Verlag, New York.

[Ma3]   Mañé, B. On the dimension of the compact invariant sets of certain nonlinear maps, Lecture Notes in Mathematics, 898, pp. 230–242, Springer-Verlag, New York (1981).

[Mr1]   Marion, M. Attractors for reaction-diffusion equations; Existence and estimate of their dimension, *Appl. Anal.*, 25 (1987), 101–147.

[Mr2]   Marion, M. Finite dimensional attractors to partly dissipative reaction-difffusion systems, in *AMS Contemporary Mathematics Series*, 99 (1989).

[MT]   Marion, M., and Temam, R. Nonlinear Galerkin Methods, *SIAM J. Numer. Analysis* 26, 5 (1989), 1139–1157.

[Mo1]   Mora, X. Finite-dimensional attracting manifolds in reaction-diffusion equations, *Contemp. Math.*, 17 (1983), 353–360.

[Mo2]   Mora, X. Finite-dimensional attracting manifolds for damped semilinear wave equations, in *Contributions to Nonlinear Partial Differential Equations II*, to appear.

[MSM] Mora, X., and Solà-Morales, J. Existence and non-existence of finite-dimensional globally attracting invariant manifolds in semilinear damped wave equations, Universidad Autonoma de Barcelona, July 1986, Preprint.

[NST1] Nicolaenko, B., Scheurer, B., and Temam, R. Some global dynamical properties of the Kuramoto-Sivashinsky equations: Nonlinear stability and attractors, *Physica*, **16D** (1985), 155–183.

[NST2] Nicolaenko, B., Scheurer, B., and Temam, R. Attractors for the Kuramoto-Sivashinsky equation, *A.M.S. Lectures in Applied Mathematics*, **23**, (1986), 149–170.

[NST3] Nicolaenko, B., Scheurer, B., and Temam, R. Some global dynamical properties of a class of pattern formation equations, *Comm. in PDEs* **14** (2), (1988), 245–297.

[NS1] Nicolaenko, B., and She, Z.S. Symmetry breaking homoclinic chaos in Kolmogorov flows, *Nonlinear World* (World Scientific Publ.) (1990), 602–617.

[NS2] Nicolaenko, B., and She, Z.S. Temporal intermittency and turbulence production in the Kolmogorov flow, *Topological Structures in Turbulence*, Cambridge University Press (1990), 265–277.

[NS3] Nicolaenko, B., and She, Z.S. Symmetry breaking homoclinic chaos and vorticity bursts for periodic Navier-Stokes flows, *European J. of Mechanics, B/Fluids*, **10**, No. 2 (1991), 67–74.

[R] Richards, J. On the gap between numbers which are the sum of two squares, *Adv. in Math.*, **46** (1982), 1–12.

[Ru1] Ruelle, D. Strange attractors, *Math. Intelligencer*, **2** (1979-80), 126–137.

[Ru2] Ruelle, D. Small random perturbations of dynamical systems and the definition of attractors, *Comm. Math. Phys.*, **82** (1981), 137–151.

[SaS] Sacker, J., and Sell, G.R. Exponential Dichotomies for Dynamical Systems, *J. Diff. Eqn.*, **22** (1976), 497–522.

[SYC] Sauer, T., Yorke, J. A., and Casdagli, M. Embedology, *J. Stat. Phys.*, **65**, no. 3/4 (1991), 579–616.

[ST] Saut, J. C., and Temam, R. Generic properties of Navier-Stokes equations: Genericity with respect to the boundary values, *Indiana Univ. Math. J.*, **29** (1980), 427–446.

[Sch]   Scheffer, V. Hausdorff measure and the Navier-Stokes equations, *Comm. Math. Phys.*, **55** (1977), 97–112.

[SeT]   Sermange, M., and Temam, R. Some mathematical questions related to the MHD equations, *Comm. Pure Appl. Math.*, **36** (1983), 635–664.

[Sh]   Shaw, R. Strange attractors, chaotic behavior and information flow, *Z. Naturforsch.*, A36 (1981), 80–112.

[Si1]   Sivashinsky, G. Nonlinear analysis of hydrodynamic instability in laminar flames, Part I. Derivation of basic equations, *Acta Astronaut.*, **4** (1977), 1177–1206.

[Si2]   Sivashinsky, G. On flame propagation under conditions of stoichiometry, *SIAM J. Appl. Math.*, **39** (1980), 67–82.

[SM]   Sivashinsky, G., and Michelson, D. M. On irregular wavy flow of a liquid down a vertical plane, *Progr. Theoret. Phys.*, **63** (1980), 2112–2114.

[T1]   Temam, R. *Infinite-Dimensional Dynamical Systems in Mechanics and Physics*, Appl. Math. Sci., **68**, Springer-Verlag, New York, 1988.

[T2]   Temam, R. *Navier-Stokes Equations, Theory and Numerical Analysis*, 3rd rev. ed., North-Holland, Amsterdam, 1984.

[T3]   Temam, R. *Navier-Stokes Equations and Nonlinear Functional Analysis*, CBMS-NSF Regional Conference Series in Applied Mathematics, SIAM, Philadelphia, 1983; augmented 2nd edition (1994).

[T4]   Temam, R. Attractors for Navier-Stokes equations, in *Nonlinear Partial Differential Equations and Their Applications*, Collège de France Seminar, Vol. VII, H. Brézis, J. L. Lions (Eds.), Pitman, London, 1985.

[T5]   Temam, R. Induced Trajectories and Approximate Inertial Manifolds, *Math. Mod. and Numer. Analysis (M2AN)*, **23**, 3 (1989), 541–561.

[TWs]   Temam, R., and Wang, S., Inertial forms of Navier-Stokes equations on the sphere, *J. Functional Analysis*, **117** (1993), 215–242.

[TWx]   Temam, R., and Wang., X., Estimates on the lowest dimension of inertial manifolds for the Kuramoto-Sivashinsky equation in the general case, *Differential Integral Equ.* (1993), to appear.

[Ti]   Titi, E.S. Une variété approximante de l'attracteur universel des équations de Navier-Stokes, non linéaires, de dimension, *C.R. Acad. Sci. Paris*, Sér. I, **307** (1988), 383-385.

[W]   Walters, P. *An Introduction to Ergodic Theory*, Springer-Verlag, 1982.

[Y]   Yomdin, Y. Volume Growth and Entropy, preprint, (1986).

MASSON Éditeur
120, boulevard Saint-Germain
75280 Paris Cedex 06
Dépôt légal : octobre 1994

SNEL S.A.
Rue Saint-Vincent 12 – 4020 Liège
septembre 1994